MY SIDE OF THE MOUNTAIN

ITP

Gorge
tree
Mountain meadow
Gribley Beech
apple tree
house site
walnut tree
cattail supply
My Side of the Mountain
signed S. Gribley

MY SIDE OF THE MOUNTAIN

written and illustrated by

JEAN CRAIGHEAD GEORGE

Published by The Trumpet Club
1540 Broadway, New York, New York 10036

ISBN 0-440-84773-7

This edition published by arrangement with Dutton Children's Books, a division of Penguin Books USA Inc.
Printed in the United States of America
November 1991

10 9 8
OPM

This book is dedicated to many people—

to that gang of youngsters who inhabited the trees and waters of the Potomac River so many years ago, and to the bit of Sam Gribley in the children and adults around me now.

Contents

AUTHOR'S PREFACE

When I was in elementary school, I packed my suitcase and told my mother I was going to run away from home. As I envisioned it, I would live by a waterfall in the woods and catch fish on hooks made from the forks of tree limbs, as I had been taught by my father. I would walk among the wildflowers and trees, listen to the birds, read the weather report in the clouds and the wind, and stride down mountainsides independent and free. Wisely, my mother did not try to dissuade me. She had been through this herself. She checked my bag to see if I had my toothbrush and a postcard to let her know how I was getting along, and kissed me good-by. Forty minutes later I was home.

When my daughter, Twig, was in elementary school, she told me she was going to run away to the woods. I checked her backpack for her toothbrush and watched her go down the front steps, her shoulders squared confidently. I blew her a kiss and sat down to wait. Presently, she was back.

Although wishing to run to the woods and live on our own seems to be an inherited characteristic in our family, we are not unique. Almost everyone I know has dreamed at some time of running away to a distant mountain or island, castle or sailing ship, to live there in beauty and peace. Few of us make it, however.

It is one thing to wish to go, and another matter to do it. I might have been able to do what Sam Gribley does in this book—live off the land, make a home, survive by wits and library research, for I had the knowledge. My father, who was a naturalist and scientist, taught me the plants and animals of eastern forests and showed me where the wild edible fruits and tubers grew. On weekends along the Potomac River near Washington, D.C., where I was born and grew up, he and I boiled water in leaves and made rabbit traps. Together we made tables and chairs out of saplings bound with the braided inner bark of the basswood tree. My brothers, two of the first falconers in the United States, helped me in the training of a falcon. I had the know-how for surviving in the woods; and yet I came home.

"But not Sam," I said to myself when I sat down at my typewriter and began putting on paper this story, one that I had been writing in my head for many, many years.

The writing came easily—Sam needed a home. I remembered a huge tree my brothers had camped in on an island in the Potomac River. A tree would be Sam's home. And I knew how he would survive when foraging became tough. "A falcon will be his provider," I said to myself.

With ideas coming fast, the first draft was done in two weeks. Five revisions later, it was finished and off to the publisher. Back came a phone call from Sharon Bannigan, the editor of E. P. Dutton's children's book department at that time.

"Elliott Macrae, the publisher," she said, "won't print the book. He says parents should not encourage their kids to leave home."

Discouraged, I hung up the phone and walked out into the woods behind the house. As always when I am in the wildwood, I very quickly forgot what was troubling me. A sentinel crow was protecting its flock by watching the sky for hawks; a squirrel was building a nest of leaves for the winter; a spider was tapping out a message to his mate on a line of her web.

Better to run to the woods than the city, I thought. Here, there is the world to occupy the mind.

The telephone rang. Sharon Bannigan was back on the wire, and she was almost singing. Elliott Macrae had changed his mind. And what, I asked her, had worked the miracle?

"I simply told him it is better to have children run to the woods than the city," she said. "He thought about that. Since he has a home in the wilds of the Adirondack Mountains and goes off there alone himself, he suddenly understood your book. *My Side of the Mountain* will be published in the spring of '59."

From that date to this, I have been answering children's letters about Sam. Most want to know if he is a real person. Some, convinced that he is, have biked to Delhi, New York, from as far away as Long Island, New York, to find his tree, his falcon, weasel, and raccoon. To these and all others who ask, I say, "There is no real Sam, except inside me." His adventures are the fulfillment of that day long ago when I told my mother I was going to run away, got as far as the edge of the woods, and came back. Perhaps Sam will fulfill your dreams, too. Be you writer or reader, it is very pleasant to run away in a book.

MY SIDE OF THE MOUNTAIN

IN WHICH
I Hole Up in a Snowstorm

I am on my mountain in a tree home that people have passed without ever knowing that I am here. The house is a hemlock tree six feet in diameter, and must be as old as the mountain itself. I came upon it last summer and dug and burned it out until I made a snug cave in the tree that I now call home.

"My bed is on the right as you enter, and is made of ash slats and covered with deerskin. On the left is a small fireplace about knee high. It is of clay and stones. It has a chimney that leads the smoke out through a knothole. I chipped out three other knotholes to let fresh air in. The air coming in is bitter cold. It must be below zero outside, and yet I can sit here inside my tree and write with bare hands. The fire is small, too. It doesn't take much fire to warm this tree room.

"It is the fourth of December, I think. It may be the fifth. I am not sure because I have not recently counted the notches in the aspen pole that is my calendar. I have been just too busy gathering nuts and berries, smoking venison, fish, and small game to keep up with the exact date.

"The lamp I am writing by is deer fat poured into a turtle shell with a strip of my old city trousers for a wick.

"It snowed all day yesterday and today. I have not been outside since the storm began, and I am bored for the first time since I ran away from home eight months ago to live on the land.

"I am well and healthy. The food is good. Sometimes I eat turtle soup, and I know how to make acorn pancakes. I keep my supplies in the wall of the tree in wooden pockets that I chopped myself.

"Every time I have looked at those pockets during the last two days, I have felt just like a squirrel, which reminds me: I didn't see a squirrel one whole day before that storm began. I guess they are holed up and eating their stored nuts, too.

"I wonder if The Baron, that's the wild weasel who lives behind the big boulder to the north of my tree, is also denned up. Well, anyway, I think the storm is dying down because the tree is not crying so much. When the wind really blows, the whole tree moans right down to the roots, which is where I am.

"Tomorrow I hope The Baron and I can tunnel out into the sunlight. I wonder if I should dig the snow. But that would mean I would have to put it somewhere, and the only place to put it is in my nice snug tree.

Maybe I can pack it with my hands as I go. I've always dug into the snow from the top, never up from under.

"The Baron must dig up from under the snow. I wonder where he puts what he digs? Well, I guess I'll know in the morning."

When I wrote that last winter, I was scared and thought maybe I'd never get out of my tree. I had been scared for two days—ever since the first blizzard hit the Catskill Mountains. When I came up to the sunlight, which I did by simply poking my head into the soft snow and standing up, I laughed at my dark fears.

Everything was white, clean, shining, and beautiful. The sky was blue, blue, blue. The hemlock grove was laced with snow, the meadow was smooth and white, and the gorge was sparkling with ice. It was so beautiful and peaceful that I laughed out loud. I guess I laughed because my first snowstorm was over and it had not been so terrible after all.

Then I shouted, "I did it!" My voice never got very far. It was hushed by the tons of snow.

I looked for signs from The Baron Weasel. His footsteps were all over the boulder, also slides where he had played. He must have been up for hours, enjoying the new snow.

Inspired by his fun, I poked my head into my tree and whistled. Frightful, my trained falcon, flew to my fist, and we jumped and slid down the mountain, making big

holes and trenches as we went. It was good to be whistling and carefree again, because I was sure scared by the coming of that storm.

I had been working since May, learning how to make a fire with flint and steel, finding what plants I could eat, how to trap animals and catch fish—all this so that when the curtain of blizzard struck the Catskills, I could crawl inside my tree and be comfortably warm and have plenty to eat.

During the summer and fall I had thought about the coming of winter. However, on that third day of December when the sky blackened, the temperature dropped, and the first flakes swirled around me. I must admit that I wanted to run back to New York. Even the first night that I spent out in the woods, when I couldn't get the fire started, was not as frightening as the snowstorm that gathered behind the gorge and mushroomed up over my mountain.

I was smoking three trout. It was nine o'clock in the morning. I was busy keeping the flames low so they would not leap up and burn the fish. As I worked, it occurred to me that it was awfully dark for that hour of the morning. Frightful was leashed to her tree stub. She seemed restless and pulled at her tethers. Then I realized that the forest was dead quiet. Even the woodpeckers that had been tapping around me all morning were silent. The squirrels were nowhere to be seen. The juncos and chickadees and nuthatches were gone. I looked to see what The Baron Weasel was doing. He was not around. I looked up.

From my tree you can see the gorge beyond the meadow. White water pours between the black wet boulders and cascades into the valley below. The water that day was as dark as the rocks. Only the sound told me it was still falling. Above the darkness stood another darkness. The clouds of winter, black and fearsome. They looked as wild as the winds that were bringing them. I grew sick with fright. I knew I had enough food. I knew everything was going to be perfectly all right. But knowing that didn't help. I was scared. I stamped out the fire and pocketed the fish.

I tried to whistle for Frightful, but couldn't purse my shaking lips tight enough to get out anything but *pfffff.* So I grabbed her by the hide straps that are attached to her legs and we dove through the deerskin door into my room in the tree.

I put Frightful on the bedpost, and curled up in a ball on the bed. I thought about New York and the noise and the lights and how a snowstorm always seemed very friendly there. I thought about our apartment, too. At that moment it seemed bright and lighted and warm. I had to keep saying to myself: There were eleven of us in it! Dad, Mother, four sisters, four brothers, and me. And not one of us liked it, except perhaps little Nina, who was too young to know. Dad didn't like it even a little bit. He had been a sailor once, but when I was born, he gave up the sea and worked on the docks in New York. Dad didn't like the land. He liked the sea, wet and big and endless.

Sometimes he would tell me about Great-grandfather Gribley, who owned land in the Catskill Mountains and felled the trees and built a home and plowed the land—only to discover that he wanted to be a sailor. The farm failed, and Great-grandfather Gribley went to sea.

As I lay with my face buried in the sweet greasy smell of my deerskin, I could hear Dad's voice saying, "That land is still in the family's name. Somewhere in the Catskills is an old beech with the name *Gribley* carved on it. It marks the northern boundary of Gribley's folly—the land is no place for a Gribley."

"The land is no place for a Gribley," I said. "The land is no place for a Gribley, and here I am three hundred feet from the beech with *Gribley* carved on it."

I fell asleep at that point, and when I awoke I was hungry. I cracked some walnuts, got down the acorn flour I had pounded, with a bit of ash to remove the bite, reached out the door for a little snow, and stirred up some acorn pancakes. I cooked them on a top of a tin can, and as I ate them, smothered with blueberry jam, I knew that the land was just the place for a Gribley.

IN WHICH
I Get Started on This Venture

I left New York in May. I had a penknife, a ball of cord, an ax, and $40, which I had saved from selling magazine subscriptions. I also had some flint and steel which

I had bought at a Chinese store in the city. The man in the store had showed me how to use it. He had also given me a little purse to put it in, and some tinder to catch the sparks. He had told me that if I ran out of tinder, I should burn cloth, and use the charred ashes.

I thanked him and said, "This is the kind of thing I am not going to forget."

On the train north to the Catskills I unwrapped my flint and steel and practiced hitting them together to make sparks. On the wrapping paper I made these notes.

"A hard brisk strike is best. Remember to hold the steel in the left hand and the flint in the right, and hit the steel with the flint.

"The trouble is the sparks go every which way."

And that *was* the trouble. I did not get a fire going that night, and as I mentioned, this was a scary experience.

I hitched rides into the Catskill Mountains. At about four o'clock a truck driver and I passed through a beautiful dark hemlock forest, and I said to him, "This is as far as I am going."

He looked all around and said, "You live here?"

"No," I said, "but I am running away from home, and this is just the kind of forest I have always dreamed I would run to. I think I'll camp here tonight." I hopped out of the cab.

"Hey, boy," the driver shouted. "Are you serious?"

"Sure," I said.

"Well, now, ain't that sumpin'? You know, when I was your age, I did the same thing. Only thing was, I was a farm boy and ran to the city, and you're a city boy running to the woods. I was scared of the city—do you think you'll be scared of the woods?"

"Heck, no!" I shouted loudly.

As I marched into the cool shadowy woods, I heard the driver call to me, "I'll be back in the morning, if you want to ride home."

He laughed. Everybody laughed at me. Even Dad. I told Dad that I was going to run away to Great-grandfather Gribley's land. He had roared with laughter and told me about the time he had run away from home. He got on a boat headed for Singapore, but when the whistle blew for departure, he was down the gangplank and home in bed before anyone knew he was gone. Then he told me, "Sure, go try it. Every boy should try it."

I must have walked a mile into the woods until I found a stream. It was a clear athletic stream that rushed and ran and jumped and splashed. Ferns grew along its bank, and its rocks were upholstered with moss.

I sat down, smelled the piney air, and took out my penknife. I cut off a green twig and began to whittle. I have always been good at whittling. I carved a ship once that my teacher exhibited for parents' night at school.

First I whittled an angle on one end of the twig. Then I cut a smaller twig and sharpened it to a point. I whittled an angle on that twig, and bound the two angles face to face with a strip of green bark. It was supposed to be a fishhook.

According to a book on how to survive on the land that I read in the New York Public Library, this was the way to make your own hooks. I then dug for worms. I had hardly chopped the moss away with my ax before I hit frost. It had not occurred to me that there would be frost in the ground in May, but then, I had not been on a mountain before.

This did worry me, because I was depending on fish to keep me alive until I got to my great-grandfather's mountain, where I was going to make traps and catch game.

I looked into the stream to see what else I could eat, and as I did, my hand knocked a rotten log apart. I remembered about old logs and all the sleeping stages of insects that are in it. I chopped away until I found a cold white grub.

I swiftly tied a string to my hook, put the grub on, and walked up the stream looking for a good place to fish. All the manuals I had read were very emphatic about where fish lived, and so I had memorized this: "In streams, fish usually congregate in pools and deep calm water. The heads of riffles, small rapids, the tail of a pool, eddies below rocks or logs, deep undercut banks, in the shade of overhanging bushes—all are very likely places to fish."

This stream did not seem to have any calm water, and I must have walked a thousand miles before I found a pool by a deep undercut bank in the shade of overhanging bushes. Actually, it wasn't that far, it just seemed that way because as I went looking and finding nothing, I was sure I was going to starve to death.

I squatted on this bank and dropped in my line. I did so want to catch a fish. One fish would set me upon my way, because I had read how much you can learn from one fish. By examining the contents of its stomach you can find what the other fish are eating or you can use the internal organs as bait.

The grub went down to the bottom of the stream. It swirled around and hung still. Suddenly the string came

to life, and rode back and forth and around in a circle. I pulled with a powerful jerk. The hook came apart, and whatever I had went circling back to its bed.

Well, that almost made me cry. My bait was gone, my hook was broken, and I was getting cold, frightened, and mad. I whittled another hook, but this time I cheated and used string to wind it together instead of bark. I walked back to the log and luckily found another grub. I hurried to the pool, and I flipped a trout out of the water before I knew I had a bite.

The fish flopped, and I threw my whole body over it. I could not bear to think of it flopping itself back into the stream.

I cleaned it like I had seen the man at the fish market do, examined its stomach, and found it empty. This horrified me. What I didn't know was that an empty stomach means the fish are hungry and will eat about anything. However, I thought at the time that I was a goner. Sadly, I put some of the internal organs on my hook, and before I could get my line to the bottom I had another bite. I lost that one, but got the next one. I stopped when I had five nice little trout and looked around for a place to build a camp and make a fire.

It wasn't hard to find a pretty spot along that stream. I selected a place beside a mossy rock in a circle of hemlocks.

I decided to make a bed before I cooked. I cut off some boughs for a mattress, then I leaned some dead limbs against the boulder and covered them with hemlock limbs. This made a kind of tent. I crawled in, lay down, and felt alone and secret and very excited.

But ah, the rest of this story! I was on the northeast side of the mountain. It grew dark and cold early. Seeing the shadows slide down on me, I frantically ran around gathering firewood. This is about the only thing

I did right from that moment until dawn, because I remembered that the driest wood in a forest is the dead limbs that are still on the trees, and I gathered an enormous pile of them. That pile must still be there, for I never got a fire going.

I got sparks, sparks, sparks. I even hit the tinder with the sparks. The tinder burned all right, but that was as far as I got. I blew on it, I breathed on it, I cupped it in my hands, but no sooner did I add twigs than the whole thing went black.

Then it got too dark to see. I clicked steel and flint together, even though I couldn't see the tinder. Finally, I gave up and crawled into my hemlock tent, hungry, cold, and miserable.

I can talk about that first night now, although it is still embarrassing to me because I was so stupid, and scared, that I hate to admit it.

I had made my hemlock bed right in the stream valley where the wind drained down from the cold mountaintop. It might have been all right if I had made it on the other side of the boulder, but I didn't. I was right on the main highway of the cold winds as they tore down upon the valley below. I didn't have enough hemlock boughs under me, and before I had my head down, my stomach was cold and damp. I took some boughs off the roof and stuffed them under me, and then my shoulders were cold. I curled up in a ball and was almost asleep when a whippoorwill called. If you have ever been within forty feet of a whippoorwill, you will understand why I couldn't even shut my eyes. They are deafening!

Well, anyway, the whole night went like that. I don't think I slept fifteen minutes, and I was so scared and tired that my throat was dry. I wanted a drink but didn't dare go near the stream for fear of making a misstep and falling in and getting wet. So I sat tight,

and shivered and shook—and now I am able to say—I cried a little tiny bit.

Fortunately, the sun has a wonderfully glorious habit of rising every morning. When the sky lightened, when the birds awoke, I knew I would never again see anything so splendid as the round red sun coming up over the earth.

I was immediately cheered, and set out directly for the highway. Somehow, I thought that if I was a little nearer the road, everything would be all right.

I climbed a hill and stopped. There was a house. A house warm and cozy, with smoke coming out the chimney and lights in the windows, and only a hundred feet from my torture camp.

Without considering my pride, I ran down the hill and banged on the door. A nice old man answered. I told him everything in one long sentence, and then said, "And so, can I cook my fish here, because I haven't eaten in years."

He chuckled, stroked his whiskery face, and took the fish. He had them cooking in a pan before I knew what his name was.

When I asked him, he said Bill something, but I never heard his last name because I fell asleep in his rocking chair that was pulled up beside his big hot glorious wood stove in the kitchen.

I ate the fish some hours later, also some bread, jelly, oatmeal, and cream. Then he said to me, "Sam Gribley, if you are going to run off and live in the woods, you better learn how to make a fire. Come with me."

We spent the afternoon practicing. I penciled these notes on the back of a scrap of paper, so I wouldn't forget.

"When the tinder glows, keep blowing and add fine dry needles one by one—and keep blowing, steadily, lightly, and evenly. Add one inch dry twigs to the needles and then give her a good big handful of small dry stuff. Keep blowing."

THE MANNER IN WHICH
I Find Gribley's Farm

The next day I told Bill good-by, and as I strode, warm and fed, onto the road, he called to me, "I'll see you tonight. The back door will be open if you want a roof over your head."

I said, "Okay," but I knew I wouldn't see Bill again. I knew how to make fire, and that was my weapon. With fire I could conquer the Catskills. I also knew how to fish. To fish and to make a fire. That was all I needed to know, I thought.

Three rides that morning took me to Delhi. Somewhere around here was Great-grandfather's beech tree with the name *Gribley* carved on it. This much I knew from Dad's stories.

By six o'clock I still had not found anyone who had even heard of the Gribleys, much less Gribley's beech, and so I slept on the porch of a schoolhouse and ate chocolate bars for supper. It was cold and hard, but I was so tired I could have slept in a wind tunnel.

At dawn I thought real hard: Where would I find out about the Gribley farm? Some old map, I said. Where would I find an old map? The library? Maybe. I'd try it and see.

The librarian was very helpful. She was sort of young, had brown hair and brown eyes, and loved books as much as I did.

The library didn't open until ten-thirty. I got there at nine. After I had lolled and rolled and sat on the steps for fifteen or twenty minutes, the door whisked open, and this tall lady asked me to come on in and browse around until opening time.

All I said to her was that I wanted to find the old Gribley farm, and that the Gribleys hadn't lived on it for maybe a hundred years, and she was off. I can still hear her heels click, when I think of her, scattering herself around those shelves finding me old maps, histories of the Catskills, and files of letters and deeds that must have come from attics around Delhi.

Miss Turner—that was her name—found it. She found Gribley's farm in an old book of Delaware County. Then she worked out the roads to it, and drew me maps and everything. Finally she said, "What do you want to know for? Some school project?"

"Oh, no, Miss Turner, I want to go live there."

"But, Sam, it is all forest and trees now. The house is probably only a foundation covered with moss."

"That's just what I want. I am going to trap animals and eat nuts and bulbs and berries and make myself a house. You see, I am Sam Gribley, and I thought I would like to live on my great-grandfather's farm."

Miss Turner was the only person that believed me. She smiled, sat back in her chair, and said, "Well, I declare."

The library was just opening when I gathered the notes we had made and started off. As I pushed open the door, Miss Turner leaned over and said to me, "Sam, we have some very good books on plants and trees and animals, in case you get stuck."

I knew what she was thinking, and so I told her I would remember that.

With Miss Turner's map, I found the first stone wall that marked the farm. The old roads to it were all grown up and mostly gone, but by locating the stream at the bottom of the mountain I was able to begin at the bridge and go north and up a mile and a half. There, caterpillaring around boulders, roller-coastering up ravines and down hills, was the mound of rocks that had once been Great-grandfather's boundary fence.

And then, do you know, I couldn't believe I was there. I sat on the old gray stones a long time, looking through the forest, up that steep mountain, and saying to myself, "It must be Sunday afternoon, and it's raining, and Dad is trying to keep us all quiet by telling us about Great-grandfather's farm; and he's telling it so real that I can see it."

And then I said, "No. I am here, because I was never this hungry before."

I wanted to run all the way back to the library and tell Miss Turner that I had found it. Partly because she would have liked to have known, and partly because Dad had said to me as I left, "If you find the place, tell someone at Delhi. I may visit you someday." Of course, he was kidding, because he thought I'd be home the next day, but after many weeks, maybe he would think I meant what I said, and he might come see me.

However, I was too hungry to run back. I took my hook and line and went back down the mountain to the stream.

I caught a big old catfish. I climbed back to the stone wall in great spirits.

It was getting late and so I didn't try to explore. I went right to work making a fire. I decided that even if I didn't have enough time to cut boughs for a bed, I was going to have cooked fish and a fire to huddle around during those cold night hours. May is not exactly warm in the Catskills.

By firelight that night I wrote this:

"Dear Bill [that was the old man]:

"After three tries, I finally got a handful of dry grass on the glow in the tinder. Grass is even better than pine needles, and tomorrow I am going to try the outside bark of the river birch. I read somewhere that it has combustible oil in it that the Indians used to start fires. Anyway, I did just what you showed me, and had cooked catfish for dinner. It was good.

Your friend,
Sam."

After I wrote that I remembered I didn't know his last name, and so I stuffed the note in my pocket, made myself a bed of boughs and leaves in the shelter of the stone wall, and fell right to sleep.

I must say this now about that first fire. It was magic. Out of dead tinder and grass and sticks came a live warm light. It cracked and snapped and smoked and filled the woods with brightness. It lighted the trees and made them warm and friendly. It stood tall and bright and held back the night. Oh, this was a different night than the first dark frightful one. Also I was stuffed on catfish. I have since learned to cook it more, but never have I enjoyed a meal as much as that one, and never have I felt so independent again.

IN WHICH
I Find Many Useful Plants

The following morning I stood up, stretched, and looked about me. Birds were dripping from the trees, little birds, singing and flying and pouring over the limbs.

"This must be the warbler migration," I said, and I laughed because there were so many birds. I had never seen so many. My big voice rolled through the woods, and their little voices seemed to rise and answer me.

They were eating. Three or four in a maple tree near me were darting along the limbs, pecking and snatching at something delicious on the trees. I wondered if there was anything there for a hungry boy. I pulled a limb down, and all I saw were leaves, twigs, and flowers. I ate a flower. It was not very good. One manual I had read said to watch what the birds and animals were eating in order to learn what is edible and nonedible in the forest. If the animal life can eat it, it is safe for humans. The book did suggest that a raccoon had tastes more nearly like ours. Certainly the birds were no example.

Then I wondered if they were not eating something I couldn't see—tiny insects perhaps; well, anyway, whatever it was, I decided to fish. I took my line and hook and walked down to the stream.

I lay on a log and dangled my line in the bright water. The fish were not biting. That made me hungrier. My stomach pinched. You know, it really does hurt to be terribly hungry.

A stream is supposed to be full of food. It is the easiest place to get a lot of food in a hurry. I needed something in a hurry, but what? I looked through the clear water and saw the tracks of mussels in the mud. I ran along the log back to shore, took off my clothes, and plunged into that icy water.

I collected almost a peck of mussels in very little time at all, and began tying them in my sweater to carry them back to camp.

But I don't have to carry them anywhere, I said to myself. I have my fire in my pocket, I don't need a table. I can sit right here by the stream and eat. And so I did. I wrapped the mussels in leaves and sort of steamed them in coals. They are not quite as good as clams—a little stronger, I would say—but by the time I had eaten three, I had forgotten what clams tasted like and knew only how delicious freshwater mussels were. I actually got full.

I wandered back to Great-grandfather's farm and began to explore. Most of the acreage was maple and beech, some pine, dogwoods, ash; and here and there a glorious hickory. I made a sketch of the farm on my road map, and put *x's* where the hickories were. They were gold trees to me. I would have hickory nuts in the fall. I could also make salt from hickory limbs. I cut off one and chopped it into bits and scraps. I stuck them in my sweater.

The land was up and down and up and down, and I wondered how Great-grandfather ever cut it and plowed it. There was one stream running through it, which I was glad to see, for it meant I did not have to go all the way down the mountain to the big creek for fish and water.

Around noon I came upon what I was sure was the old foundation of the house. Miss Turner was right. It was ruins—a few stones in a square, a slight depression for the basement, and trees growing right up through what had once been the living room. I wandered around to see what was left of the Gribley home.

After a few looks I saw an apple tree. I rushed up to it, hoping to find an old apple. No apples beneath it. About forty feet away, however, I found a dried one in the crotch of a tree, stuck there by a squirrel and forgotten. I ate it. It was pretty bad—but nourishing, I hoped. There was another apple tree and three walnuts. I scribbled *x*'s. These were wonderful finds.

I poked around the foundations, hoping to uncover some old iron implements that I could use. I found nothing. Too many leaves had fallen and turned to loam, too many plants had grown up and died down over the old home site. I decided to come back when I had made myself a shovel.

Whistling and looking for food and shelter, I went on up the mountain, following the stone walls, discovering many things about my property. I found a marsh. In it were cattails and arrow-leaf—good starchy foods.

At high noon I stepped onto a mountain meadow. An enormous boulder rose up in the center of it. At the top of the meadow was a fringe of white birch. There were maples and oaks to the west, and a hemlock forest to the right that pulled me right across the sweet grasses, into it.

Never, never have I seen such trees. They were giants—old, old giants. They must have begun when the world began.

I started walking around them. I couldn't hear myself step, so dense and damp were the needles. Great boulders covered with ferns and moss stood among them. They looked like pebbles beneath those trees.

Standing before the biggest and the oldest and the most kinglike of them all, I suddenly had an idea.

THIS IS ABOUT
The Old, Old Tree

I knew enough about the Catskill Mountains to know that when the summer came, they were covered with people. Although Great-grandfather's farm was somewhat remote, still hikers and campers and hunters and fishermen were sure to wander across it.

Therefore I wanted a house that could not be seen. People would want to take me back where I belonged if they found me.

I looked at that tree. Somehow I knew it was home, but I was not quite sure how it was home. The limbs were high and not right for a tree house. I could build a bark extension around it, but that would look silly. Slowly I circled the great trunk. Halfway around the whole plan became perfectly obvious. To the west, between two of the flanges of the tree that spread out to be roots, was a cavity. The heart of the tree was rotting away. I scraped at it with my hands; old, rotten insect-ridden dust came tumbling out. I dug on and on, using my ax from time to time as my excitement grew.

With much of the old rot out, I could crawl in the tree and sit cross-legged. Inside I felt as cozy as a turtle in its shell. I chopped and chopped until I was hungry and exhausted. I was now in the hard good wood, and chopping it out was work. I was afraid December would come before I got a hole big enough to lie in. So I sat down to think.

You know, those first days, I just never planned right. I had the beginnings of a home, but not a bite to eat, and I had worked so hard that I could hardly move forward to find that bite. Furthermore, it was discouraging to feed that body of mine. It was never satisfied, and gathering food for it took time and got it hungrier. Trying to get a place to rest it took time and got it more tired, and I really felt I was going in circles

and wondered how primitive man ever had enough time and energy to stop hunting food and start thinking about fire and tools.

I left the tree and went across the meadow looking for food. I plunged into the woods beyond, and there I discovered the gorge and the white cascade splashing down the black rocks into the pool below.

I was hot and dirty. I scrambled down the rocks and slipped into the pool. It was so cold I yelled. But when I came out on the bank and put on my two pairs of trousers and three sweaters, which I thought was a better way to carry clothes than in a pack, I tingled and burned and felt coltish. I leapt up the bank, slipped, and my face went down in a patch of dogtooth violets.

You would know them anywhere after a few looks at them at the Botanical Gardens and in colored flower books. They are little yellow lilies on long slender stems with oval leaves dappled with gray. But that's not all. They have wonderfully tasty bulbs. I was filling my pockets before I got up from my fall.

"I'll have a salad type lunch," I said as I moved up the steep sides of the ravine. I discovered that as late as it was in the season, the spring beauties were still blooming in the cool pockets of the woods. They are all right raw, that is if you are as hungry as I was. They taste a little like lima beans. I ate these as I went on hunting food, feeling better and better, until I worked my way back to the meadow where the dandelions were blooming. Funny I hadn't noticed them earlier. Their greens are good, and so are their roots—a little strong and milky, but you get used to that.

A crow flew into the aspen grove without saying a

word. The little I knew of crows from following them in Central Park, they always have something to say. But this bird was sneaking, obviously trying to be quiet. Birds are good food. Crow is certainly not the best, but I did not know that then, and I launched out to see where it was going. I had a vague plan to try to noose it. This is the kind of thing I wasted time on in those days when time was so important. However, this venture turned out all right, because I did not have to noose that bird.

I stepped into the woods, looked around, could not see the crow, but noticed a big stick nest in a scrabbly pine. I started to climb the tree. Off flew the crow. What made me keep on climbing in face of such discouragement, I don't know, but I did, and that noon I had crow eggs and wild salad for lunch.

At lunch I also solved the problem of carving out my tree. After a struggle I made a fire. Then I sewed a big skunk cabbage leaf into a cup with grass strands. I had read that you can boil water in a leaf, and ever since then I had been very anxious to see if this were true. It seems impossible, but it works. I boiled the eggs in a leaf. The water keeps the leaf wet, and although the top dries up and burns down to the water level, that's as far as the burning goes. I was pleased to see it work.

Then here's what happened. Naturally, all this took a lot of time, and I hadn't gotten very far on my tree, so I was fretting and stamping out the fire when I stopped with my foot in the air.

The fire! Indians made dugout canoes with fire. They burned them out, an easier and much faster way of getting results. I would try fire in the tree. If I was very careful, perhaps it would work. I ran into the hemlock forest with a burning stick and got a fire going inside the tree.

Thinking that I ought to have a bucket of water in case things got out of hand, I looked desperately around me. The water was far across the meadow and down the ravine. This would never do. I began to think the whole inspiration of a home in the tree was no good. I really did have to live near water for cooking and drinking and comfort. I looked sadly at the magnificent hemlock and was about to put the fire out and desert it when I said something to myself. It must have come out of some book: "Hemlocks usually grow around mountain streams and springs."

I swirled on my heel. Nothing but boulders around

me. But the air was damp, somewhere—I said—and darted around the rocks, peering and looking and sniffing and going down into pockets and dales. No water. I was coming back, circling wide, when I almost fell in it. Two sentinel boulders, dripping wet, decorated with flowers, ferns, moss, weeds—everything that loved water—guarded a bathtub-sized spring.

"You pretty thing," I said, flopped on my stomach, and pushed my face into it to drink. I opened my eyes. The water was like glass, and in it were little insects with oars. They rowed away from me. Beetles skittered like bullets on the surface, or carried a silver bubble of air with them to the bottom. Ha, then I saw a crayfish.

I jumped up, overturned rocks, and found many crayfish. At first I hesitated to grab them because they can pinch. I gritted my teeth, thought about how much more it hurts to be hungry, and came down upon them. I did get pinched, but I had my dinner. And that was the first time I had planned ahead! Any planning that I did in those early days was such a surprise to me and so successful that I was delighted with even a small plan. I wrapped the crayfish in leaves, stuffed them in my pockets, and went back to the burning tree.

Bucket of water, I thought. Bucket of water? Where was I going to get a bucket? How did I think, even if I found water, I could get it back to the tree? That's how citified I was in those days. I had never lived without a bucket before—scrub buckets, water buckets—and so when a water problem came up, I just thought I could run to the kitchen and get a bucket.

"Well, dirt is as good as water," I said as I ran back to my tree. "I can smother the fire with dirt."

Days passed working, burning, cutting, gathering food, and each day I cut another notch on an aspen pole that I had stuck in the ground for a calendar.

IN WHICH
I Meet One of My Own Kind and Have a Terrible Time Getting Away

Five notches into June, my house was done. I could stand in it, lie down in it, and there was room left over for a stump to sit on. On warm evenings I would lie on my stomach and look out the door, listen to the frogs and nighthawks, and hope it would storm so that I could crawl into my tree and be dry. I had gotten soaked during a couple of May downpours, and now that my house was done, I wanted the chance to sit in my hemlock and watch a cloudburst wet everything but me. This opportunity didn't come for a long time. It was dry.

One morning I was at the edge of the meadow. I had cut down a small ash tree and was chopping it into lengths of about eighteen inches each. This was the beginning of my bed that I was planning to work on after supper every night.

With the golden summer upon me, food was much easier to get, and I actually had several hours of free time after supper in which to do other things. I had been eating frogs' legs, turtles, and best of all, an occasional rabbit. My snares and traps were set now. Furthermore, I had a good supply of cattail roots I had dug in the marsh.

If you ever eat cattails, be sure to cook them well, otherwise the fibers are tough and they take more chewing to get the starchy food from them than they are worth. However, they taste just like potatoes after you've been eating them a couple of weeks, and to my way of thinking are extremely good.

Well, anyway, that summer morning when I was gathering material for a bed, I was singing and chopping and playing a game with a raccoon I had come to know. He had just crawled in a hollow tree and had gone to bed for the day when I came to the meadow. From time to time I would tap on his tree with my ax. He would hang his sleepy head out, snarl at me, close his eyes, and slide out of sight.

The third time I did this, I knew something was happening in the forest. Instead of closing his eyes, he pricked up his ears and his face became drawn and tense. His eyes were focused on something down the mountain. I stood up and looked. I could see nothing.

This device is set along an animal's runway.

game snare

bait

This one will work sometimes, too.

I squatted down and went back to work. The raccoon dove out of sight.

"Now what's got you all excited?" I said, and tried once more to see what he had seen.

I finished the posts for the bed and was looking around for a bigger ash to fell and make slats for the springs when I nearly jumped out of my shoes.

"Now what are you doing up here all alone?" It was a human voice. I swung around and stood face to face with a little old lady in a pale blue sunbonnet and a loose brown dress.

"Oh! Gosh!" I said. "Don't scare me like that. Say one word at a time until I get used to a human voice." I must have looked frightened because she chuckled, smoothed down the front of her dress, and whispered, "Are you lost?"

"Oh, no, ma'am," I stuttered.

"Then a little fellow like you should not be all alone way up here on this haunted mountain."

"Haunted?" said I.

"Yes, indeed. There's an old story says there are little men up here who play ninepins right down in that gorge in the twilight." She peered at me. "Are you one of them?"

"Oh, no, no, no, no," I said. "I read that story. It's just make-believe." I laughed, and she puckered her forehead.

"Well, come on," she said, "make some use of yourself and help me fill this basket with strawberries."

I hesitated—she meant *my* strawberry supply.

"Now, get on with you. A boy your age should be doing something worthwhile, 'stead of playing mumbly peg with sticks. Come on, young man." She jogged me out into the meadow.

We worked quite a while before we said any more. Frankly, I was wondering how to save my precious, precious strawberries, and I may say I picked slowly. Every time I dropped one in her basket, I thought how good it would taste.

"Where do ye live?" I jumped. It is terribly odd to hear a voice after weeks of listening only to birds and raccoons, and what is more, to hear the voice ask a question like that.

"I live here," I said.

"Ye mean Delhi. Fine. You can walk me home."

Nothing I added did any good. She would not be shaken from her belief that I lived in Delhi. So I let it go.

We must have reaped every last strawberry before she stood up, put her arm in mine and escorted me down the mountain. I certainly was not escorting her. Her wiry little arms were like crayfish pinchers. I couldn't have gotten away if I had tried. So I walked and listened.

She told me all the local and world news, and it was rather pleasant to hear about the National League, an atom bomb test, and a Mr. Riley's three-legged dog that chased her chickens. In the middle of all this chatter she said, "That's the best strawberry patch in the entire Catskill range. I come up here every spring. For forty years I've come to that meadow for my strawberries. It gits harder every year, but there's no jam can beat the jam from that mountain. I know. I've been around here all my life." Then she went right into the New York Yanks without putting in a period.

As I helped her across the stream on big boulders, I heard a cry in the sky. I looked up. Swinging down the valley on long pointed wings was a large bird. I was struck by the ease and swiftness of its flight.

"Duck hawk," she said. "Nest around here every year. My man used to shoot 'em. He said they killed chickens, but I don't believe it. The only thing that kills chickens is Mr. Riley's three-legged dog."

She tipped and teetered as she crossed the rocks, but kept right on talking and stepping as if she knew that no matter what, she would get across.

We finally reached the road. I wasn't listening to her very much. I was thinking about the duck hawk. This bird, I was sure, was the peregrine falcon, the king's hunting bird.

"I will get one. I will train it to hunt for me," I said to myself.

Finally I got the little lady to her brown house at the edge of town.

She turned fiercely upon me. I started back.

"Where are you going, young man?"

I stopped. Now, I thought, she is going to march me into town. Into town? Well, that's where I'll go then, I said to myself. And I turned on my heel, smiled at her, and replied, "To the library."

The King's Provider

Miss Turner was glad to see me. I told her I wanted some books on hawks and falcons, and she located a few, although there was not much to be had on the subject. We worked all afternoon, and I learned enough. I departed when the library closed. Miss Turner whispered to me as I left, "Sam, you need a haircut."

I hadn't seen myself in so long that this had not occurred to me. "Gee, I don't have any scissors."

She thought a minute, got out her library scissors, and sat me down on the back steps. She did a fine job, and I looked like any other boy who had played hard all day, and who, with a little soap and water after supper, would be going off to bed in a regular house.

I didn't get back to my tree that night. The May apples were ripe, and I stuffed on those as I went through the woods. They taste like a very sweet banana, are earthy and a little slippery. But I liked them.

At the stream I caught a trout. Everybody thinks a trout is hard to catch because of all the fancy gear and flies and lines sold for trout fishing, but, honestly, they are easier to catch than any other fish. They have big mouths and snatch and swallow whole anything they see when they are hungry. With my wooden hook in its mouth, the trout was mine. The trouble is that trout are not hungry when most people have time to fish. I knew they were hungry that evening because the creek was swirling, and minnows and everything else were jumping out of the water. When you see that, go fish. You'll get them.

I made a fire on a flat boulder in the stream, and cooked the trout. I did this so I could watch the sky. I wanted to see the falcon again. I also put the trout head on the hook and dropped it in the pool. A snapping turtle would view a trout head with relish.

I waited for the falcon patiently. I didn't have to go anywhere. After an hour or so, I was rewarded. A slender speck came from the valley and glided above the stream. It was still far away when it folded its wings and bombed the earth. I watched. It arose, clumsy and big—carrying food—and winged back to the valley.

I sprinted down the stream and made myself a lean-to near some cliffs where I thought the bird had disappeared. Having learned that day that duck hawks prefer to nest on cliffs, I settled for this site.

Early the next morning, I got up and dug the tubers of the arrow-leaf that grew along the stream bank. I baked these and boiled mussels for breakfast, then I curled up behind a willow and watched the cliff.

The falcons came in from behind me and circled the stream. They had apparently been out hunting before I had gotten up, as they were returning with food. This was exciting news. They were feeding young, and I was somewhere near the nest.

I watched one of them swing in to the cliff and disappear. A few minutes later it winged out empty-footed. I marked the spot mentally and said, "Ha!"

After splashing across the stream in the shallows, I stood at the bottom of the cliff and wondered how on earth I was going to climb the sheer wall.

I wanted a falcon so badly, however, that I dug in with my toes and hands and started up. The first part was easy; it was not too steep. When I thought I was stuck, I found a little ledge and shinnied up to it.

I was high, and when I looked down, the stream spun. I decided not to look down anymore. I edged up to another ledge, and lay down on it to catch my breath. I was shaking from exertion and I was tired.

I looked up to see how much higher I had to go when my hand touched something moist. I pulled it back and saw that it was white—bird droppings. Then I saw them. Almost where my hand had been sat three fuzzy whitish gray birds. Their wide-open mouths gave them a startled look.

"Oh, hello, hello," I said. "You are cute."

When I spoke, all three blinked at once. All three heads turned and followed my hand as I swung it up and toward them. All three watched my hand with opened mouths. They were marvelous. I chuckled. But I couldn't reach them.

I wormed forward, and *wham!*—something hit my shoulder. It pained. I turned my head to see the big female. She had hit me. She winged out, banked, and started back for another strike.

Now I was scared, for I was sure she would cut me wide open. With sudden nerve, I stood up, stepped forward, and picked up the biggest of the nestlings. The females are bigger than the males. They are the "falcons." They are the pride of kings. I tucked her in my sweater and leaned against the cliff, facing the bulletlike dive of the falcon. I threw out my foot as she struck, and the sole of my tennis shoe took the blow.

The female was now gathering speed for another attack, and when I say speed, I mean 50 to 60 miles an hour. I could see myself battered and torn, lying in the valley below, and I said to myself, "Sam Gribley, you had better get down from here like a rabbit."

I jumped to the ledge below, found it was really quite wide, slid on the seat of my pants to the next ledge, and stopped. The hawk apparently couldn't count. She did not know I had a youngster, for she checked her nest, saw the open mouths, and then she forgot me.

I scrambled to the riverbed somehow, being very careful not to hurt the hot fuzzy body that was against my own. However, Frightful, as I called her right then and there because of the difficulties we had had in getting together, did not think so gently of me. She dug her talons into my skin to brace herself during the bumpy ride to the ground.

I stumbled to the stream, placed her in a nest of buttercups, and dropped beside her. I fell asleep.

When I awoke my eyes opened on two gray eyes in a white stroobly head. Small pinfeathers were sticking out of the stroobly down, like feathers in an Indian quiver. The big blue beak curled down in a snarl and up in a smile.

"Oh, Frightful," I said, "you are a raving beauty."

Frightful fluffed her nubby feathers and shook. I picked her up in the cup of my hands and held her under my chin. I stuck my nose in the deep warm fuzz. It smelled dusty and sweet.

I liked that bird. Oh, how I liked that bird from that smelly minute. It was so pleasant to feel the beating life and see the funny little awkward movements of a young thing.

The legs pushed out between my fingers, I gathered them up, together with the thrashing wings, and tucked the bird in one piece under my chin. I rocked.

"Frightful," I said. "You will enjoy what we are going to do."

I washed my bleeding shoulder in the creek, tucked the torn threads of my sweater back into the hole they had come out of, and set out for my tree.

A BRIEF ACCOUNT OF *What I Did About the First Man Who Was After Me*

At the edge of the meadow, I sensed all was not well at camp. How I knew there was a human being there was not clear to me then. I can only say that after living so long with the birds and animals, the movement of a human is like the difference between the explosion of a cap pistol and a cannon.

I wormed toward camp. When I could see the man

I felt to be there, I stopped and looked. He was wearing a forester's uniform. Immediately I thought they had sent someone out to bring me in, and I began to shake. Then I realized that I didn't have to go back to meet the man at all. I was perfectly free and capable of settling down anywhere. My tree was just a pleasant habit.

I circled the meadow and went over to the gorge. On the way I checked a trap. It was a deadfall. A figure four under a big rock. The rock was down. The food was rabbit.

I picked a comfortable place just below the rim of the gorge where I could pop up every now and then and watch my tree. Here I dressed down the rabbit and fed Frightful some of the more savory bites from a young falcon's point of view: the liver, the heart, the brain. She ate in gulps. As I watched her swallow I sensed a great pleasure. It is hard to explain my feelings at that moment. It seemed marvelous to see life pump through that strange little body of feathers, wordless noises, milk eyes—much as life pumped through me.

The food put the bird to sleep. I watched her eyelids close from the bottom up, and her head quiver. The fuzzy body rocked, the tail spread to steady it, and the little duck hawk almost sighed as she sank into the leaves, sleeping.

I had lots of time. I was going to wait for the man to leave. So I stared at my bird, the beautiful details of the new feathers, the fernlike lashes along the lids, the saucy bristles at the base of the beak. Pleasant hours passed.

Frightful would awaken, I would feed her, she would fall back to sleep, and I would watch the breath rock her body ever so slightly. I was breathing the same way, only not as fast. Her heart beat much faster than mine. She was designed to her bones for a swifter life.

It finally occurred to me that I was very hungry. I stood up to see if the man were gone. He was yawning and pacing.

The sun was slanting on him now, and I could see him quite well. He was a fire warden. Of course, it has not rained, I told myself, for almost three weeks, and the fire planes have been circling the mountains and valleys, patrolling the mountains. Apparently the smoke from my fire was spotted, and a man was sent to check it. I recalled the bare trampled ground around the tree, the fireplace of rocks filled with ashes, the wood chips from the making of my bed, and resolved hereafter to keep my yard clean.

So I made rabbit soup in a tin can I found at the bottom of the gorge. I seasoned it with wild garlic and jack-in-the-pulpit roots.

Jack-in-the-pulpits have three big leaves on a stalk and are easily recognized by the curly striped awning above a stiff, serious preacher named Jack. The jack-in-the-pulpit root, or corm, tastes and looks like potato. It should never be eaten raw.

The fire I made was only of the driest wood, and I made it right at the water's edge. I didn't want a smoky fire on this particular evening.

After supper I made a bough bed and stretched out with Frightful beside me. Apparently, the more you stroke and handle a falcon, the easier they are to train.

I had all sorts of plans for hoods and jesses, as the straps on a falcon are called, and I soon forgot about the man.

Stretched on the boughs, I listened to the wood pewees calling their haunting good nights until I fell sound asleep.

IN WHICH
I Learn to Season My Food

The fire warden made a fire some time in the colder hours of the night. At dawn he was asleep beside white smoldering ashes. I crawled back to the gorge, fed Frightful rabbit bites, and slipped back to the edge of the meadow to check a box trap I had set the day before. I made it by tying small sticks together like a log cabin. This trap was better than the snares or deadfalls. It had caught numerous rabbits, several squirrels, and a groundhog.

I saw, as I inched toward it, that it was closed. The sight of a closed trap excites me to this day. I still can't believe that animals don't understand why delicious food is in such a ridiculous spot.

Well, this morning I pulled the trap deep into the woods to open it. The trapped animal was light. I couldn't guess what it was. It was also active, flipping and darting from one corner to the next. I peeked in to locate it, so that I could grab it quickly behind the head without getting bitten. I was not always successful at this, and had scars to prove it.

I put my eye to the crack. A rumpus arose in the darkness. Two bright eyes shone, and out through that hole that was no wider than a string bean came a weasel. He flew right out at me, landed on my shoulder, gave me a lecture that I shall never forget, and vanished under the scant cover of trillium and bloodroot leaves.

He popped up about five feet away and stood on his hind feet to lecture me again. I said, "Scat!" so he darted right to my knee, put his broad furry paws on my pants, and looked me in the face. I shall never forget the fear and wonder that I felt at the bravery of that weasel. He stood his ground and berated me. I could see by the flashing of his eyes and the curl of his lip that he was furious at me for trapping him. He couldn't talk, but I knew what he meant.

Wonder filled me as I realized he was absolutely unafraid. No other animal, and I knew quite a few by now, had been so brave in my presence. Screaming, he jumped on me. This surprised and scared me. He leapt from my lap to my head, took a mouthful of hair and wrestled it. My goose bumps rose. I was too frightened to move. A good thing, too, because I guess he figured I was not going to fight back and his scream of anger changed to a purr of peace. Still, I couldn't move.

Presently, down he climbed, as stately as royalty, and off he marched, never looking back. He sank beneath the leaves like a fish beneath the water. Not a stem rippled to mark his way.

And so The Baron and I met for the first time, and it was the beginning of a harassing but wonderful friendship.

Frightful had been watching all this. She was tense with fright. Although young and inexperienced, she knew an enemy when she saw one. I picked her up and whispered into her birdy-smelling neck feathers.

"You wild ones know."

Since I couldn't go home, I decided to spend the day in the marsh down the west side of the mountain. There were a lot of cattails and frogs there.

Frightful balanced on my fist as we walked. She had learned that in the short span of one afternoon and a night. She is a very bright bird.

On our way we scared up a deer. It was a doe. I watched her dart gracefully away, and said to Frightful, "That's what I want. I need a door for my house, tethers for you, and a blanket for me. How am I going to get a deer?"

This was not the first time I had said this. The forest was full of deer, and I already had drawn plans on a piece of birch bark for deadfalls, pit traps, and snares. None seemed workable.

The day passed. In the early evening we stole home, tree by tree, to find that the warden had gone. I cleaned up my front yard, scattered needles over the bare spots, and started a small fire with very dry wood that would not smoke much. No more wardens for me. I liked my tree, and although I could live somewhere else, I certainly did not want to.

Once home, I immediately started to work again. I had a device I wanted to try, and put some hickory sticks in a tin can and set it to boiling while I fixed dinner. Before going to bed, I noted this on a piece of birch bark:

"This night I am making salt. I know that people in the early days got along without it, but I think some of these wild foods would taste better with some flavoring. I understand that hickory sticks, boiled dry, leave a salty residue. I am trying it."

In the morning I added:

"It is quite true. The can is dry, and thick with a black substance. It is very salty, and I tried it on frogs' legs for breakfast. It is just what I have needed."

And so I went into salt production for several days, and chipped out a niche inside the tree in which to store it.

"*June 19*

"I finished my bed today. The ash slats work very well, and are quite springy and comfortable. The bed just fits in the right-hand side of the tree. I have hem-

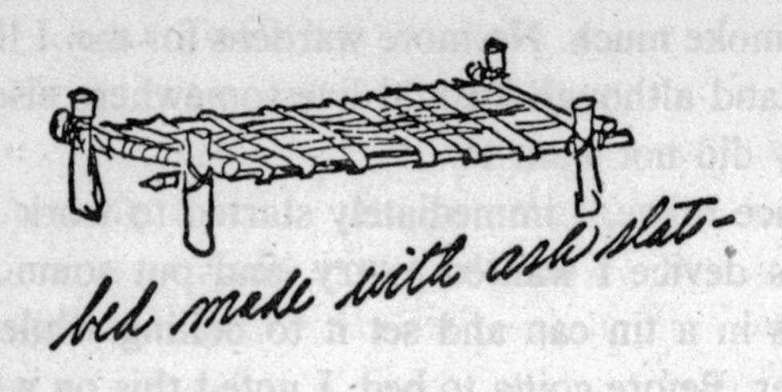

lock boughs on it now, but hope to have deer hide soon. I am making a figure-four trap as tall as me with a log on it that I can barely lift. It doesn't look workable. I wish there was another way of getting a deer.

"June 20

"I decided today to dig a pit to trap a deer, so I am whittling a shovel out of a board I found in the stream this morning. That stream is very useful. It has given me tin cans for pots, and now an oaken board for a shovel.

"Frightful will hop from the stump to my fist. She still can't fly. Her wing feathers are only about an inch long. I think she likes me."

How a Door Came to Me

One morning before the wood pewees were up, I was smoking a mess of fish I had caught in the stream. When I caught more than I could eat, I would bone them, put them on a rack of sticks, and slowly smoke them until they dried out. This is the best way to preserve extra food. However, if you try it, remember to use a hard wood—hickory is the best. I tried pine on the first batch, and ruined them with black tarry smoke. Well, it was very silent—then came a scream. I jumped into my tree. Presently I had enough nerve to look out.

"Baron Weasel!" I said in astonishment. I was sure it was the same weasel I had met in the trap. He was on the boulder in front of the hemlock, batting the ferns with his front feet and rearing and staring at me.

"Now, you stay right there," I said. Of course, he flipped and came off the rock like a jet stream. He was at the door before I could stop him, and loping around my feet like a bouncing ball.

"You look glad all over, Baron. I hope all that frisking means joy," I said. He took my pants leg in his teeth, tugged it, and then rippled softly back to the boulder. He went down a small hole. He popped up again, bit a fern near by, and ran around the boulder. I crept out to look for him—no weasel. I poked a stick in the hole at the base of the rock trying to provoke him. I felt a little jumpy, so that when a shot rang out through the woods I leapt a foot in the air and dove into my hole. A cricket chirped, a catbird scratched the leaves. I waited. One enormous minute later a dark form ran onto the meadow. It stumbled and fell.

I had the impression that it was a deer. Without

waiting to consider what I might be running toward, I burst to the edge of the meadow.

No one was in sight, I ran into the grass. There lay a dead deer! With all my strength I dragged the heavy animal into the woods. I then hurried to my tree, gathered up the hemlock boughs on my bed, rushed back and threw them over the carcass. I stuck a few ferns in them so they would look as if they were growing there and ran back to camp, breathless.

Hurriedly I put out the fire, covered it with dirt, hid my smoking rack in the spring, grabbed Frightful and got in my tree.

Someone was poaching, and he might be along in a minute to collect his prize. The shot had come from the side of the mountain, and I figured I had about four minutes to clean up before the poacher arrived.

Then when I was hidden and ready, Frightful started her cry of hunger. I had not fed her yet that morning. Oh, how was I going to explain to her the awful need to be quiet? How did a mother falcon warn her young of danger? I took her in my hands and stroked her stomach. She fought me and then she lay still in my hand, her feet up, her eyes bright. She stiffened and drooped. I kept on stroking her. She was hypnotized. I would stop for a few moments, she would lie still, then pop to her feet. I was sure this wasn't what her mother did to keep her quiet, but it worked.

Bushes cracked, leaves scuttled, and a man with a rifle came into the meadow. I could just see his head and shoulders. He looked around and banged toward the hemlock forest. I crawled up on my bed and stroked the hungry Frightful.

I couldn't see the man from my bed, but I could hear him.

I heard him come to the tree. I could see his boots. He stopped by the ashes of the fire; and then went on. I could see my heart lift my sweater. I was terrified.

I stayed on the bed all morning, telling the fierce little bundle of feathers in my hand that there was deer meat in store for her if she would just wait with me.

Way down the other side of the mountain, I heard another shot. I sure hoped that deer dropped on the poacher's toes and that he would now go home.

At noon I went to my prize. Frightful sat beside me as I skinned and quartered it. She ate deer until she was misshapen.

I didn't make any notes as to how long it took me to do all the work that was required to get the deer ready for smoking and the hide scraped and ready for tanning, but it was many, many days.

However, when I sat down to a venison steak, that was a meal! All it was, was venison. I wrote this on a piece of birch bark. "I think I grew an inch on venison!" Frightful and I went to the meadow when the meal was done, and I flopped in the grass. The stars came up, the ground smelled sweet, and I closed my eyes. I heard, "*Pip, pop, pop, pop.*"

"Who's making that noise?" I said sleepily to Frightful. She ruffled her feathers.

I listened. "*Pop, pip.*" I rolled over and stuck my face in the grass. Something gleamed beneath me, and in the fading light I could see an earthworm coming out of its hole.

Nearby another one arose and there was a *pop.* Little bubbles of air snapped as these voiceless animals of the earth came to the surface. That got me to smiling. I was glad to know this about earthworms. I don't know why, but this seemed like one of the nicest things I had learned in the woods—that earthworms, lowly, confined to the darkness of the earth, could make just a little stir in the world.

IN WHICH
Frightful Learns Her ABC's

Free time was spent scraping the fur off the deer hide to get it ready for tanning. This much I knew: in order to tan hide, it has to be steeped in tannic acid. There is tannic acid in the woods in oak trees, but it took me several weeks to figure out how to get it. You need a lot of oak chips in water. Water and oak give off tannic acid. My problem was not oak or water but getting a vessel big enough to put the deer hide in.

Coming home from the stream one night I had an inspiration.

It had showered the day before, and as Frightful and I passed an old stump, I noticed that it had collected the rain. "A stump, an oak stump, would be perfect," I said right out loud to that pretty bird.

So I felled an oak over by the gorge, burned a hole in it, carried water to it, and put my deerskin in it. I let it steep, oh, maybe five days before I took it out and dried it. It dried stiff as a board, and I had to chew, rub, jump on it, and twist it to get it soft. When this was done, however, I had my door. I hung it on pegs inside my entrance, and because it was bigger than it had to be, I would cut off pieces now and then when I needed them. I cut off two thin strips to make jesses, or leg straps, for Frightful. All good falcons wear jesses and leashes so they can be tethered for their training.

I smoked the meat I couldn't eat and stored it. I used everything I could on that animal. I even used one of its bones for a spearhead. I was tired of catching frogs by the jump-and-miss system. I made two sharp points, and strapped them to the end of a long stick, one on each side, to make a kind of fork. It worked beautifully. Frogs were one of my favorite meals, and I found I could fix them many ways; however, I got to like frog soup fixed in this way: "Clean, skin, and boil until tender. Add wild onions, also water lily buds and wild carrots. Thicken with acorn flour. Serve in turtle shell."

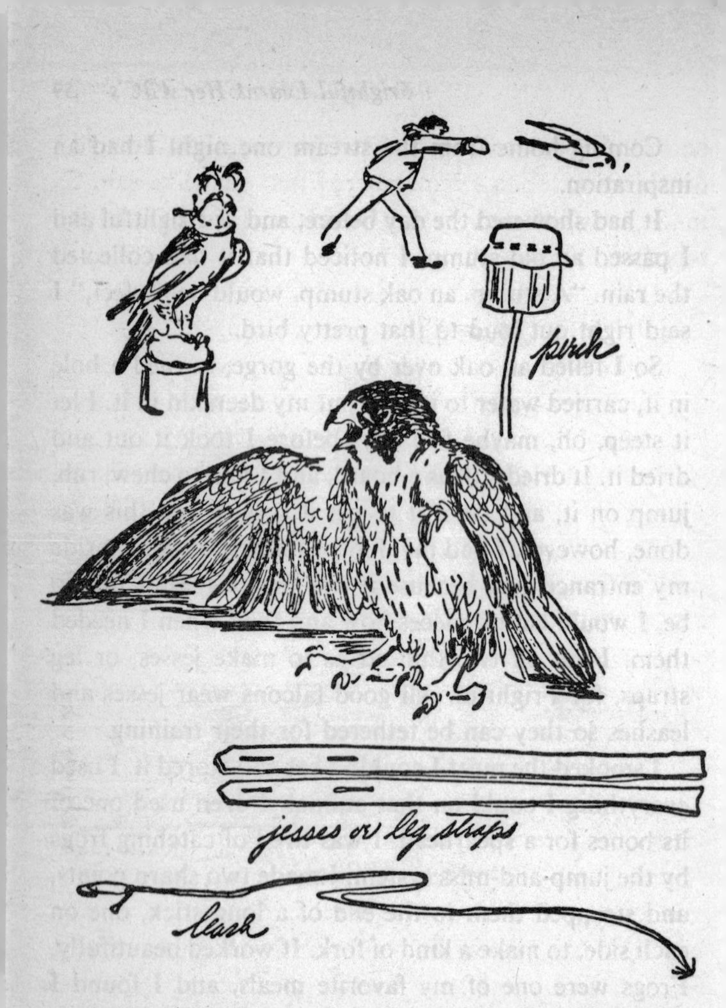

By now my two pairs of pants were threadbare and my three sweaters were frayed. I dreamed of a deerskin suit, and watched my herd with clothes in mind.

The deer for my suit did not come easily. I rigged up a figure-four trap under the log, and baited it with elderberries rolled into a ball. That just mushed up and didn't work. Then I remembered that deer like salt. I made a ball of hickory salt with turtle fat to hold it together.

Every evening Frightful and I, sometimes accompanied by The Baron Weasel, would go to the edge of the meadow and look toward the aspen grove to see if the great log had fallen. One night we saw three deer standing around it quietly, reaching toward the smell of salt. At that moment, The Baron jumped at my pants leg, but got my ankle with an awful nip. I guess I had grown some; my pants and socks did not meet anymore. I screamed, and the deer fled.

I chased The Baron home. I had the uneasy feeling that he was laughing as he darted, flipped, buckled, and disappeared.

The Baron was hard to understand. What did he want from me? Occasionally I left him bites of turtle or venison, and although he smelled the offerings, he never ate them. The catbird would get them. Most animals stick around if you feed them. But The Baron did not eat anything. Yet he seemed to like me. Gradually it occurred to me that he didn't have a mate or a family. Could he be a lonely bachelor, taking up with odd company for lack of an ordinary life? Well, whatever, The Baron liked me for what I was, and I appreciated that. He was a personable little fellow.

Every day I worked to train Frightful. It was a long process. I would put her on her stump with a long leash and step back a few feet with some meat in my hand. Then I would whistle. The whistle was supposed eventually to mean food to her. So I would whistle, show her the meat, and after many false flaps she would finally fly to my hand. I would pet her and feed her. She could fly fairly well, so now I made sure that she never ate unless she flew to my fist.

One day at breakfast I whistled for Frightful. I had no food, she wasn't even hungry, but she came to me anyway. I was thrilled. She had learned a whistle meant "come."

I looked into her steely eyes that morning and thought I saw a gentle recognition. She puffed up her feathers as she sat on my hand. I call this a "feather word." It means she is content.

Now each day I stepped farther and farther away from Frightful to make her fly greater and greater distances. One day she flew a good fifty feet, and we packed up and went gathering seeds, bark, and tubers to celebrate.

I used my oldest sweater for gathering things. It was not very convenient, and each time I filled it I mentally designed bigger and better pockets on my deer-hide suit-to-be.

The summer was wonderful. There was food in abundance and I gathered it most of the morning, and stored it away in the afternoon. I could now see that my niches were not going to be big enough for the amount of food I would need for the winter, so I began burning out another tree. When the hickory nuts, walnuts, and acorns appeared, I was going to need a bin. You'd be surprised what a pile of nuts it takes to make one turtle shell full of nut meats—and not a snapping-turtle shell either, just a box-turtle shell!

With the easy living of the summer also came a threat. Hikers and vacationers were in the woods, and more than once I pulled inside my tree, closed my deer-flap door, and hid while bouncing noisy people crossed the meadow on their way to the gorge. Apparently the gorge was a sight for those who wanted a four-mile hike up the mountain.

One morning I heard a group arriving. I whistled for Frightful. She came promptly. We dove into the tree. It was dark inside the tree with the flap closed, and I realized that I needed a candle. I planned a lamp of a turtle shell with a deer-hide wick, and as I was cutting off a piece of hide, I heard a shrill scream.

The voices of the hikers became louder. I wondered if one of them had fallen into the gorge. Then I said to Frightful, "That was no cry of a human, pretty bird. I'll bet you a rabbit for dinner that our deer trap worked. And here we are stored in a tree like a nut and unable to claim our prize."

We waited and waited until I couldn't be patient any more, and I was about to put my head out the door when a man's voice said, "Look at these trees!"

A woman spoke. "Harold, they're huge. How old do you think they are?"

"Three hundred years old, maybe four hundred," said Harold.

They tramped around, actually sat on The Baron's boulder, and were apparently going to have lunch, when things began to happen out there and I almost gave myself away with hysterics.

"Harold, what's the matter with that weasel? It's running all over this rock." A scream! A scuttering and scraping of boots on the rocks.

"He's mad!" That was the woman.

"Watch it, Grace, he's coming at your feet." They ran.

By this time I had my hand over my mouth to keep back the laughter. I snorted and choked, but they never heard me. They were in the meadow—run right out of the forest by that fiery Baron Weasel.

I still laugh when I think of it.

It was not until dark that Frightful and I got to the deer, and a beauty it was.

The rest of June was spent smoking it, tanning it, and finally, starting on my deerskin suit. I made a bone needle, cut out the pants by ripping up one pair of old city pants for a pattern. I saved my city pants and burned them bit by bit to make charred cloth for the flint and steel.

"Frightful," I said while sewing one afternoon. She was preening her now silver-gray, black, and white feathers. "There is no end to this. We need another deer. I can't make a blouse."

We didn't get another deer until fall, so with the scraps I made big square pockets for food gathering. One hung in front of me, and the other down my back. They were joined by straps. This device worked beautifully.

Sometime in July I finished my pants. They fit well, and were the best-looking pants I had ever seen. I was terribly proud of them.

With pockets and good tough pants I was willing to pack home many more new foods to try. Daisies, the bark of a poplar tree that I saw a squirrel eating, and puffballs. They are mushrooms, the only ones I felt were safe to eat, and even at that, I kept waiting to die the first night I ate them. I didn't, so I enjoyed them from that night on. They are wonderful. Mushrooms are dangerous and I would not suggest that one eat them from the forest. The mushroom expert at the Botanical Gardens told me that. He said even he didn't eat wild ones.

The inner bark of the poplar tree tasted like wheat kernels, and so I dried as much as I could and powdered it into flour. It was tedious work, and in August when the acorns were ready, I found that they made better flour and were much easier to handle.

I would bake the acorns in the fire, and grind them between stones. This was tedious work, too, but now that I had a home and smoked venison and did not have to hunt food every minute, I could do things like make flour. I would simply add spring water to the flour and bake this on a piece of tin. When done, I had the best pancakes ever. They were flat and hard, like I imagined Indian bread to be. I liked them, and would carry the leftovers in my pockets for lunch.

One fine August day I took Frightful to the meadow. I had been training her to the lure. That is, I now tied her meat on a piece of wood, covered with hide and feathers. I would throw it in the air and she would swoop out of the sky and catch it. She was absolutely free during these maneuvers, and would fly high into the air and hover over me like a leaf. I made sure she was very hungry before I turned her loose. I wanted her back.

After a few tries she never missed the lure. Such marksmanship thrilled me. Bird and lure would drop to the earth, I would run over, grab her jesses, and we would sit on the big boulder in the meadow while she ate. Those were nice evenings. The finest was the night I wrote this:

"Frightful caught her first prey. She is now a trained falcon. It was only a sparrow, but we are on our way. It happened unexpectedly. Frightful was climbing into the sky, circling and waiting for the lure, when I stepped forward and scared a sparrow.

"The sparrow flew across the meadow. Out of the sky came a black streak—I've never seen anything drop so fast. With a great backwatering of wings, Frightful broke her fall, and at the same time seized the sparrow. I took it away from her and gave her the lure. That sounds mean, but if she gets in the habit of eating what she catches, she will go wild."

IN WHICH
I Find a Real Live Man

One of the gasping joys of summer was my daily bath in the spring. It was cold water, I never stayed in long, but it woke me up and started me into the day with a vengeance.

I would tether Frightful to a hemlock bough above me and splash her from time to time. She would suck in her chest, look startled, and then shake. While I bathed and washed, she preened. Huddled down in the water between the ferns and moss, I scrubbed myself with the bark of the slippery elm. It gets soapy when you rub it.

The frogs would hop out and let me in, and the

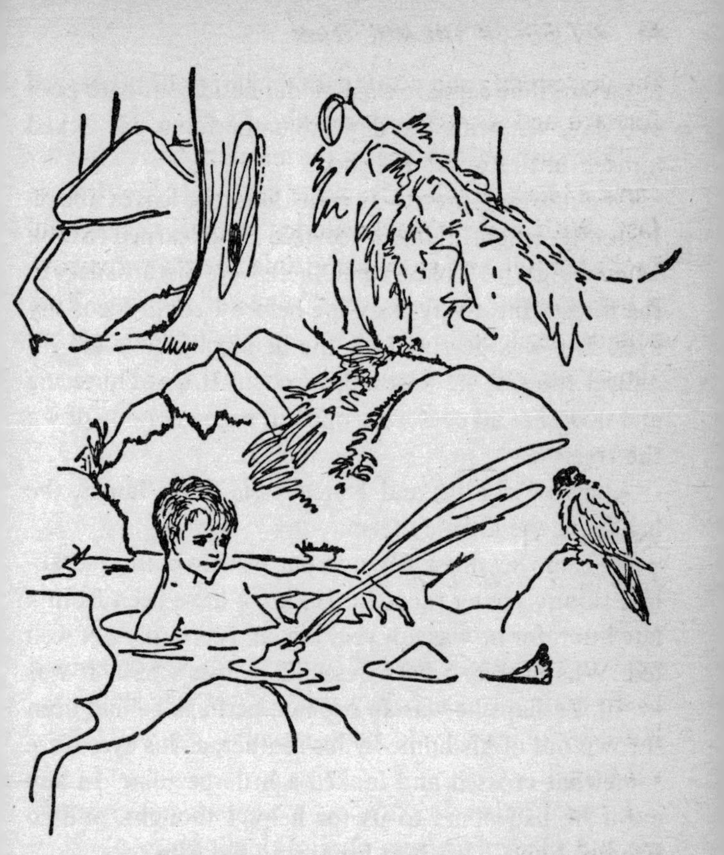

woodthrush would come to the edge of the pool to see what was happening. We were a gay gathering—me shouting, Frightful preening, the woodthrush cocking its pretty head. Occasionally The Baron Weasel would pop up and glance furtively at us. He didn't care for water. How he stayed glossy and clean was a mystery to me, until he came to the boulder beside our bath pool one day, wet with the dew from the ferns. He licked himself until he was polished.

One morning there was a rustle in the leaves above. Instantly, Frightful had it located. I had learned to look where Frightful looked when there were disturbances in the forest. She always saw life before I could focus my eyes. She was peering into the hemlock above us. Finally I too saw it. A young raccoon. It was chittering and now that all eyes were upon it, began coming down the tree.

And so Frightful and I met Jessie Coon James, the bandit of the Gribley farm.

He came headfirst down to our private bath, a scrabbly, skinny young raccoon. He must have been from a late litter, for he was not very big, and certainly not well fed. Whatever had been Jessie C. James's past, it was awful. Perhaps he was an orphan, perhaps he had been thrown out of his home by his mother, as his eyes were somewhat crossed and looked a little peculiar. In any event he had come to us for help, I thought, and so Frightful and I led him home and fed him.

In about a week he fattened up. His crumply hair smoothed out, and with a little ear scratching and back rubbing, Jessie C. James became a devoted friend. He also became useful. He slept somewhere in the dark tops of the hemlocks all day long, unless he saw us start for the stream. Then, tree by tree, limb by limb, Jessie followed us. At the stream he was the most useful mussel digger that any boy could have. Jessie could find mussels where three men could not. He would start to eat them, and if he ate them, he got full and wouldn't dig anymore, so I took them away from him until he found me all I wanted. Then I let him have some.

Mussels are good. Here are a few notes on how to fix them.

"Scrub mussels in spring water. Dump them into boiling water with salt. Boil five minutes. Remove and cool in the juice. Take out meat. Eat by dipping in acorn paste flavored with a smudge of garlic, and green apples."

Frightful took care of the small game supply, and now that she was an expert hunter, we had rabbit stew, pheasant potpie, and an occasional sparrow, which I generously gave to Frightful. As fast as we removed the rabbits and pheasants new ones replaced them.

Beverages during the hot summer became my chore, largely because no one else wanted them. I found some sassafras trees at the edge of the road one day, dug up a good supply of roots, peeled and dried them. Sassafras tea is about as good as anything you want to drink. Pennyroyal makes another good drink. I dried great bunches of this, and hung them from the roof of the tree room together with the leaves of winterberry. All these fragrant plants I also used in cooking to give a new taste to some not-so-good foods.

The room in the tree smelled of smoke and mint. It was the best-smelling tree in the Catskill Mountains.

Life was leisurely. I was warm, well fed. One day while I was down the mountain, I returned home by way of the old farmhouse site to check the apple crop. They were summer apples, and were about ready to be picked. I had gathered a pouchful and had sat down under the tree to eat a few and think about how I would dry them for use in the winter when Frightful dug her talons into my shoulder so hard I winced.

"Be gentle, bird!" I said to her.

I got her talons out and put her on a log, where I watched her with some alarm. She was as alert as a high tension wire, her head cocked so that her ears, just membranes under her feathers, were pointed east. She evidently heard a sound that pained her. She opened her beak. Whatever it was, I could hear nothing, though I strained my ears, cupped them, and wished she would speak.

Frightful was my ears as well as my eyes. She could hear things long before I. When she grew tense, I listened or looked. She was scared this time. She turned round and round on the log, looked up in the tree for a perch, lifted her wings to fly, and then stood still and listened.

Then I heard it. A police siren sounded far down the road. The sound grew louder and louder, and I grew afraid. Then I said, "No, Frightful, if they are after me there won't be a siren. They'll just slip up on me quietly."

No sooner had I said this than the siren wound down, and apparently stopped on the road at the foot of the mountain. I got up to run to my tree, but had not gotten past the walnut before the patrol cars started up and screamed away.

We started home although it was not late in the afternoon. However, it was hot, and thunderheads were building up. I decided to take a swim in the spring and work on the moccasins I had cut out several days ago.

With the squad car still on my mind, we slipped quietly into the hemlock forest. Once again Frightful almost sent me through the crown of the forest by digging her talons into my shoulder. I looked at her. She was staring at our home. I looked, too. Then I stopped, for I could make out the form of a man stretched between the sleeping house and the store tree.

Softly, tree by tree, Frightful and I approached him. The man was asleep. I could have left and camped in the gorge again, but my enormous desire to see another human being overcame my fear of being discovered.

We stood above the man. He did not move, so Frightful lost interest in my fellow being. She tried to hop to her stump and preen. I grabbed her leash however, as I wanted to think before awakening him. Frightful flapped. I held her wings to her body as her flapping was noisy to me. Apparently not so to the man. The man did not stir. It is hard to realize that the rustle of a falcon's wings is not much of a noise to a man from the city, because by now, one beat of her wings and I would awaken from a sound sleep as if a shot had gone off. The stranger slept on. I realized how long I'd been in the mountains.

Right at that moment, as I looked at his unshaven face, his close-cropped hair, and his torn clothes, I thought of the police siren, and put two and two together.

"An outlaw!" I said to myself. "Wow!" I had to think what to do with an outlaw before I awoke him.

Would he be troublesome? Would he be mean? Should I go live in the gorge until he moved on? How I wanted to hear his voice, to tell him about The Baron and Jessie C. James, to say words out loud. I really did not want to hide from him; besides, he might be hungry, I thought. Finally I spoke.

"Hi!" I said. I was delighted to see him roll over, open his eyes, and look up. He seemed startled, so I reassured him. "It's all right, they've gone. If you don't tell on me I won't tell on you." When he heard this, he sat up and seemed to relax.

"Oh," he said. Then he leaned against the tree and added, "Thanks." He evidently was thinking this over, for he propped his head on his elbow and studied me closely.

"You're a sight for sore eyes," he said, and smiled. He had a nice smile—in fact, he looked nice and not like

an outlaw at all. His eyes were very blue and, although tired, they did not look scared or hunted.

However, I talked quickly before he could get up and run away.

"I don't know anything about you, and I don't want to. You don't know anything about me, and don't want to, but you may stay here if you like. No one is going to find you here. Would you like some supper?" It was still early, but he looked hungry.

"Do you have some?"

"Yes, venison or rabbit?"

"Well . . . venison." His eyebrows puckered in question marks. I went to work.

He arose, turned around and around, and looked at his surroundings. He whistled softly when I kindled a spark with the flint and steel. I was now quite quick at this, and had a tidy fire blazing in a very few minutes. I was so used to myself doing this that it had not occurred to me that it would be interesting to a stranger.

"Desdemondia!" he said. I judged this to be some underworld phrase. At this moment Frightful, who had been sitting quietly on her stump, began to preen. The outlaw jumped back, then saw she was tied and said, "And who is this ferocious-looking character?"

"That is Frightful; don't be afraid. She's quite wonderful and gentle. She would be glad to catch you a rabbit for supper if you would prefer that to venison."

"Am I dreaming?" said the man. "I go to sleep by a campfire that looked like it was built by a boy scout, and I awaken in the middle of the eighteenth century."

I crawled into the store tree to get the smoked venison and some cattail tubers. When I came out again, he was speechless.

"My storehouse," I explained.

"I see," he answered. From that moment on he did not talk much. He just watched me. I was so busy cooking the best meal that I could possibly get together that I didn't say much either. Later I wrote down that menu, as it was excellent.

"Brown puffballs in deer fat with a little wild garlic, fill pot with water, put venison in, boil. Wrap tubers in leaves and stick in coals. Cut up apples and boil in can with dogtooth violet bulbs. Raspberries to finish meal."

When the meal was ready, I served it to the man in my nicest turtle shell. I had to whittle him a fork out of the crotch of a twig, as Jessie Coon James had gone off with the others. He ate and ate and ate, and when he was done he said, "May I call you Thoreau?"

"That will do nicely," I said. Then I paused—just to let him know that I knew a little bit about him too. I smiled and said, "I will call you Bando."

His eyebrows went up, he cocked his head, shrugged his shoulders and answered, "That's close enough."

With this he sat and thought. I felt I had offended him, so I spoke. "I will be glad to help. I will teach you how to live off the land. It is very easy. No one need find you."

His eyebrows gathered together again. This was characteristic of Bando when he was concerned, and so I was sorry I had mentioned his past. After all, outlaw or no outlaw, he was an adult, and I still felt unsure of myself around adults. I changed the subject.

"Let's get some sleep," I said.

'Where do you sleep?" he asked. All this time sitting and talking with me, and he had not seen the entrance to my tree. I was pleased. Then I beckoned, walked a few feet to the left, pushed back the deer-hide door, and showed Bando my secret.

"Thoreau," he said. "You are quite wonderful." He went in. I lit the turtle candle for him, he explored, tried the bed, came out and shook his head until I thought it would roll off.

We didn't say much more that night. I let him sleep on my bed. His feet hung off, but he was comfortable, he said. I stretched out by the fire. The ground was dry, the night warm, and I could sleep on anything now.

I got up early and had breakfast ready when Bando

came stumbling out of the tree. We ate crayfish, and he really honestly seemed to like them. It takes a little time to acquire a taste for wild foods, so Bando surprised me the way he liked the menu. Of course he was hungry, and that helped.

That day we didn't talk much, just went over the mountain collecting foods. I wanted to dig up the tubers of the Solomon's seal from a big garden of them on the other side of the gorge. We fished, we swam a little, and I told him I hoped to make a raft pretty soon, so I could float into deeper water and perhaps catch bigger fish.

When Bando heard this, he took my ax and immediately began to cut young trees for this purpose. I watched him and said, "You must have lived on a farm or something."

At that moment a bird sang.

"The wood pewee," said Bando, stopping his work. He stepped into the woods, seeking it. Now I was astonished.

"How would you know about a wood pewee in your business?" I grew bold enough to ask.

"And just what do you think my business is?" he said as I followed him.

"Well, you're not a minister."

"Right!"

"And you're not a doctor or a lawyer."

"Correct."

"You're not a businessman or a sailor."

"No, I am not."

"Nor do you dig ditches."

"I do not."

"Well . . ."

"Guess."

Suddenly I wanted to know for sure. So I said it.

"You are a murderer or a thief or a racketeer; and you are hiding out."

Bando stopped looking for the pewee. He turned and stared at me. At first I was frightened. A bandit might do anything. But he wasn't mad, he was laughing. He had a good deep laugh and it kept coming out of him. I smiled, then grinned and laughed with him.

"What's funny, Bando?" I asked.

"I like that," he finally said. "I like that a lot." The tickle deep inside him kept him chuckling. I had no more to say, so I ground my heel in the dirt while I waited for him to get over the fun and explain it all to me.

"Thoreau, my friend, I am just a college English teacher lost in the Catskills. I came out to hike around the woods, got completely lost yesterday, found your fire and fell asleep beside it. I was hoping the scoutmaster and his troop would be back for supper and help me home."

"Oh, no." My comment. Then I laughed. "You see, Bando, before I found you, I heard squad cars screaming up the road. Occasionally you read about bandits that hide out in the forest, and I was just so sure that you were someone they were looking for."

We gave up the pewee and went back to the raft-making, talking very fast now, and laughing a lot. He was fun. Then something sad occurred to me.

"Well, if you're not a bandit, you will have to go home very soon, and there is no point in teaching you how to live on fish and bark and plants."

"I can stay a little while," he said. "This is summer vacation. I must admit I had not planned to eat crayfish on my vacation, but I am rather getting to like it.

"Maybe I can stay until your school opens," he went on. "That's after Labor Day, isn't it?"

I was very still, thinking how to answer that.

Bando sensed this. Then he turned to me with a big grin.

"You really mean you are going to try to winter it out here?"

"I think I can."

"Well!" He sat down, rubbed his forehead in his hands, and looked at me. "Thoreau, I have led a varied life—dishwasher, sax player, teacher. To me it has been an interesting life. Just now it seems very dull." He sat awhile with his head down, then looked up at the mountains and the rocks and trees. I heard him sigh.

"Let's go fish. We can finish this another day."

That is how I came to know Bando. We became very good friends in the week or ten days that he stayed with me, and he helped me a lot. We spent several days gathering white oak acorns and groundnuts, harvesting the blueberry crop and smoking fish.

We flew Frightful every day just for the pleasure of lying on our backs in the meadow and watching her mastery of the sky. I had lots of meat, so what she caught those days was all hers. It was a pleasant time, warm, with occasional thundershowers, some of which we stayed out in. We talked about books. He did know a lot of books, and could quote exciting things from them.

One day Bando went to town and came back with five pounds of sugar.

"I want to make blueberry jam," he announced. "All those excellent berries and no jam."

He worked two days at this. He knew how to make jam. He'd watched his pa make it in Mississippi, but we got stuck on what to put it in.

I wrote this one night:

"*August 29*

"The raft is almost done. Bando has promised to stay until we can sail out into the deep fishing holes.

"Bando and I found some clay along the stream bank. It was as slick as ice. Bando thought it would make good pottery. He shaped some jars and lids. They look good—not Wedgwood, he said, but containers. We dried them on the rock in the meadow, and later Bando made a clay oven and baked them in it. He thinks they might hold the blueberry jam he has been making.

"Bando got the fire hot by blowing on it with some homemade bellows that he fashioned from one of my skins that he tied together like a balloon. A reed is the nozzle.

"*August 30*

"It was a terribly hot day for Bando to be firing clay jars, but he stuck with it. They look jam-worthy, as he says, and he filled three of them tonight. The jam is good, the pots remind me of crude flower pots without the hole in the bottom. Some of the lids don't fit. Bando says he will go home and read more about pottery making so that he can do a better job next time.

"We like the jam. We eat it on hard acorn pancakes.

"Later. Bando met The Baron Weasel today for the first time. I don't know where The Baron has been this past week, but suddenly he appeared on the rock, and nearly jumped down Bando's shirt collar. Bando said he liked The Baron best when he was in his hole.

"*September 3*

"Bando taught me how to make willow whistles today. He and I went to the stream and cut two fat twigs about eight inches long. He slipped the bark on them. That means he pulled the wood out of the bark, leaving a tube. He made a mouthpiece at one end, cut a hole beneath it, and used the wood to slide up and down like a trombone.

"We played music until the moon came up. Bando could even play jazz on the willow whistles. They are wonderful instruments, sounding much like the wind in

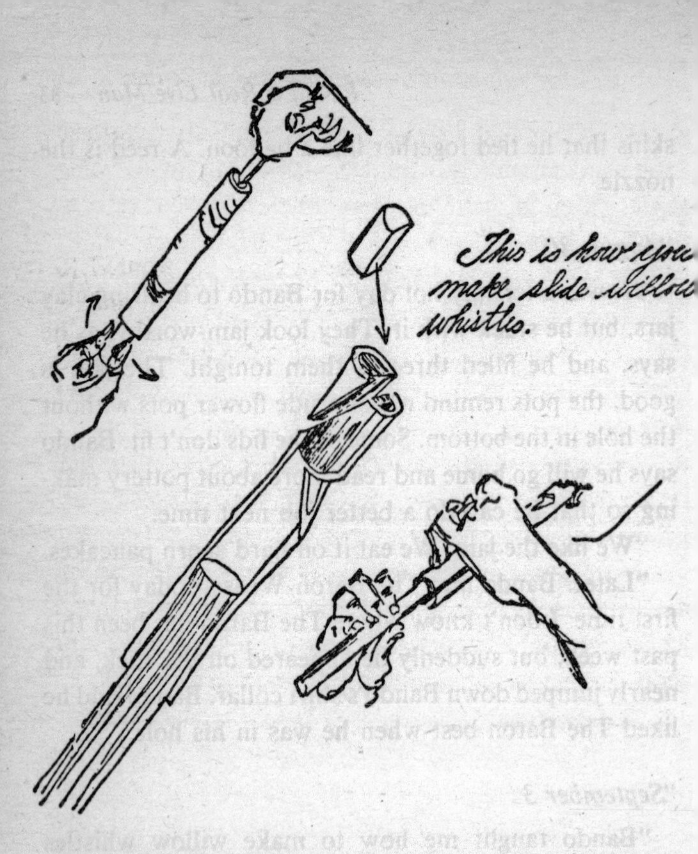

the top of the hemlocks. Sad tunes are best suited to willow whistles. When we played 'The Young Voyageur' tears came to our eyes, it was so sad."

There were no more notes for many days. Bando had left me saying: "Good-by, I'll see you at Christmas." I was so lonely that I kept sewing on my moccasins to keep myself busy. I sewed every free minute for four days, and when they were finished, I began a glove to protect my hand from Frightful's sharp talons.

One day when I was thinking very hard about being alone, Frightful gave her gentle call of love and contentment. I looked up.

"Bird," I said. "I had almost forgotten how we used to talk." She made tiny movements with her beak and fluffed her feathers. This was a language I had forgotten since Bando came. It meant she was glad to see me and hear me, that she was well fed, and content. I picked her up and squeaked into her neck feathers. She moved her beak, turned her bright head, and bit my nose very gently.

Jessie Coon James came down from the trees for the first time in ten days. He finished my fish dinner. Then just before dusk, The Baron came up on his boulder and scratched and cleaned and played with a fern leaf.

I had the feeling we were all back together again.

IN WHICH
The Autumn Provides Food and Loneliness

September blazed a trail into the mountains. First she burned the grasses. The grasses seeded and were harvested by the mice and the winds.

Then she sent the squirrels and chipmunks running boldly through the forest, collecting and hiding nuts.

Then she frosted the aspen leaves and left them sunshine yellow.

Then she gathered the birds together in flocks, and the mountaintop was full of songs and twitterings and flashing wings. The birds were ready to move to the south.

And I, Sam Gribley, felt just wonderful, just wonderful.

I pushed the raft down the stream and gathered arrowleaf bulbs, cattail tubers, bulrush roots, and the nutlike tubers of the sedges.

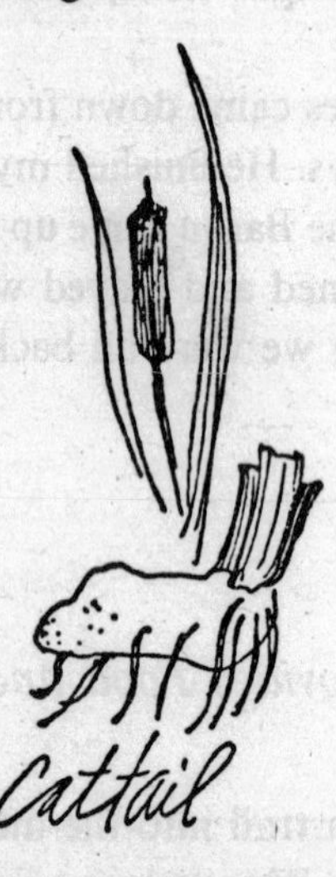

And then the crop of crickets appeared and Frightful hopped all over the meadow snagging them in her great talons and eating them. I tried them, because I had heard they are good. I think it was another species of cricket that was meant. I think the field cricket would taste excellent if you were starving. I was not starving, so I preferred to listen to them. I abandoned the crickets and went back to the goodness of the earth.

I smoked fish and rabbit, dug wild onions by the pouchful, and raced September for her crop.

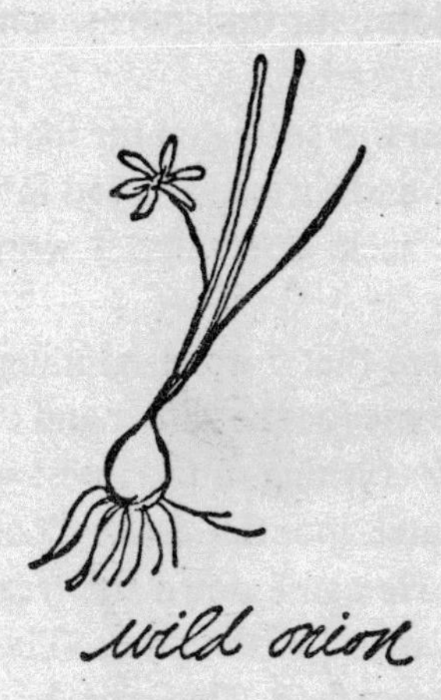

wild onion

"October 15

"Today The Baron Weasel looked moldy. I couldn't get near enough to see what was the matter with him, but it occurs to me that he might be changing his summer fur for his white winter mantle. If he is, it is an itchy process. He scratches a lot."

Seeing The Baron changing his mantle for winter awoke the first fears in me. I wrote that note on a little birch bark, curled up on my bed, and shivered.

The snow and the cold and the long lifeless months are ahead, I thought. The wind was blowing hard and cool across the mountain. I lit my candle, took out the rabbit and squirrel hides I had been saving, and began rubbing and kneading them to softness.

The Baron was getting a new suit for winter. I must have one too. Some fur underwear, some mittens, fur-lined socks.

Frightful, who was sitting on the foot post of the bed, yawned, fluffed, and thrust her head into the slate gray feathers of her back. She slept. I worked for several hours.

I must say here that I was beginning to wonder if I should not go home for the winter and come back again in the spring. Everything in the forest was getting prepared for the harsh months. Jessie Coon James was as fat as a barrel. He came down the tree slowly, his fat falling in a roll over his shoulders. The squirrels were working and storing food. They were building leaf nests. The skunks had burrows and plugged themselves in at dawn with bunches of leaves. No drafts could reach them.

As I thought of the skunks and all the animals preparing themselves against the winter, I realized suddenly that my tree would be as cold as the air if I did not somehow find a way to heat it.

"NOTES:

"Today I rafted out into the deep pools of the creek to fish. It was a lazy sort of autumn day, the sky clear, the leaves beginning to brighten, the air warm. I stretched out on my back because the fish weren't biting, and hummed.

"My line jerked and I sat up to pull, but was too late. However, I was not too late to notice that I had drifted into the bank—the very bank where Bando had dug the clay for the jam pots.

"At that moment I knew what I was going to do. I was going to build a fireplace of clay, even fashion a little chimney of clay. It would be small, but enough to warm the tree during the long winter.

"Next Day

"I dragged the clay up the mountain to my tree in my second best pair of city pants. I tied the bottoms of the legs, stuffed them full, and as I looked down on my strange cargo, I thought of scarecrows and Halloween. I thought of the gang dumping ashcans on Third Avenue and soaping up the windows. Suddenly I was terribly lonely. The air smelled of leaves and the cool wind from the stream hugged me. The warblers in the trees above me seemed gay and glad about their trip south. I stopped halfway up the mountain and dropped my head. I was lonely and on the verge of tears. Suddenly there was a flash, a pricking sensation on my leg, and

I looked down in time to see The Baron leap from my pants to the cover of fern.

"He scared the loneliness right out of me. I ran after him and chased him up the mountain, losing him from time to time in the ferns and crowfeet. We stormed into camp an awful sight, The Baron bouncing and screaming ahead of me, and me dragging that half scarecrow of clay.

"Frightful took one look and flew to the end of her leash. She doesn't like The Baron, and watches him—well, like a hawk. I don't like to leave her alone. End notes. Must make fireplace."

It took three days to get the fireplace worked out so that it didn't smoke me out of the tree like a bee. It was an enormous problem. In the first place, the chimney sagged because the clay was too heavy to hold itself up, so I had to get some dry grasses to work into it so it could hold its own weight.

I whittled out one of the old knotholes to let the smoke out, and built the chimney down from this. Of course when the clay dried, it pulled away from the tree, and all the smoke poured back in on me.

So I tried sealing the leak with pine pitch, and that worked all right, but then the funnel over the fire bed cracked, and I had to put wooden props under that.

The wooden props burned, and I could see that this wasn't going to work either; so I went down the mountain to the site of the old Gribley farmhouse and looked around for some iron spikes or some sort of metal.

I took the wooden shovel that I had carved from the board and dug around what I thought must have been the back door or possibly the woodhouse.

I found a hinge, old handmade nails that would come in handy, and finally, treasure of treasures, the axle of an old wagon. It was much too big. I had no hacksaw to cut it into smaller pieces, and I was not strong enough to heat it and hammer it apart. Besides, I didn't have anything but a small wooden mallet I had made.

I carried my trophies home and sat down before my tree to fix dinner and feed Frightful. The evening was cooling down for a frost. I looked at Frightful's warm feathers. I didn't even have a deer hide for a blanket. I had used the two I had for a door and a pair of pants. I wished that I might grow feathers.

I tossed Frightful off my fist and she flashed through the trees and out over the meadow. She went with a determination strange to her. "She is going to leave," I cried. "I have never seen her fly so wildly." I pushed the smoked fish aside and ran to the meadow. I whistled and whistled and whistled until my mouth was dry and no more whistle came.

I ran onto the big boulder. I could not see her. Wildly I waved the lure. I licked my lips and whistled again. The sun was a cold steely color as it dipped below the mountain. The air was now brisk, and Frightful was gone. I was sure that she had suddenly taken off on the migration; my heart was sore and pounding. I had enough food, I was sure. Frightful was not absolutely necessary for my survival; but I was now so fond of her. She was more than a bird. I knew I must have her back to talk to and play with if I was going to make it through the winter.

I whistled. Then I heard a cry in the grasses up near the white birches.

In the gathering darkness I saw movement. I think I flew to the spot. And there she was; she had caught herself a bird. I rolled into the grass beside her and clutched her jesses. She didn't intend to leave, but I was going to make sure that she didn't. I grabbed so swiftly that my hand hit a rock and I bruised my knuckles.

The rock was flat and narrow and long; it was the answer to my fireplace. I picked up Frightful in one hand and the stone in the other; and I laughed at the cold steely sun as it slipped out of sight, because I knew I was going to be warm. This flat stone was what I needed to hold up the funnel and finish my fireplace.

And that's what I did with it. I broke it into two pieces, set one on each side under the funnel, lit the fire, closed the flap of the door and listened to the wind bring the first frost to the mountain. I was warm.

Then I noticed something dreadful. Frightful was sitting on the bedpost, her head under her wings. She was toppling. She jerked her head out of her feathers. Her eyes looked glassy. She is sick, I said. I picked her up and stroked her, and we both might have died there if I had not opened the tent flap to get her some water.

The cold night air revived her. "Air," I said. "The fireplace used up all the oxygen. I've got to ventilate this place."

We sat out in the cold for a long time because I was more than a little afraid of what our end might have been.

I put out the fire, took the door down and wrapped up in it. Frightful and I slept with the good frost nipping our faces.

"NOTES:

"I cut out several more knotholes to let air in and out of the tree room. I tried it today. I have Frightful on my fist watching her. It's been about two hours and she hasn't fainted and I haven't gone numb. I can still write and see clearly.

"Test: Frightful's healthy face."

IN WHICH
We All Learn About Halloween

"October 28

"I have been up and down the mountain every day for a week, watching to see if walnuts and hickory nuts are ripe. Today I found the squirrels all over the trees, harvesting them furiously, and so I have decided that ripe or not, I must gather them. It's me or the squirrels.

"I tethered Frightful in the hickory tree while I went to the walnut tree and filled pouches. Frightful protected the hickory nuts. She keeps the squirrels so busy scolding her that they don't have time to take the nuts. They are quite terrified by her. It is a good scheme. I shout and bang the tree and keep them away while I gather.

"I have never seen so many squirrels. They hang from the slender branches, they bounce through the limbs, they seem to come from the whole forest. They must pass messages along to each other—messages that tell what kind of nuts and where the trees are."

A few days later, my storehouse rolling with nuts, I began the race for apples. Entering this race were squirrels, raccoons, and a fat old skunk who looked as if he could eat not another bite. He was ready to sleep his autumn meal off, and I resented him because he did not need my apples. However, I did not toy with him.

I gathered what apples I could, cut some in slices, and dried them on the boulder in the sun. Some I put in the storeroom tree to eat right away. They were a little wormy, but it was wonderful to eat an apple again.

Then one night this was all done, the crop was gathered. I sat down to make a few notes when The Baron came sprinting into sight.

He actually bounced up and licked the edges of my turtle-shell bowl, stormed Frightful, and came to my feet.

"Baron Weasel," I said. "It is nearing Halloween. Are you playing tricks or treats?" I handed him the remains of my turtle soup dinner, and, fascinated, watched him devour it.

"NOTES:

"The Baron chews with his back molars, and chews with a ferocity I have not seen in him before. His eyes gleam, the lips curl back from his white pointed teeth, and he frowns like an angry man. If I move toward him, a rumble starts in his chest that keeps me back. He flashes glances at me. It is indeed strange to be looked in the eye by this fearless wild animal. There is something human about his beady glance. Perhaps because that glance tells me something. It tells me he knows who I am and that he does not want me to come any closer."

The Baron Weasel departed after his feast. Frightful, who was drawn up as skinny as a stick, relaxed and fluffed her feathers, and then I said to her, "See, he got his treats. No tricks." Then something occurred to me. I reached inside the door and pulled out my calendar stick. I counted 28, 29, 30, 31.

"Frightful, that old weasel knows. It is Halloween. Let's have a Halloween party."

Swiftly I made piles of cracked nuts, smoked rabbit, and crayfish. I even added two of my apples. This food was an invitation to the squirrels, foxes, raccoons, opossums, even the birds that lived around me to come have a party.

When Frightful is tethered to her stump, some of the animals and birds will only come close enough to scream at her. So bird and I went inside the tree, propped open the flap, and waited.

Not much happened that night. I learned that it takes a little time for the woodland messages to get around. But they do. Before the party I had been very careful about leaving food out because I needed every mouthful. I took the precaution of rolling a stone in front of my store tree. The harvest moon rose. Frightful and I went to sleep.

At dawn, we abandoned the party. I left the treats out, however. Since it was a snappy gold-colored day, we went off to get some more rabbit skins to finish my winter underwear.

We had lunch along the creek—stewed mussels and wild potatoes. We didn't get back until dusk because I discovered some wild rice in an ox bow of the stream. There was no more than a handful.

Home that night, everything seemed peaceful enough. A few nuts were gone, to the squirrels, I thought. I baked a fish in leaves, and ate a small, precious amount of wild rice. It was marvelous! As I settled

down to scrape the rabbit skins of the day, my neighbor the skunk marched right into the campground and set to work on the smoked rabbit. I made some Halloween notes:

"The moon is coming up behind the aspens. It is as big as a pumpkin and as orange. The winds are cool, the stars are like electric light bulbs. I am just inside the doorway, with my turtle-shell lamp burning so that I can see to write this.

"Something is moving beyond the second hemlock. Frightful is very alert, as if there are things all around us. Halloween was over at midnight last night, but for us it is just beginning. That's how I feel, anyhow, but it just may be my imagination.

"I wish Frightful would stop pulling her feathers in and drawing herself up like a spring. I keep thinking that she feels things.

"Here comes Jessie C. James. He will want the venison.

"He didn't get the venison. There was a snarl, and a big raccoon I've never seen walked past him, growling and looking ferocious. Jessie C. stood motionless—I might say, scared stiff. He held his head at an angle and let the big fellow eat. If Jessie so much as rolled his eyes that old coon would sputter at him."

It grew dark, and I couldn't see much. An eerie yelp behind the boulder announced that the red fox of the meadow was nearing. He gave me goose bumps. He stayed just beyond my store tree, weaving back and forth on silent feet. Every now and then he would cry—a wavery owllike cry. I wrote some more.

"The light from my turtle lamp casts leaping shadows. To the beechnuts has come a small gray animal. I can't make out what—now, I see it. It's a flying squirrel. That surprises me, I've never seen a flying squirrel around here, but of course I haven't been up much after sunset."

When it grew too dark to see, I lit a fire, hoping it would not end the party. It did not, and the more I watched, the more I realized that all these animals were familiar with my camp. A white-footed mouse walked over my woodpile as if it were his.

I put out the candle and fell asleep when the fire turned to coals. Much later I was awakened by screaming. I lifted my head and looked into the moonlit forest. A few guests, still lingering at the party, saw me move, and dashed bashfully into the ground cover. One was big and slender. I thought perhaps a mink. As I slowly came awake, I realized that screaming was coming from behind me. Something was in my house. I jumped up and shouted, and two raccoons skittered under my feet. I reached for my candle, slipped on hundreds of nuts, and fell. When I finally got a light and looked about me, I was dismayed to see what a mess my guests had made of my tree house. They had found the cache of acorns and beechnuts and had tossed them all over my bed and floor. The party was getting rough.

I chased the raccoons into the night and stumbled over a third animal and was struck by a wet stinging spray. It was skunk! I was drenched. As I got used to the indignity and the smell, I saw the raccoons cavort around my fireplace and dodge past me. They were back in my tree before I could stop them.

A bat winged in from the darkness and circled the tallow candle. It was Halloween and the goblins were at work. I thought of all the ash cans I had knocked over on the streets of New York. It seemed utterly humorless.

Having invited all these neighbors, I was now faced with the problem of getting rid of them. The raccoons were feeling so much at home that they snatched up beechnuts, bits of dried fish and venison and tossed them playfully into the air. They were too full to eat any more, but were having a marvelous time making toys out of my hard-won winter food supply.

I herded the raccoons out of the tree and laced the door. I was breathing "relief" when I turned my head to the left, for I sensed someone watching me. There in the moonlight, his big ears erect on his head, sat the red fox. He was smiling—I know he was. I shouted, "Stop laughing!" and he vanished like a magician's handkerchief.

All this had awakened Frightful, who was flopping in the dark in the tree. I reached in around the deer flap to stroke her back to calmness. She grabbed me so hard I yelled—and the visitors moved to the edge of my camp at my cry.

Smelling to the sky, bleeding in the hand, and robbed of part of my hard-won food, I threw wood on the fire and sent an enormous shaft of light into the night. Then I shouted. The skunk moved farther away. The raccoons galloped off a few feet and galloped back. I snarled at them. They went to the edge of the darkness and stared at me. I had learned something that night from that very raccoon bossing Jessie C. James—to animals, might is right. I was biggest and I was oldest, and I was going to tell them so. I growled and snarled and hissed and snorted. It worked. They understood and moved away. Some looked back and their eyes glowed. The red eyes chilled me. Never had there been a more real Halloween night. I looked up, expecting to see a witch. The last bat of the season darted in the moonlight. I dove on my bed, and tied the door. There are no more notes about Halloween.

IN WHICH
I Find Out What to Do with Hunters

That party had a moral ending. Don't feed wild animals! I picked up and counted my walnuts and hickory nuts. I was glad to discover there was more mess than loss. I decided that I would not only live until spring but that I still had more nuts than all the squirrels on Gribley's (including flying squirrels).

In early November I was awakened one morning by a shot from a rifle. The hunting season had begun! I had forgotten all about that. To hide from a swarm of hunters was truly going to be a trick. They would be behind every tree and on every hill and dale. They would be shooting at everything that moved, and here was I in deerskin pants and dirty brown sweater, looking like a deer.

I decided, like the animals, to stay holed up the first

day of the season. I whittled a fork and finished my rabbit-skin winter underwear. I cracked a lot of walnuts.

The second day of the hunting season I stuck my head out of my door and decided my yard was messy. I picked it up so that it looked like a forest floor.

The third day of the hunting season some men came in and camped by the gorge. I tried to steal down the other side of the mountain to the north stream, found another camp of hunters there, and went back to my tree.

By the end of the week both Frightful and I were in need of exercise. Gunshots were still snapping around the mountain. I decided to go see Miss Turner at the library. About an hour later I wrote this:

"I got as far as the edge of the hemlock grove when a shot went off practically at my elbow. I didn't have Frightful's jesses in my hand and she took off at the blast. I climbed a tree. There was a hunter so close to me he could have bitten me, but apparently he was busy watching his deer. I was able to get up into the high branches without being seen. First, I looked around for Frightful. I could see her nowhere. I wanted to whistle for her but didn't think I should. I sat still and looked and wondered if she'd go home.

"I watched the hunter track his deer. The deer was still running. From where I was I could see it plainly, going toward the old Gribley farm site. Quietly I climbed higher and watched. Then of all things, it jumped the stone fence and fell dead.

"I thought I would stay in the tree until the hunter quartered his kill and dragged it out to the road. Ah, then, it occurred to me that he wasn't even going to find that deer. He was going off at an angle, and from what I could see, the deer had dropped in a big bank of dry ferns and would be hard to find.

"It got to be nerve-racking at this point. I could see my new jacket lying in the ferns, and the hunter looking for it. I closed my eyes and mentally steered him to the left.

"Then, good old Frightful! She had winged down the mountain and was sitting in a sapling maple not far from the deer. She saw the man and screamed. He looked in her direction; heaven knows what he thought she was, but he turned and started toward her. She rustled her wings, climbed into the sky, and disappeared over my head. I did want to whistle to her, but feared for my deer, myself, and her.

"I hung in the tree and waited about a half an hour. Finally the man gave up his hunt. His friends called, and he went on down the mountain. I went down the tree.

"In the dry ferns lay a nice young buck. I covered it carefully with some of the stones from the fence, and more ferns, and rushed home. I whistled, and down from the top of my own hemlock came Frightful. I got a piece of birch bark to write all this on so I wouldn't get too anxious and go for the deer too soon.

"We will wait until dark to go get our dinner and my new jacket. I am beginning to think I'll have all the deer hide and venison I can use. There must be other lost game on this mountain."

I got the deer after dark, and I was quite right. Before the season was over I got two more deer in the same way. However, with the first deer to work on, the rest of the season passed quickly. I had lots of scraping and preparing to do. My complaint was that I did not dare light a fire and cook that wonderful meat. I was afraid of being spotted. I ate smoked venison, nut meats, and hawthorn berries. Hawthorn berries taste a little bit like apples. They are smaller and drier than apples. They also have big seeds in them. The hawthorn bush is easy to tell because it has big red shiny thorns on it.

Each day the shooting lessened as the hunters left the hills and went home. As they cleared out, Frightful and I were freer and freer to roam.

The air temperature now was cold enough to preserve the venison, so I didn't smoke the last two deer, and about two weeks after I heard that first alarming shot, I cut off a beautiful steak, built a bright fire, and when the embers were glowing, I had myself a real dinner. I soaked some dried puffballs in water, and when they were big and moist, I fried them with wild onions and skimpy old wild carrots and stuffed myself until I felt kindly toward all men. I wrote this:

"November 26

"Hunters are excellent friends if used correctly. Don't let them see you; but follow them closely. Preferably use the tops of trees for this purpose, for hunters don't look up. They look down and to the right and left and straight ahead. So if you stay in the trees, you can not only see what they shoot, but where it falls, and if you are extremely careful, you can sometimes get to it before they do and hide it. That's how I got my third deer."

I had a little more trouble tanning these hides because the water in my oak stump kept freezing at night. It was getting cold. I began wearing my rabbit-fur underwear most of the morning. It was still too warm at noon to keep it on, but it felt good at night. I slept in it until I got my blanket made. I did not scrape the deer hair off my blanket. I liked it on. Because I had grown, one deerskin wouldn't cover me. I sewed part of another one to it.

The third hide I made into a jacket. I just cut a rectangle with a hole in it for my head and sewed on straight wide sleeves. I put enormous pockets all over

it, using every scrap I had, including the pouches I had made last summer. It looked like a cross between a Russian military blouse and a carpenter's apron, but it was warm, roomy and, I thought, handsome.

IN WHICH
Trouble Begins

I stood in my doorway the twenty-third of November dressed from head to toe in deerskins. I was lined with rabbit fur. I had mittens and squirrel-lined moccasins. I was quite excited by my wardrobe.

I whistled and Frightful came to my fist. She eyed me with her silky black eyes and pecked at my suit.

"Frightful," I said, "this is not food. It is my new suit. Please don't eat it." She peeped softly, fluffed her feathers, and looked gently toward the meadow.

"You are beautiful, too, Frightful," I said, and I touched the slate gray feathers of her back. Very gently I stroked the jet black ones that came down from her eyes. Those beautiful marks gave her much of her superb dignity. In a sense she had also come into a new suit. Her plumage had changed during the autumn, and she was breathtaking.

I walked to the spring and we looked in. I saw us quite clearly, as there were no longer any frogs to plop in the water and break the mirror with circles and ripples.

"Frightful," I said as I turned and twisted and looked. "We would be quite handsome if it were not for my hair. I need another haircut."

I did the best job I was able to do with a penknife.

I made a mental note to make a hat to cover the stray ends.

Then I did something which took me by surprise. I smelled the clean air of November, turned once more to see how the back of my suit looked, and walked down the mountain. I stepped over the stream on the stones. I walked to the road.

Before I could talk myself out of it, I was on my way to town.

As I walked down the road, I kept pretending I was going to the library; but it was Sunday, and I knew the library was closed.

I tethered Frightful just outside town on a stump. I didn't want to attract any attention. Kicking stones as I went, and whistling, I walked to the main intersection of town as if I came every Sunday.

I saw the drugstore and began to walk faster, for I was beginning to sense that I was not exactly what everybody saw every day. Eyes were upon me longer than they needed to be.

By the time I got to the drugstore, I was running. I slipped in and went to the magazine stand. I picked up a comic book and began to read.

Footsteps came toward me. Below the bottom pictures I saw a pair of pants and saddle shoes. One shoe went *tap, tap.* The feet did a kind of hop step, and I watched them walk to the other side of me. *Tap, tap, tap,* again; a hop step and the shoes and pants circled me. Then came the voice. "Well, if it isn't Daniel Boone!"

I looked into a face about the age of my own—but a little more puppyish—I thought. It had about the same coloring—brown eyes, brown hair—a bigger nose than mine, and more ears, but a very assured face. I said, "Well?" I grinned, because it had been a long time since I had seen a young man my age.

The young man didn't answer, he simply took my sleeve between his fingers and examined it closely. "Did you chew it yourself?" he asked.

I looked at the spot he was examining and said, "Well, no, I pounded it on a rock there, but I did have to chew it a bit around the neck. It stuck me."

We looked at each other then. I wanted to say something, but didn't know where to begin. He picked at my sleeve again.

"My kid brother has one that looks more real than that thing. Whataya got that on for anyway?"

I looked at his clothes. He had on a nice pair of gray slacks, a white shirt opened at the neck, and a leather jacket. As I looked at these things, I found my voice.

"Well, I'd rip anything like you have on all to pieces in about a week."

He didn't answer; he walked around me again.

"Where did you say you came from?"

"I didn't say, but I come from a farm up the way."

"Whatja say your name was?"

"Well, you called me Daniel Boone."

"Daniel Boone, eh?" He walked around me once more, and then peered at me.

"You're from New York. I can tell the accent." He leaned against the cosmetic counter. "Come on, now, tell me, is this what the kids are wearing in New York now? Is this gang stuff?"

"I am hardly a member of a gang," I said. "Are you?"

"Out here? Naw, we bowl." The conversation went to bowling for a while, then he looked at his watch.

"I gotta go. You sure are a sight, Boone. Whatja doing anyway, playing cowboys and Indians?"

"Come on up to the Gribley farm and I'll show you what I'm doing. I'm doing research. Who knows when we're all going to be blown to bits and need to know how to smoke venison."

"Gee, you New York guys can sure double talk. What does that mean, burn a block down?"

"No, it means smoke venison," I said. I took a piece out of my pocket and gave it to him. He smelled it and handed it back.

"Man," he said, "whataya do, eat it?"

"I sure do," I answered.

"I don't know whether to send you home to play with my kid brother or call the cops." He shrugged his shoulders and repeated that he had to go. As he left, he called back, "The Gribley farm?"

"Yes. Come on up if you can find it."

I browsed through the magazines until the clerk got anxious to sell me something and then I wandered out. Most of the people were in church. I wandered around the town and back to the road.

It was nice to see people again. At the outskirts of town a little boy came bursting out of a house with his shoes off, and his mother came bursting out after him. I caught the little fellow by the arm and I held him until his mother picked him up and took him back. As she went up the steps, she stopped and looked at me. She stepped toward the door, and then walked back a few steps and looked at me again. I began to feel conspicuous and took the road to my mountain.

I passed the little old strawberry lady's house. I almost went in, and then something told me to go home.

I found Frightful, untied her, stroked her creamy breast feathers, and spoke to her. "Frightful, I made a friend today. Do you think that is what I had in mind all the time?" The bird whispered.

I was feeling sad as we kicked up the leaves and started home through the forest. On the other hand, I was glad I had met Mr. Jacket, as I called him. I never asked his name. I had liked him although we hadn't even had a fight. All the best friends I had, I always fought, then got to like them after the wounds healed.

The afternoon darkened. The nuthatches that had been clinking around the trees were silent. The chickadees had vanished. A single crow called from the edge of the road. There were no insects singing, there were no catbirds, or orioles, or vireos, or robins.

"Frightful," I said. "It is winter. It is winter and I have forgotten to do a terribly important thing—stack up a big woodpile." The stupidity of this sent Mr. Jacket right out of my mind, and I bolted down the valley to my mountain. Frightful flapped to keep her balance. As I crossed the stones to my mountain trail, I said to that bird, "Sometimes I wonder if I will make it to spring."

IN WHICH
I Pile Up Wood and Go on with Winter

Now I am almost to that snowstorm. The morning after I had the awful thought about the wood, I got up early. I was glad to hear the nuthatches and chickadees. They gave me the feeling that I still had time to chop. They were bright, busy, and totally unworried about storms. I shouldered my ax and went out.

I had used most of the wood around the hemlock house, so I crossed to the top of the gorge. First I took all the dry limbs off the trees and hauled them home. Then I chopped down dead trees. With wood all around me, I got in my tree and put my arm out. I made an *x* in the needles. Where the *x* lay, I began stacking wood. I wanted to be able to reach my wood from the tree when the snow was deep. I piled a big stack at this point. I reached out the other side of the door and made another *x*. I piled wood here. Then I stepped around my piles and had a fine idea. I decided that if I used up one pile, I could tunnel through the snow to the next and the next. I made many woodpiles leading out into the forest.

I watched the sky. It was as blue as summer, but ice was building up along the waterfall at the gorge. I knew winter was coming, although each day the sun would rise in a bright sky and the days would follow cloudless. I piled more wood. This is when I realized that I was scared. I kept cutting wood and piling it like a nervous child biting his nails.

It was almost with relief that I saw the storm arrive.

Now I am back where I began. I won't tell it again, I shall go on now with my relief and the fun and wonderfulness of living on a mountaintop in winter.

The Baron Weasel loved the snow, and was up and about in it every day before Frightful and I had had our breakfast. Professor Bando's jam was my standby on those cold mornings. I would eat mounds of it on my hard acorn pancakes, which I improved by adding hickory nuts. With these as a bracer for the day, Frightful and I would stamp out into the snow and reel down the mountain. She would fly above my head as I slid and plunged and rolled to the creek.

The creek was frozen. I would slide out onto it and break a little hole and ice fish. The sun would glance off the white snow, the birds would fly through the trees, and I would come home with a fresh meal from the valley. I found there were still plants under the snow, and I would dig down and get teaberry leaves and wintergreen. I got this idea from the deer, who found a lot to eat under the snow. I tried some of the mosses that they liked, but decided moss was for the deer.

Around four o'clock we would all wander home. The nuthatches, the chickadees, the cardinals, Frightful, and me. And now came the nicest part of wonderful days. I would stop in the meadow and throw Frightful off my fist. She would wind into the sky and wait above me as I kicked the snow-bent grasses. A rabbit would pop up, or sometimes a pheasant. Out of the sky, from a pinpoint of a thing, would dive my beautiful falcon. And, oh, she was beautiful when she made a strike—all power and beauty. On the ground she would cover her quarry. Her perfect feathers would stand up on her body and her wings would arch over the food. She never touched it until I came and picked her up. I would go home and feed her, then crawl into my tree room, light a little fire on my hearth, and Frightful and I would begin the winter evening.

I had lots of time to cook and try mixing different plants with different meats to make things taste better—and I must say I originated some excellent meals.

When dinner was done, the fire would blaze on; Frightful would sit on the foot post of the bed and preen and wipe her beak and shake. Just the fact that she was alive was a warming thing to know.

I would look at her and wonder what made a bird a bird and a boy a boy. The forest would become silent. I would know that The Baron Weasel was about, but I would not hear him.

Then I would get a piece of birch bark and write, or I would make new things out of deer hide, like a hood for Frightful, and finally I would take off my suit and my moccasins and crawl into my bed under the sweet-smelling deerskin. The fire would burn itself out and I would be asleep.

Those were nights of the very best sort.

One night I read some of my old notes about how to pile wood so I could get to it under the snow, and I laughed until Frightful awoke. I hadn't made a single tunnel. I walked on the snow to get wood like The Baron Weasel went for food or the deer went for moss.

IN WHICH
I Learn About Birds and People

Frightful and I settled down to living in snow. We went to bed early, slept late, ate the mountain harvest, and explored the country alone. Oh, the deer walked with us, the foxes followed in our footsteps, the winter birds flew over our heads, but mostly we were alone in the white wilderness. It was nice. It was very, very nice. My deerskin rabbit-lined suit was so warm that even when my breath froze in my nostrils, my body was snug and comfortable. Frightful fluffed on the coldest days, but a good flight into the air around the mountain would warm her, and she would come back to my fist with a thump and a flip. This was her signal of good spirits.

I did not become lonely. Many times during the summer I had thought of the "long winter months ahead" with some fear. I had read so much about the loneliness of the farmer, the trapper, the woodsman during the bleakness of winter that I had come to believe it. The winter was as exciting as the summer—maybe more so. The birds were magnificent and almost tame. They talked to each other, warned each other, fought for food, for kingship, and for the right to make the most noise. Sometimes I would sit in my doorway, which became an entrance to behold—a portico of pure white snow, adorned with snowmen—and watch them with endless interest. They reminded me of Third Avenue, and I gave them the names that seemed to fit.

There was Mr. Bracket. He lived on the first floor of our apartment house, and no one could sit on his step or even make a noise near his door without being chased. Mr. Bracket, the chickadee, spent most of his time chasing the young chickadees through the woods. Only his mate could share his favorite perches and feeding places.

Then there were Mrs. O'Brien, Mrs. Callaway, and Mrs. Federio. On Third Avenue they would all go off to the market together first thing in the morning, talking and pushing and stopping to lecture to children in gutters and streets. Mrs. Federio always followed Mrs. O'Brien, and Mrs. O'Brien always followed Mrs. Callaway in talking and pushing and even in buying an apple. And there they were again in my hemlock; three busy chickadees. They would flit and rush around and click and fly from one eating spot to another. They were noisy, scolding and busily following each other. All the other chickadees followed them, and they made way only for Mr. Bracket.

The chickadees, like the people on Third Avenue, had their favorite routes to and from the best food supplies. They each had their own resting perches and each had a little shelter in a tree cavity to which they would fly when the day was over. They would chatter and call good night and make a big fuss before they parted; and then the forest would be as quiet as the apartment house on Third Avenue when all the kids were off the streets and all the parents had said their last words to each other and everyone had gone to their own little hole.

Sometimes when the wind howled and the snows blew, the chickadees would be out for only a few hours. Even Mr. Bracket, who had been elected by the chickadees to test whether or not it was too stormy for good hunting, would appear for a few hours and disappear. Sometimes I would find him just sitting quietly on a limb next to the bole of a tree, all fluffed up and doing nothing. There was no one who more enjoyed doing nothing on a bad day than Mr. Bracket of Third Avenue.

Frightful, the two Mr. Brackets, and I shared this feeling. When the ice and sleet and snow drove down through the hemlocks, we all holed up.

I looked at my calendar pole one day, and realized that it was almost Christmas. Bando will come, I thought. I'll have to prepare a feast and make a present for him. I took stock of the frozen venison and decided that there were enough steaks for us to eat nothing but venison for a month. I scooped under the snow for teaberry plants to boil down and pour over snowballs for dessert.

I checked my cache of wild onions to see if I had enough to make onion soup, and set aside some large firm groundnuts for mashed potatoes. There were still piles of dogtooth violet bulbs and Solomon's seal roots and a few dried apples. I cracked walnuts, hickory nuts, and beechnuts, then began a pair of deer-hide moccasins to be lined with rabbit fur for Bando's present. I finished these before Christmas, so I started a hat of the same materials.

Two days before Christmas I began to wonder if Bando would come. He had forgotten, I was sure—or he was busy, I said. Or he thought that I was no longer here and decided not to tramp out through the snows to find out. On Christmas Eve Bando still had not arrived, and I began to plan for a very small Christmas with Frightful.

About four-thirty Christmas Eve I hung a small red cluster of teaberries on the deerskin door. I went in my tree room for a snack of beechnuts when I heard a faint "halloooo" from far down the mountain. I snuffed out my tallow candle, jumped into my coat and moccasins, and plunged out into the snow. Again a "halloooo" floated over the quiet snow. I took a bearing on the sound and bounced down the hill to meet Bando. I ran into him just as he turned up the valley to follow the stream bed. I was so glad to see him that I hugged him and pounded him on the back.

"Never thought I'd make it," he said. "I walked all the way from the entrance of the State Park; pretty good, eh?" He smiled and slapped his tired legs. Then he grabbed my arm, and with three quick pinches, tested the meat on me.

"You've been living well," he said. He looked closely at my face. "But you're gonna need a shave in a year or two." I thanked him and we sprang up the mountain, cut across through the gorge and home.

"How's the Frightful?" he asked as soon as we were inside and the light was lit.

I whistled. She jumped to my fist. He got bold and stroked her. "And the jam?" he asked.

"Excellent, except the crocks are absorbent and are sopping up all the juice."

"Well, I brought you some more sugar; we'll try next year. Merry Christmas, Thoreau!" he shouted, and looked about the room.

"I see you have been busy. A blanket, new clothes, and an ingenious fireplace—with a real chimney—and say, you have silverware!" He picked up the forks I had carved.

We ate smoked fish for dinner with boiled dogtooth violet bulbs. Walnuts dipped in jam were dessert. Bando was pleased with his jam.

When we were done, Bando stretched out on my bed. He propped his feet up and lit his pipe.

"And now, I have something to show you," he said. He reached in his coat pocket and took out a newspaper clipping. It was from a New York paper, and it read:

WILD BOY SUSPECTED LIVING OFF DEER
AND NUTS IN WILDERNESS OF CATSKILLS

I looked at Bando and leaned over to read the headline myself.

"Have you been talking?" I asked.

"Me? Don't be ridiculous. You have had several visitors other than me."

"The fire warden—the old lady!" I cried out.

"Now, Thoreau, this could only be a rumor. Just because it is in print, doesn't mean it's true. Before you get excited, sit still and listen." He read:

" 'Residents of Delhi, in the Catskill Mountains, report that a wild boy, who lives off deer and nuts, is hiding out in the mountains.

" 'Several hunters stated that this boy stole deer from them during hunting season.' "

"I did not!" I shouted. "I only took the ones they had wounded and couldn't find."

"Well, that's what they told their wives when they came home without their deer. Anyway, listen to this:

" 'This wild boy has been seen from time to time by Catskill residents, some of whom believe he is crazy!' "

"Well, that's a terrible thing to say!"

"Just awful," he stated. "Any normal red-blooded American boy wants to live in a tree house and trap his own food. They just don't do it, that's all."

"Read on," I said.

" 'Officials say that there is no evidence of any boy living alone in the mountains, and add that all abandoned houses and sheds are routinely checked for just such events. Nevertheless, the residents are sure that such a boy exists!' End story."

"That's a lot of nonsense!" I leaned back against the bedstead and smiled.

"Ho, ho, don't think that ends it," Bando said, and reached in his pocket for another clipping. "This one is dated December fifth, the other was November twenty-third. Shall I read?"

"Yes."

OLD WOMAN REPORTS MEETING WILD BOY
WHILE PICKING STRAWBERRIES IN CATSKILLS

" 'Mrs. Thomas Fielder, ninety-seven, resident of Delhi, N.Y., told this reporter that she met a wild boy on Bitter Mountain last June while gathering her annual strawberry jelly supply.

" 'She said the boy was brown-haired, dusty, and wandering aimlessly around the mountains. However, she added, he seemed to be in good flesh and happy.

" 'The old woman, a resident of the mountain resort town for ninety-seven years, called this office to report her observation. Local residents report that Mrs. Fielder is a fine old member of the community, who only occasionally sees imaginary things.' "

Bando roared. I must say I was sweating, for I really did not expect this turn of events.

"And now," went on Bando, "and now the queen of

the New York papers. This story was buried on page nineteen. No sensationalism for this paper.

BOY REPORTED LIVING OFF LAND IN CATSKILLS

" 'A young boy of seventeen or eighteen, who left home with a group of boy scouts, is reported to be still scouting in that area, according to the fire warden of the Catskill Mountains.

" 'Evidence of someone living in the forest—a fireplace, soup bones, and cracked nuts—was reported by Warden Jim Handy, who spent the night in the wilderness looking for the lad. Jim stated that the young man had apparently left the area, as there was no evidence of his camp upon a second trip—' "

"What second trip?" I asked.

Bando puffed his pipe, looked at me wistfully and said, "Are you ready to listen?"

"Sure," I answered.

"Well, here's the rest of it. '. . . there was no trace of his camp on a second trip, and the warden believes that the young man returned to his home at the end of the summer.'

"You know, Thoreau, I could scarcely drag myself away from the newspapers to come up here. You make a marvelous story."

I said, "Put more wood on the fire, it is Christmas. No one will be searching these mountains until May Day."

Bando asked for the willow whistles. I got them for him, and after running the scale several times, he said, "Let us serenade the ingenuity of the American newspaperman. Then let us serenade the conservationists who have protected the American wilderness, so that a boy can still be alone in this world of millions of people."

I thought that was suitable, and we played "Holy Night." We tried "The Twelve Days of Christmas," but the whistles were too stiff and Bando too tired.

"Thoreau, my body needs rest. Let's give up," he said after two bad starts. I banked the fire and blew out the candle and slept in my clothes.

It was Christmas when we awoke. Breakfast was light—acorn pancakes, jam, and sassafras tea. Bando went for a walk, I lit the fire in the fireplace and spent the morning creating a feast from the wilderness.

I gave Bando his presents when he returned. He liked them. He was really pleased; I could tell by his eyebrows. They went up and down and in and out. Furthermore, I know he liked the presents because he wore them.

The onion soup was about to be served when I heard a voice shouting in the distance, "I know you are there! I know you are there! Where are you?"

"*Dad!*" I screamed, and dove right through the door onto my stomach. I all but fell down the mountain shouting, "Dad! Dad! Where are you?" I found him resting in a snowdrift, looking at the cardinal pair that lived near the stream. He was smiling, stretched out on his back, not in exhaustion, but in joy.

"Merry Christmas!" he whooped. I ran toward him. He jumped to his feet, tackled me, thumped my chest, and rubbed snow in my face.

Then he stood up, lifted me from the snow by the pockets on my coat, and held me off the ground so that we were eye to eye. He sure smiled. He threw me down in the snow again and wrestled with me for a few minutes. Our formal greeting done, we strode up the mountain.

"Well, son," he began. "I've been reading about you in the papers and I could no longer resist the temptation to visit you. I still can't believe you did it."

His arm went around me. He looked real good, and I was overjoyed to see him.

"How did you find me?" I asked eagerly.

"I went to Mrs. Fielder, and she told me which mountain. At the stream I found your raft and ice-fishing holes. Then I looked for trails and footsteps. When I thought I was getting warm, I hollered."

"Am I that easy to find?"

"You didn't have to answer, and I'd probably have frozen in the snow." He was pleased and not angry at me at all. He said again, "I just didn't think you'd do it. I was sure you'd be back the next day. When you weren't, I bet on the next week; then the next month. How's it going?"

"Oh, it's a wonderful life, Dad!"

When we walked into the tree, Bando was putting the final touches on the venison steak.

"Dad, this is my friend, Professor Bando; he's a teacher. He got lost one day last summer and stumbled onto my camp. He liked it so well that he came back for Christmas. Bando, meet my father."

Bando turned the steak on the spit, rose, and shook my father's hand.

"I am pleased to meet the man who sired this boy," he said grandly. I could see that they liked each other and that it was going to be a splendid Christmas. Dad stretched out on the bed and looked around.

"I thought maybe you'd pick a cave," he said. "The papers reported that they were looking for you in old sheds and houses, but I knew better than that. However, I never would have thought of the inside of a tree. What a beauty! Very clever, son, very, very clever. This is a comfortable bed."

He noticed my food caches, stood and peered into them. "Got enough to last until spring?"

"I think so," I said. "If I don't keep getting hungry visitors all the time." I winked at him.

"Well, I would wear out my welcome by a year if I could, but I have to get back to work soon after Christmas."

"How's Mom and all the rest?" I asked as I took down the turtle-shell plates and set them on the floor.

"She's marvelous. How she manages to feed and

clothe those eight youngsters on what I bring her, I don't know; but she does it. She sends her love, and says that she hopes you are eating well-balanced meals."

The onion soup was simmering and ready. I gave Dad his.

"First course," I said.

He breathed deeply of the odor and downed it boiling hot.

"Son, this is better onion soup than the chef at the Waldorf can make."

Bando sipped his, and I put mine in the snow to cool.

"Your mother will stop worrying about your diet when she hears of this."

Bando rinsed Dad's soup bowl in the snow, and with great ceremony and elegance—he could really be elegant when the occasion arose—poured him a turtle shell of sassafras tea. Quoting a passage from one of Dickens's food-eating scenes, he carved the blackened steak. It was pink and juicy inside. Cooked to perfection. We were all proud of it. Dad had to finish his tea before he could eat. I was short on bowls. Then I filled his shell. A mound of sort of fluffy mashed cattail tubers, mushrooms, and dogtooth violet bulbs, smothered in gravy thickened with acorn powder. Each plate had a pile of soaked and stewed honey locust beans—mixed with hickory nuts. The beans are so hard it took three days to soak them.

It was a glorious feast. Everyone was impressed, including me. When we were done, Bando went down to the stream and cut some old dried and hollow reeds. He came back and carefully made us each a flute with the tip of his penknife. He said the willow whistles were too old for such an occasion. We all played Christmas carols until dark. Bando wanted to try some complicat-

ed jazz tunes, but the late hour, the small fire dancing and throwing heat, and the snow insulating us from the winds made us all so sleepy that we were not capable of more than a last slow rendition of taps before we put ourselves on and under skins and blew out the light.

Before anyone was awake the next morning, I heard Frightful call hungrily. I had put her outside to sleep, as we were very crowded. I went out to find her. Her Christmas dinner had been a big piece of venison, but the night air had enlarged her appetite. I called her to my fist and we went into the meadow to rustle up breakfast for the guests. She was about to go after a rabbit, but I thought that wasn't proper fare for a post-Christmas breakfast, so we went to the stream. Frightful caught herself a pheasant while I kicked a hole in the ice and did a little ice fishing. I caught about six trout and whistled Frightful to my hand. We returned to the hemlock. Dad and Bando were still asleep, with their feet in each other's faces, but both looking very content.

I built the fire and was cooking the fish and making pancakes when Dad shot out of bed.

"Wild boy!" he shouted. "What a sanguine smell. What a purposeful fire. Breakfast in a tree. Son, I toil from sunup to sundown, and never have I lived so well!"

I served him. He choked a bit on the acorn pancakes—they are a little flat and hard—but Bando got out some of his blueberry jam and smothered the pancakes with an enormous portion. Dad went through the motions of eating this. The fish, however, he enjoyed, and he asked for more. We drank sassafras tea, sweetened with some of the sugar Bando had brought me, rubbed our turtle shells clean in the snow, and went out into the forest.

Dad had not met Frightful. When she winged down out of the hemlock, he ducked and flattened out in the snow shouting, "Blast off."

He was very cool toward Frightful until he learned that she was the best provider we had ever had in our family, and then he continually praised her beauty and admired her talents. He even tried to pet her, but Frightful was not to be won. She snagged him with her talons.

They stayed away from each other for the rest of Dad's visit, although Dad never ceased to admire her from a safe distance.

Bando had to leave two or three days after Christmas. He had some papers to grade, and he started off reluctantly one morning, looking very unhappy about the way of life he had chosen. He shook hands all around and then turned to me and said, "I'll save all the newspaper clippings for you, and if the reporters start getting too hot on your trail, I'll call the New York papers and give them a bum steer." I could see he rather liked the idea, and departed a little happier.

Dad lingered on for a few more days, ice fishing, setting my traps and snares, and husking walnuts. He whittled some cooking spoons and forks.

On New Year's Day he announced that he must go.

"I told your mother I would only stay for Christmas. It's a good thing she knows me or she might be worried."

"She won't send the police out to look for you?" I asked hurriedly. "Could she think you never found me?"

"Oh, I told her I'd call her Christmas night if I didn't." He poked around for another hour or two, trying to decide just how to leave. Finally he started down the mountain. He had hardly gone a hundred feet before he was back.

"I've decided to leave by another route. Somebody might backtrack me and find you. And that would be too bad." He came over to me and put his hand on my shoulder. "You've done very well, Sam." He grinned and walked off toward the gorge.

I watched him bound from rock to rock. He waved from the top of a large rock and leaped into the air. That was the last I saw of Dad for a long time.

IN WHICH
I Have a Good Look at Winter and Find Spring in the Snow

With Christmas over, the winter became serious. The snows deepened, the wind blew, the temperatures dropped until the air snapped and talked. Never had humanity seemed so far away as it did in those cold still months of January, February, and March. I wandered the snowy crags, listening to the language of the birds by day and to the noises of the weather by night. The wind howled, the snow avalanched, and the air creaked.

I slept, ate, played my reed whistle, and talked to Frightful.

To be relaxed, warm, and part of the winter wilderness is an unforgettable experience. I was in excellent condition. Not a cold, not a sniffle, not a moment of fatigue. I enjoyed the feeling that I could eat, sleep and be warm, and outwit the storms that blasted the mountains and the subzero temperatures that numbed them.

It snowed on. I plowed through drifts and stamped paths until eventually it occurred to me that I had all the materials to make snowshoes for easier traveling.

Here are the snowshoe notes:

"I made slats out of ash saplings, whittling them thin enough to bow. I soaked them in water to make them bend more easily, looped the two ends together, and wound them with hide.

"With my penknife I made holes an inch apart all around the loop.

"I strung deer hide crisscross through the loops. I made a loop of hide to hold my toe and straps to tie the shoes on.

"When I first walked in these shoes, I tripped on my toes and fell, but by the end of the first day I could walk from the tree to the gorge in half the time."

I lived close to the weather. It is surprising how you watch it when you live in it. Not a cloud passed unnoticed, not a wind blew untested. I knew the moods of the storms, where they came from, their shapes and colors. When the sun shone, I took Frightful to the meadow and we slid down the mountain on my snapping-turtle-shell sled. She really didn't care much for this.

When the winds changed and the air smelled like snow, I would stay in my tree, because I had gotten lost in a blizzard one afternoon and had had to hole up in a rock ledge until I could see where I was going. That day the winds were so strong I could not push against them, so I crawled under the ledge; for hours I wondered if I would be able to dig out when the storm blew on. Fortunately I only had to push through about a foot of snow. However, that taught me to stay home when the air said "snow." Not that I was afraid of being caught far from home in a storm, for I could find food and shelter and make a fire anywhere, but I had become as attached to my hemlock house as a brooding bird to her nest. Caught out in the storms and weather, I had an urgent desire to return to my tree, even as The Baron Weasel returned to his den, and the deer to their copse. We all had our little "patch" in the wilderness. We all fought to return there.

I usually came home at night with the nuthatch that roosted in a nearby sapling. I knew I was late if I tapped the tree and he came out. Sometimes when the weather was icy and miserable, I would hear him high in the tree near the edge of the meadow, yanking and yanking and flicking his tail, and then I would see him wing to bed early. I considered him a pretty good barometer, and if he went to his tree early, I went to mine early too. When you don't have a newspaper or radio to give you weather bulletins, watch the birds and animals. They can tell when a storm is coming. I called the nuthatch "Barometer," and when he holed up, I holed up, lit my light, and sat by my fire whittling or learning new tunes on my reed whistle. I was now really into the teeth of winter, and quite fascinated by its activity. There is no such thing as a "still winter night." Not only are many animals running around in the creaking cold, but the trees cry out and limbs snap and fall, and the wind gets caught in a ravine and screams until it dies. One noisy night I put this down:

"There is somebody in my bedroom. I can hear small exchanges of greetings and little feet moving up the wall. By the time I get to my light all is quiet.

"Next Day

"There was something in my room last night, a small tunnel leads out from my door into the snow. It is a marvelous tunnel, neatly packed, and it goes from a dried fern to a clump of moss. Then it turns and disappears. I would say mouse.

"That Night

"I kept an ember glowing and got a light fast before the visitor could get to the door. It *was* a mouse—a perfect little white-footed deer mouse with enormous black eyes and tidy white feet. Caught in the act of intruding, he decided not to retreat, but came toward me a few steps. I handed him a nut meat. He took it in his fragile paws, stuffed it in his cheek, flipped, and went out his secret tunnel. No doubt the tunnel leads right over to my store tree, and this fellow is having a fat winter."

There were no raccoons or skunks about in the snow, but the mice, the weasels, the mink, the foxes, the shrews, the cottontail rabbits were all busier than Coney Island in July. Their tracks were all over the mountain, and their activities ranged from catching each other to hauling various materials back to their dens and burrows for more insulation.

By day the birds were a-wing. They got up late, after I did, and would call to each other before hunting. I would stir up my fire and think about how much food it must take to keep one little bird alive in that fierce cold. They must eat and eat and eat, I thought.

Once, however, I came upon a male cardinal sitting in a hawthorn bush. It was a miserable day, gray, damp, and somewhere around the zero mark. The cardinal wasn't doing anything at all—just sitting on a twig, all fluffed up to keep himself warm. Now there's a wise bird, I said to myself. He is conserving his energy, none of this flying around looking for food and wasting effort. As I watched him, he shifted his feet twice, standing on one and pulling the other up into his warm feathers. I had often wondered why birds' feet didn't freeze, and there was my answer. He even sat down on both of them and let his warm feathers cover them like socks.

"*January 8*

"I took Frightful out today. We went over to the meadow to catch a rabbit for her; as we passed one of the hemlocks near the edge of the grove, she pulled her feathers to her body and looked alarmed. I tried to find out what had frightened her, but saw nothing.

"On the way back we passed the same tree and I noticed an owl pellet cast in the snow. I looked up. There were lots of limbs and darkness, but I could not see the owl. I walked around the tree; Frightful stared at one spot until I thought her head would swivel off. I looked, and there it was, looking like a broken limb—a great horned owl. I must say I was excited to have such a neighbor. I hit the tree with a stick and he flew off. Those great wings—they must have been five feet across—beat the wind, but there was no sound. The owl steered down the mountain through the tree limbs, and somewhere not far away he vanished in the needles and limbs.

"It is really very special to have a horned owl. I guess I feel this way because he is such a wilderness bird. He needs lots of forest and big trees, and so his presence means that the Gribley farm is a beautiful place indeed."

One week the weather gave a little to the sun, and snow melted and limbs dumped their loads and popped up into the air. I thought I'd try to make an igloo. I was cutting big blocks of snow and putting them in a circle. Frightful was dozing with her face in the sun, and the tree sparrows were raiding the hemlock cones. I worked and hummed, and did not notice the gray sheet of cloud that was sneaking up the mountain from the northwest. It covered the sun suddenly. I realized the air was damp enough to wring. I could stay as warm as a bug if I didn't get wet, so I looked at the drab mess in the sky, whistled for Frightful, and started back to the tree. We holed up just as Barometer was yanking his way home, and it was none too soon. It drizzled, it misted, it sprinkled, and finally it froze. The deer-hide door grew stiff with ice as darkness came, and it rattled like a piece of tin when the wind hit it.

I made a fire, the tree room warmed, and I puttered around with a concoction I call possum sop. A meal of frozen possum stewed with lichens, snakeweed, and lousewort. It is a different sort of dish. Of course what I really like about it are the names of all the plants with the name possum. I fooled for an hour or so brewing this dish, adding this and that, when I heard the mouse in his tunnel. I realized he was making an awful fuss, and decided it was because he was trying to gnaw through ice to get in. I decided to help him. Frightful was on her post, and I wanted to see the mouse's face when he found he was in a den with a falcon. I pushed the deerskin door. It wouldn't budge. I kicked it. It gave a little, cracking like china, and I realized that I was going to be iced in if I didn't keep that door open.

I finally got it open. There must have been an inch and a half of ice on it. The mouse, needless to say, was gone. I ate my supper and reminded myself to awaken and open the door off and on during the night. I put more wood on the fire, as it was damp in spite of the flames, and went to bed in my underwear and suit.

I awoke twice and kicked open the door. Then I fell into a sound sleep that lasted hours beyond my usual rising time. I overslept, I discovered, because I was in a block of ice, and none of the morning sounds of the forest penetrated my glass house to awaken me. The first thing I did was try to open the door; I chipped and kicked and managed to get my head out to see what had happened. I was sealed in. Now, I have seen ice storms, and I know they can be shiny and glassy and treacherous, but this was something else. There were sheets of ice binding the aspens to earth and cementing the tops of the hemlocks in arches. It was inches thick! Frightful winged out of the door and flew to a limb, where she tried to perch. She slipped, dropped to the ground, and skidded on her wings and undercoverts to a low spot where she finally stopped. She tried to get to her feet, slipped, lost her balance, and spread her wings. She finally flapped into the air and hovered there until she could locate a decent perch. She found one close against the bole of the hemlock. It was ice free.

I laughed at her, and then I came out and took a step. I landed with an explosion on my seat. The jolt splintered the ice and sent glass-covered limbs clattering to earth like a shopful of shattering crystal. As I sat there, and I didn't dare to move because I might get hurt, I heard an enormous explosion. It was followed by splintering and clattering and smashing. A maple at the edge of the meadow had literally blown up. I feared now for my trees—the ice was too heavy to bear. While down, I chipped the deer flap clean, and sort of swam back into my tree, listening to trees exploding all over the mountain. It was a fearful and dreadful sound. I lit a fire, ate smoked fish and dried apples, and went out again. I must say I toyed with the idea of making ice skates. However, I saw the iron wagon axle iced against a tree, and crawled to it. I de-iced it with the butt of my ax, and used it for a cane. I would stab it into the ground and inch along. I fell a couple of times but not as hard as that first time.

Frightful saw me start off through the woods, for I had to see this winter display, and she winged to my shoulder, glad for a good perch. At the meadow I looked hopefully for the sun, but it didn't have a chance. The sky was as thick as Indiana bean soup. Out in the open I watched one tree after another splinter and break under the ice, and the glass sparks that shot into the air and the thunder that the ice made as it shattered were something to remember.

At noon not a drip had fallen, the ice was as tight as it had been at dawn. I heard no nuthatches, the chickadees called once, but were silent again. There was an explosion near my spring. A hemlock had gone. Frightful and I crept back to the tree. I decided that if my house was going to shatter, I would just as soon be in it. Inside, I threw sticks to Frightful and she caught them in her talons. This is a game we play when we are tense and bored. Night came and the ice still lay in sheets. We slept to the occasional boom of breaking trees, although the explosions were not as frequent. Apparently the most rotted and oldest trees had collapsed first. The rest were more resilient, and unless a wind came up, I figured the damage was over.

At midnight a wind came up. It awakened me, for the screech of the iced limbs rubbing each other and the snapping of the ice were like the sounds from a madhouse. I listened, decided there was nothing I could do, buried my head under the deer hide, and went back to sleep.

Around six or seven I heard Barometer, the nuthatch. He yanked as he went food hunting through the hemlock grove. I jumped up and looked out. The sun had come through, and the forest sparkled and shone in cruel splendor.

That day I heard the *drip, drip* begin, and by evening some of the trees had dumped their loads and were slowly lifting themselves to their feet, so to speak. The aspens and birch trees, however, were still bent like Indian bows.

Three days later, the forest arose, the ice melted, and for about a day or so we had warm, glorious weather.

The mountain was a mess. Broken trees, fallen limbs were everywhere. I felt badly about the ruins until I thought that this had been happening to the mountain for thousands of years and the trees were still there, as were the animals and birds. The birds were starved, and many had died. I found their cold little bodies under bushes and one stiff chickadee in a cavity. Its foot was drawn into its feathers, its feathers were fluffed.

Frightful ate old frozen muskrat during those days, We couldn't kick up a rabbit or even a mouse. They were in the snow under the ice, waiting it out. I suppose the mice went right on tunneling to the grasses and the mosses and had no trouble staying alive, but I did wonder how The Baron Weasel was doing. I needn't have. Here are some notes about him.

"I should not have worried about The Baron Weasel; he appeared after the ice storm, looking sleek and pleased with himself. I think he dined royally on the many dying animals and birds. In any event, he was full of pep and ran up the hemlock to chase Frightful off her perch. That Baron! It's a good thing I don't have to tie Frightful much anymore, or he would certainly try to kill her. He still attacks me, more for the fun of being sent sprawling out into the snow than for food, for he hasn't put his teeth in my trousers for months."

January was a fierce month. After the ice storm came more snow. The mountaintop was never free of it, the gorge was blocked; only on the warmest days could I hear, deep under the ice, the trickle of water seeping over the falls. I still had food, but it was getting low. All the fresh-frozen venison was gone, and most of the bulbs and tubers. I longed for just a simple dandelion green.

Toward the end of January I began to feel tired, and my elbows and knees were a little stiff. This worried me. I figured it was due to some vitamin I wasn't getting, but I couldn't remember which vitamin it was or even where I would find it if I could remember it.

One morning my nose bled. It frightened me a bit, and I wondered if I shouldn't hike to the library and reread the material on vitamins. It didn't last long, however, so I figured it wasn't too serious. I decided I would live until the greens came to the land, for I was of the opinion that since I had had nothing green for months, that was probably the trouble.

On that same day Frightful caught a rabbit in the meadow. As I cleaned it, the liver suddenly looked so tempting that I could hardly wait to prepare it. For the next week, I craved liver and ate all I could get. The tiredness ended, the bones stopped aching and I had no more nosebleeds. Hunger is a funny thing. It has a kind of intelligence all its own. I ate liver almost every day until the first plants emerged, and I never had any more trouble. I have looked up vitamins since. I am not surprised to find that liver is rich in vitamin C. So are citrus fruits and green vegetables, the foods I lacked. Wild plants like sorrel and dock are rich in this vitamin. Even if I had known this at that time, it would have done me no good, for they were but roots in the earth. As it turned out, liver was the only available source of vitamin C—and on liver I stuffed, without knowing why.

So much for my health. I wonder now why I didn't have more trouble than I did, except that my mother worked in a children's hospital during the war, helping to prepare food, and she was conscious of what made up a balanced meal. We heard a lot about it as kids, so I was not unaware that my winter diet was off balance.

After that experience, I noticed things in the forest

that I hadn't paid any attention to before. A squirrel had stripped the bark off a sapling at the foot of the meadow, leaving it gleaming white. I pondered when I saw it, wondering if he had lacked a vitamin or two and had sought them in the bark. I must admit I tried a little of the bark myself, but decided that even if it was loaded with vitamins, I preferred liver.

I also noticed that the birds would sit in the sun when it favored our mountain with its light, and I, being awfully vitamin minded at the time, wondered if they were gathering vitamin D. To be on the safe side, in view of this, I sat in the sun too when it was out. So did Frightful.

My notes piled up during these months, and my journal of birch bark became a storage problem. I finally took it out of my tree and cached it under a rock ledge nearby. The mice made nests in it, but it held up even when it got wet. That's one thing about using the products of the forest. They are usually weatherproof. This is important when the weather is as near to you as your skin and as much a part of your life as eating.

I was writing more about the animals now and less about myself, which proves I was feeling pretty safe. Here is an interesting entry.

"February 6

"The deer have pressed in all around me. They are hungry. Apparently they stamp out yards in the valleys where they feed during the dawn and dusk, but many

of them climb back to the hemlock grove to hide and sleep for the day. They manage the deep snows so effortlessly on those slender hooves. If I were to know that a million years from today my children's children's children were to live as I am living in these mountains, I should marry me a wife with slender feet and begin immediately to breed a race with hooves, that the Catskill children of the future might run through the snows and meadows and marshes as easily as the deer."

I got to worrying about the deer, and for many days I climbed trees and cut down tender limbs for them. At first only two came, then five, and soon I had a ring of large-eyed white-tailed deer waiting at my tree at twilight for me to come out and chop off limbs. I was astonished to see this herd grow, and wondered what signals they used to inform each other of my services. Did they smell fatter? Look more contented? Somehow they were able to tell their friends that there was a free lunch on my side of the mountain, and more and more arrived.

One evening there were so many deer that I decided to chop limbs on the other side of the meadow. They were cutting up the snow and tearing up the ground around my tree with their pawing.

Three nights later they all disappeared. Not one deer came for limbs. I looked down the valley, and in the dim light could see the open earth on the land below. The deer could forage again. Spring was coming to the land! My heart beat faster. I think I was trembling. The valley also blurred. The only thing that can do that is tears, so I guess I was crying.

That night the great horned owls boomed out across the land. My notes read:

"*February 10*

"I think the great horned owls have eggs! The mountain is white, the wind blows, the snow is hard packed, but spring is beginning in their hollow maple. I will climb it tomorrow.

"*February 12*

"Yes, yes, yes, yes. It is spring in the maple. Two great horned owl eggs lie in the cold snow-rimmed cavity in the broken top of the tree. They were warm to my touch. Eggs in the snow. Now isn't that wonderful? I didn't stay long, for it is bitter weather and I wanted the female to return immediately. I climbed down, and as I ran off toward my tree I saw her drift on those muffled wings of the owl through the limbs and branches as she went back to her work. I crawled through the tunnel of ice that leads to my tree now, the wind beating at my back. I spent the evening whittling and thinking about the owl high in the forest with the first new life of the spring."

And so with the disappearance of the deer, the hoot of the owl, the cold land began to create new life. Spring is terribly exciting when you are living right in it.

I was hungry for green vegetables, and that night as I went off to sleep, I thought of the pokeweeds, the dandelions, the spring beauties that would soon be pressing up from the earth.

MORE ABOUT
The Spring in the Winter and the Beginning of My Story's End

The owl had broken the spell of winter. From that time on, things began to happen that you'd have to see to believe. Insects appeared while the snow was on the ground. Birds built nests, raccoons mated, foxes called to each other, seeking again their lifelong mates. At the end of February, the sap began to run in the maple trees. I tapped some trees and boiled the sap to syrup. It takes an awful lot of sap to make one cup of syrup, I discovered—thirty-two cups, to be exact.

All this and I was still in my winter fur-lined underwear. One or two birds returned, the ferns by the protected spring unrolled—very slowly, but they did. Then the activity gathered momentum, and before I was aware of the change, there were the skunk cabbages poking their funny blooms above the snow in the marsh. I picked some and cooked them, but they aren't any good. A skunk cabbage is a skunk cabbage.

From my meadow I could see the valleys turning green. My mountain was still snow-capped, so I walked into the valleys almost every day to scout them for edible plants. Frightful rode down with me on my

shoulder. She knew even better than I that the season had changed, and she watched the sky like radar. No life traveled that sky world unnoticed by Frightful. I thought she wanted to be free and seek a mate, but I could not let her. I still depended upon her talents and company. Furthermore, she was different, and if I did let her go, she probably would have been killed by another female, for Frightful had no territory other than the hemlock patch, and her hunting instincts had been trained for man. She was a captive, not a wild bird, and that is almost another kind of bird.

One day I was in the valley digging tubers and collecting the tiny new dandelion shoots when Frightful saw another duck hawk and flew from my shoulder like a bolt, pulling the leash from my hand as she went.

"Frightful!" I called. "You can't leave me now!" I whistled, held out a piece of meat, and hoped she would not get her leash caught in a treetop. She hovered above my head, looked at the falcon and then at my hand, folded her wings, and dropped to my fist.

"I saw that!" a voice said. I spun around to see a young man about my own age, shivering at the edge of the woods.

"You're the wild boy, aren't you?"

I was so astonished to see a human being in all this cold thawing silence that I just stood and looked at him. When I gathered my wits I replied. "No, I'm just a citizen."

"Aw, gee," he said with disappointment. Then he gave in to the cold and shivered until the twigs around him rattled. He stepped forward.

"Well, anyway, I'm Matt Spell. I work after school on the Poughkeepsie *New Yorker,* a newspaper. I read all the stories about the wild boy who lives in the Catskills, and I thought that if I found him and got a good story, I might get to be a reporter. Have you ever run across him? Is there such a boy?"

"Aw, it's all nonsense," I said as I gathered some dry wood and piled it near the edge of the woods. I lit it swiftly, hoping he would not notice the flint and steel. He was so cold and so glad to see the flames that he said nothing.

I rolled a log up to the fire for him and shoved it against a tree that was blocked from the raw biting wind by a stand of hawthorns. He crouched over the flames for a long time, then practically burnt the soles off his shoes warming his feet. He was that miserable.

"Why didn't you dress warmer for this kind of a trip?" I asked. "You'll die up here in this damp cold."

"I think I am dying," he said, sitting so close to the fire, he almost smothered it. He was nice looking, about thirteen or fourteen, I would have said. He had a good bold face, blue eyes, hair about the color of my stream in the thaw. Although he was big, he looked like the kind of fellow who didn't know his own strength. I liked Matt.

"I've still got a sandwich," he said. "Want half?"

"No, thanks," I said. "I brought my lunch." Frightful had been sitting on my shoulder through all this, but now the smoke was bothering her and she hopped to a higher perch. I still had her on the leash.

"There was a bird on your shoulder," Matt said. "He had nice eyes. Do you know him?"

"I'm sort of an amateur falconer," I replied. "I come up here to train my bird. It's a she—Frightful is her name."

"Does she catch anything?"

"Now and then. How hungry are you?" I asked as his second bite finished the sandwich.

"I'm starved; but don't share your lunch. I have some money, just tell me which road takes you toward Delhi."

I stood up and whistled to Frightful. She flew down. I undid her leash from her jesses. I stroked her head for a moment; then threw her into the air and walked out into the field, kicking the brush as I went.

I had noticed a lot of rabbit tracks earlier, and followed them over the muddy earth as best I could. I kicked up a rabbit and with a twist Frightful dropped out of the sky and took it.

Roast rabbit is marvelous under any conditions, but when you're cold and hungry it is superb. Matt enjoyed every bite. I worked on a small portion to be sociable, for I was not especially hungry. I dared not offer him the walnuts in my pocket, for too much had been written about that boy living off nuts.

"My whole circulatory system thanks you," Matt

said. He meant it, for his hands and feet were now warm, and the blue color had left his lips and was replaced by a good warm red.

"By the way, what's your name?"

"Sam. Sam Gribley," I said.

"Sam, if I could borrow a coat from you, I think I could make it to the bus station without freezing to death. I sure didn't think it would be so much colder in the mountains. I could mail it back to you."

"Well," I hesitated, "my house is pretty far from here. I live on the Gribley farm and just come down here now and then to hunt with the falcon; but maybe we could find an old horse blanket or something in one of the deserted barns around here."

"Aw, never mind, Sam. I'll run to keep warm. Have you any ideas about this wild boy—seen anyone that you think the stories might be referring to?"

"Let's start toward the road," I said as I stamped out the fire. I wound him through the forest until I was dizzy and he was lost, then headed for the road. At the edge of the woods I said, "Matt, I have seen that boy."

Matt Spell stopped.

"Gee, Sam, tell me about him." I could hear paper rattle, and saw that Matt's cold hands were not too stiff to write in his notebook.

We walked down the road a bit and then I said, "Well, he ran away from home one day and never went back."

"Where does he live? What does he wear?"

We sat down on a stone along the edge of the road. It was behind a pine tree, and out of the ripping wind.

"He lives west of here in a cave. He wears a bearskin coat, has long hair—all matted and full of burrs—and according to him he fishes for a living."

"You've talked to him?" he asked brightly.

"Oh, yes, I talk to him."

"Oh, this is great!" He wrote furiously. "What color are his eyes?"

"I think they are bluish gray, with a little brown in them."

"His hair?"

"Darkish—I couldn't really tell under all those coon tails."

"Coon tails? Do you suppose he killed them himself?"

"No. It looked more like one of those hats you get with cereal box tops."

"Well, I won't say anything about it then; just, coon-tail hat."

"Yeah, coon-tail hat's enough," I agreed. "And I think his shoes were just newspapers tied around his feet. That's good insulation, you know."

"Yeah?" Matt wrote that down.

"Did he say why he ran away?"

"I never asked him. Why does any boy run away?"

Matt put down his pencil and thought. "Well, I ran

away once because I thought how sorry everybody would be when I was gone. How they'd cry and wish they'd been nicer to me." He laughed.

Then I said, "I ran away once because . . . well, because I wanted to do something else."

"That's a good reason," said Matt. "Do you suppose that's why . . . by the way, what is his name?"

"I never asked him," I said truthfully.

"What do you suppose he really eats and lives on?" asked Matt.

"Fish, roots, berries, nuts, rabbits. There's a lot of food around the woods if you look for it, I guess."

"Roots? Roots wouldn't be good."

"Well, carrots are roots."

"By golly, they are; and so are potatoes, sort of. Fish?" pondered Matt, "I suppose there are lots of fish around here."

"The streams are full of them."

"You've really seen him, huh? He really is in these mountains?"

"Sure, I've seen him," I said. Finally I stood up.

"I gotta get home. I go the other way. You just follow this road to the town, and I think you can get a bus from there."

"Now, wait," he said. "Let me read it back to you to check the details."

"Sure."

Matt stood up, blew on his hands and read: "The wild

boy of the Catskills does exist. He has dark brown hair, black eyes, and wears a handsome deerskin suit that he apparently made himself. He is ruddy and in excellent health and is able to build a fire with flint and steel as fast as a man can light a match.

"His actual dwelling is a secret, but his means of support is a beautiful falcon. The falcon flies off the boy's fist, and kills rabbits and pheasants when the boy needs food. He only takes what he needs. The boy's name is not known, but he ran away from home and never went back."

"No, Matt, no," I begged.

I was about to wrestle it out with him when he said furtively, "I'll make a deal with you. Let me spend my spring vacation with you and I won't print a word of it. I'll write only what you've told me."

I looked at him and decided that it might be nice to have him. I said, "I'll meet you outside town any day you say, providing you let me blindfold you and lead you to my home and providing you promise not to have a lot of photographers hiding in the woods. Do you know what would happen if you told on me?"

"Sure, the newsreels would roll up, the TV cameras would arrive, reporters would hang in the trees, and you'd be famous."

"Yes, and back in New York City."

"I'll write what you said and not even your mother will recognize you."

"Make it some other town, and it's a deal," I said. "You might say I am working for Civil Defense doing research by learning to live off the land. Tell them not to be afraid, that crayfish are delicious and caves are warm."

Matt liked that. He sat down again. "Tell me some of the plants and animals you eat so that they will know what to do. We can make this informative."

I sat down, and listed some of the better wild plants and the more easily obtainable mammals and fish. I gave him a few good recipes and told him that I didn't recommend anyone trying to live off the land unless they liked oysters and spinach.

Matt liked that. He wrote and wrote. Finally he said, "My hands are cold. I'd better go. But I'll see you on April twelfth at three-thirty outside of town. Okay? And just to prove that I'm a man of my word, I'll bring you a copy of what I write."

"Well, you better not give me away. I have a scout in civilization who follows all these stories."

We shook hands and he departed at a brisk pace.

I returned to my patch on the mountain, talking to myself all the way. I talk to myself a lot, but everyone does. The human being, even in the midst of people, spends nine-tenths of his time alone with the private voices of his own head. Living alone on a mountain is not much different, except that your speaking voice gets rusty. I talked inside my head all the way home, think-

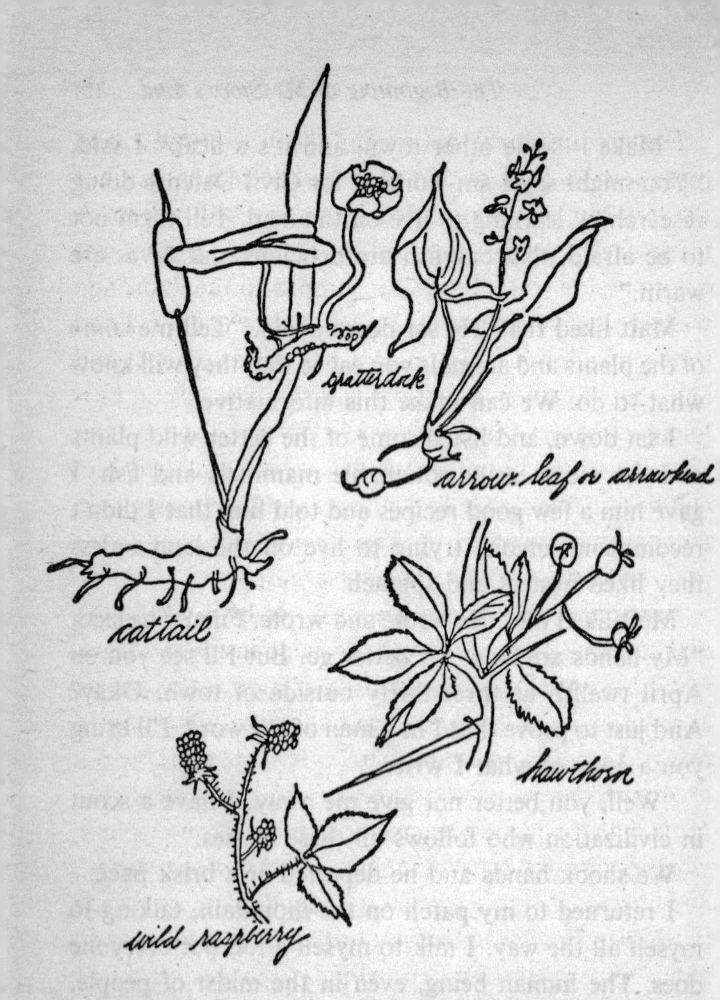

ing up schemes, holding conversations with Bando and Dad and Matt Spell. I worded the article for Matt after discussing it with Bando, and made it sound very convincing without giving myself up. I kind of wanted to write it down and send it to Matt, but I didn't.

I entered my tree, tied Frightful to the bedpost, and there was Jessie Coon James. It had been months since I'd seen him. He was curled up on my bed, asleep. A turtle shell that had been full of cracked walnuts was empty beside him. He awoke, jumped to the floor, and walked slowly between my legs and out the door. I had the feeling Jessie was hoping I had departed for good and that he could have my den. He was a comfort-loving creature. I was bigger and my hands were freer than his, so he conceded me the den. I watched him climb over The Baron's rock and shinny up a hemlock. He moved heavily into the limbs, and it occurred to me that Jessie was a she-Jessie, not a he-Jessie.

I cooked supper, and then sat down by my little fire and called a forum. It is very sociable inside my head, and I have perfected the art of getting a lot of people arguing together in silence or in a forum, as I prefer to call it. I can get four people all talking at once, and a fifth can be present, but generally I can't get him to talk. Usually these forums discuss such things as a storm and whether or not it is coming, how to make a spring suit, and how to enlarge my house without destroying the life in the tree. Tonight, however, they discussed what to do about Matt Spell. Dad kept telling me to go right down to the city and make sure he published nothing, not even a made-up story. Bando said, no, it's all right, he still doesn't know where you live; and then Matt walked into the conversation and said that he wanted to spend his spring vacation with me, and that he promised not to do anything untoward. Matt kept using "untoward"—I don't know where he got that expression, but he liked it and kept using it—that's how I knew Matt was speaking; everything was "untoward."

That night I fell asleep with all these people discussing the probability of my being found and hauled back to the city. Suddenly Frightful broke into the conversation. She said, "Don't let that Matt come up here. He eats too much." That was the first time that Frightful had ever talked in a forum. I was delighted, for I was always sure that she had more to say than a few cries. She had not missed Matt's appetite.

The forum dissolved in a good humor, everyone being delighted with Frightful. I lifted my head to look at her. She had her beak in the feathers of her back, sound asleep.

She spoke in my head, however, and said, "You really want to be found, or you would not have told Matt all you did."

"I like you better when you don't talk," I said, pulled the deer hide over me, and fell into a deep sleep.

IN WHICH
I Cooperate with the Ending

By the middle of March I could have told you it was spring without looking. Jessie did not come around anymore, she was fishing the rewarding waters of the open stream, she was returning to a tree hollow full of babies. The Baron Weasel did not come by. There were salamanders and frogs to keep him busy. The chickadees sang alone, not in a winter group, and the skunks and minks and foxes found food more abundant in the forest than at my tree house. The circumstances that had brought us all together in the winter were no more. There was food on the land and the snow was slipping away.

By April I was no longer living off my storehouse. There were bulbs, tubers, and greens to be had. Meals were varied once more. There were frogs' legs, eggs, and turtle soup on my table.

I took my baths in the spring again rather than in the turtle shell with warmed-over snow. I plunged regularly into the ice water of the spring—shouting as my breath was grabbed from my lungs. I scrubbed, ran for my tree, and dried myself before the fire, shouting as I stepped into my clothes. Then I would sing. I made up a lot of nice songs after my bath, one of which I taught to a man who was hiking along the top of the gorge one day.

He said his name was Aaron, and he was quiet and tall. I found him sitting on the edge of the cliff, looking across the valley. He was humming little tunes. He had a sad smile that never went away. I knew I would not have to hide from him just by looking at him, so I walked up and sat down beside him. I taught him my "cold water song."

I learned he wrote songs and that he was from New York. He had come to the Catskills for the Passover festivities and had wandered off for the day. He was about to go back when I sat down and said, "I heard you humming."

"Yes," he said. "I hum a good deal. Can you hum?"

"Yes," I replied, "I can hum. I hum a good deal, too, and even sing, especially when I get out of the spring in the morning. Then I really sing aloud."

"Let's hear you sing aloud."

So I said, feeling very relaxed with the sun shining on my head, "All right, I'll sing you my cold water song."

"I like that," Aaron said. "Sing it again." So I did.

"Let me suggest a few changes." He changed a few words to fit the tune and the tune to fit the words, and then we both sang it.

"Mind if I use the hum hum hum dee dee part?" he asked presently.

"You can use it all," I said. "Tunes are free up here. I got that from the red-eyed vireo."

He sat up and said, "What other songs are sung up here?"

I whistled him the "hi-chickadee" song of the black-capped Mr. Bracket; and the waterfall song of the wood thrush. He took out a card, lined it with five lines, and wrote in little marks. I stretched back in the sun and hummed the song of the brown thrasher and of Barometer, the nuthatch. Then I boomed out the song of the great horned owl and stopped.

"That's enough, isn't it?" I asked.

"I guess so." He lay back and stretched, looked into the leaves, and said, "If I do something with this, I'll come back and play it to you. I'll bring my portable organ."

"Fine," I said.

Then, after a drowsy pause, he said, "Will you be around these parts this summer?"

"I'll be around," I said. Aaron fell asleep, and I rolled over in the sun. I liked him. He hadn't asked me one personal question. Oddly enough, I wasn't sure whether that made me glad or not. Then I thought of the words Frightful had spoken in my head. "You want to be found," and I began to wonder. I had sought out a human being. This would not have happened a year ago.

I fell asleep. When I awoke, Aaron was gone and

Frightful was circling me. She saw me stir, swooped in, and sat on a rock beside me. I said, "Hi," but did not get up, just lay still listening to the birds, the snips and sputs of insects moving in the dry leaves, and the air stirring the newly leafing trees. Nothing went on in my head. It was comfortably blank. I knew the pleasures of the lizard on the log who knows where his next meal is coming from. I also knew his boredom. After an hour I did have a thought. Aaron had said that he was up in the Catskills for Passover. Then it must also be near Easter, and Matt would be coming soon. I had not counted notches in weeks.

A cool shadow crossed my face and I arose, whistled for Frightful to come to my hand, and wandered slowly home, stuffing my pockets with spring beauty bulbs as I went.

Several days later I met Matt on Route 27 at three-thirty. I tied his handkerchief around his eyes and led him, stumbling and tripping, up the mountain. I went almost directly home. I guess I didn't much care if he remembered how to get there or not. When I took off the blindfold, he looked around.

"Where are we? Where's your house?" I sat down and motioned him to sit. He did so with great willingness—in fact, he flopped.

"What do you sleep on, the ground?"

I pointed to the deerskin flaps moving in the wind in the hemlock.

"Whatdaya do, live in a tree?"

"Yep."

Matt bounced to his feet and we went in. I propped the door open so that the light streamed in, and he shouted with joy. I lit the tallow candle and we went over everything, and each invention he viewed with a shout.

While I prepared trout baked in wild grape leaves, Matt sat on the bed and told me the world news in brief. I listened with care to the trouble in Europe, the trouble in the Far East, the trouble in the south, and the trouble in America. Also to a few sensational murders, some ball scores, and his report card.

"It all proves my point," I said sagely. "People live too close together."

"Is that why you are here?"

"Well, not exactly. The main reason is that I don't like to be dependent, particularly on electricity, rails, steam, oil, coal, machines, and all those things that can go wrong."

"Well, is that why you are up here?"

"Well, not exactly. Some men climbed Mount Everest because it was there. Here is a wilderness."

"Is that why?"

"Aw, come on, Matt. See that falcon? Hear those white-throated sparrows? Smell that skunk? Well, the falcon takes the sky, the white-throated sparrow takes the low bushes, the skunk takes the earth, you take the newspaper office, I take the woods."

"Don't you get lonely?"

"Lonely? I've hardly had a quiet moment since arriving. Stop being a reporter and let's eat. Besides, there are people in the city who are lonelier than I."

"Okay. Let's eat. This is good, darned good; in fact, the best meal I've ever eaten." He ate and stopped asking questions.

We spent the next week fishing, hunting, trapping, gathering greens and bulbs. Matt talked less and less, slept, hiked, and pondered. He also ate well, and kept Frightful very busy. He made himself a pair of moccasins out of deer hide, and a hat that I can't even describe. We didn't have a mirror so he never knew how it looked, but I can say this: when I happened to meet him as we came fishing along a stream bed, I was always startled. I never did get used to that hat.

Toward the end of the week, who should we find sleeping in my bed after returning from a fishing trip, but Bando! Spring vacation, he said. That night we played our reed whistles for Matt, by an outdoor fire. It was that warm. Matt and Bando also decided to make a guest house out of one of the other trees. I said "Yes, let's" because I felt that way, although I knew what it meant.

A guest house meant I was no longer a runaway. I was no longer hiding in the wilderness. I was living in the woods like anyone else lives in a house. People drop by, neighbors come for dinner, there are three meals to get, the shopping to do, the cleaning to accomplish. I felt exactly as I felt when I was home. The only differ-

ence was that I was a little harder to visit out here, but not too hard. There sat Matt and Bando.

We all burned and dug out another hemlock. I worked with them, wondering what was happening to me. Why didn't I cry "No"? What made me happily build a city in the forest—because that is what we were doing.

When the tree was done, Bando had discovered that the sap was running in willow trees and the limbs were just right for slide whistles. He spent the evening making us trombones. We played them together. That word *together.* Maybe that was the answer to the city.

Matt said rather uncomfortably just before bedtime, "There may be some photographers in these hills."

"Matt!" I hardly protested. "What did you write?"

It was Bando who pulled out the article.

He read it, a few follow-ups, and comments from many other papers. Then he leaned back against his leaning tree, as it had come to be, and puffed silently on his pipe.

"Let's face it, Thoreau; you can't live in America today and be quietly different. If you are going to be different, you are going to stand out, and people are going to hear about you; and in your case, if they hear about you, they will remove you to the city or move to you and you won't be different anymore." A pause. "Did the owls nest, Thoreau?"

I told him about the owls and how the young played around the hemlock, and then we went to bed a little sad—all of us. Time was running out.

Matt had to return to school, and Bando stayed on to help burn out another tree for another guest house. We chopped off the blackened wood, made one bed, and started the second before he had to return to his teaching.

I wasn't alone long. Mr. Jacket found me.

I was out on the raft trying to catch an enormous snapping turtle. It would take my line, but when I got its head above water, it would eye me with those cold ancient eyes and let go. Frightful was nearby. I was making a noose to throw over the turtle's head the next time it surfaced when Frightful lit on my shoulder with a thud and a hard grip. She was drawn up and tense, which in her language said "people," so I wasn't surprised to hear a voice call from across the stream, "Hi, Daniel Boone. What are you doing?" There stood Mr. Jacket.

"I am trying to get this whale of a snapper," I said in such an ordinary voice that it was dull.

I went on with the noose making, and he called to me, "Hit it with a club."

I still couldn't catch the old tiger, so I rafted to shore and got Mr. Jacket. About an hour later we had the turtle, had cleaned it, and I knew that Mr. Jacket was Tom Sidler.

"Come on up to the house," I said, and he came on up to the house, and it was just like after school on Third Avenue. He wanted to see everything, of course, and he did think it unusual, but he got over it in a hurry and settled down to helping me prepare the meat for turtle soup.

He dug the onions for it while I got it boiling in a tin can. Turtle is as tough as rock and has to be boiled for hours before it gets tender. We flavored the soup with hickory salt, and cut a lot of Solomon's seal tubers into it. Tom said it was too thin, and I thickened it with mashed up nuts—I had run out of acorn flour. I tried some orris root in it—pretty fair.

"Wanta stay and eat it and spend the night?" I asked him somewhere along the way. He said, "Sure," but added that he had better go home and tell his mother. It took him about two hours to get back and the turtle was still tough, so we went out to the meadow to fly Frightful. She caught her own meal, we tied her to her perch, and climbed in the gorge until almost dark. We ate turtle soup. Tom slept in the guest tree.

I lay awake wondering what had happened. Everything seemed so everyday.

I liked Tom and he liked me, and he came up often, almost every weekend. He told me about his bowling team and some of his friends, and I began to feel I knew a lot of people in the town below the mountain. This made my wilderness small. When Tom left one weekend I wrote this down:

"Tom said that he and Reed went into an empty house, and when they heard the real estate man come in, they slid down the laundry chute to the basement and crawled out the basement window. He said a water main broke and flooded the school grounds and all the kids took off their shoes and played baseball in it."

I drew a line through all this and then I wrote:

"I haven't seen The Baron Weasel. I think he has deserted his den by the boulder. A catbird is nesting nearby. Apparently it has learned that Frightful is tied some of the time, because it comes right up to the fireplace for scraps when the leash is snapped."

I drew a line through this too, and filled up the rest of the piece of bark with a drawing of Frightful.

I went to the library the next day and took out four books.

Aaron came back. He came right to the hemlock forest and called. I didn't ask him how he knew I was there. He stayed a week, mostly puttering around with the willow whistles. He never asked what I was doing on the mountain. It was as if he already knew. As if he had talked to someone, or read something, and there was nothing more to question. I had the feeling that I was an old story somewhere beyond the foot of the mountain. I didn't care.

Bando got a car and he came up more often. He never mentioned any more newspaper stories, and I never asked him. I just said to him one day, "I seem to have an address now."

He said, "You do."

I said, "Is it Broadway and Forty-second Street?"

He said, "Almost." His eyebrows knitted and he looked at me sadly.

"It's all right, Bando. Maybe you'd better bring me a shirt and some blue jeans when you come next time. I was thinking, if they haven't sold that house in town, maybe Tom and I could slide down the laundry chute."

Bando slowly turned a willow whistle over in his hands. He didn't play it.

IN WHICH
The City Comes to Me

The warblers arrived, the trees turned summer green, and June burst over the mountain. It smelled good, tasted good, and was gentle to the eyes.

I was stretched out on the big rock in the meadow one morning. Frightful was jabbing at some insect in the grass below me when suddenly a flashbulb exploded and a man appeared.

"Wild boy!" he said, and took another picture. "What are you doing, eating nuts?"

I sat up. My heart was heavy. It was so heavy that I posed for him holding Frightful on my fist. I refused to take him to my tree, however, and he finally left. Two other photographers came, and a reporter. I talked a little. When they left, I rolled over on my stomach and wondered if I could get in touch with the Department of Interior and find out more about the public lands in the West. My next thought was the baseball game in the flooded school yard.

Four days passed, and I talked to many reporters and photographers. At noon of the fifth day a voice called from the glen: "I know you are there!"

"*Dad!*" I shouted, and once again burst down the mountainside to see my father.

As I ran toward him, I heard sounds that stopped me. The sound of branches and twigs breaking, of the flowers being crushed. Hordes were coming. For a long moment I stood wondering whether to meet Dad or run forever. I was self-sufficient, I could travel the world over, never needing a penny, never asking anything of anyone. I could cross to Asia in a canoe via the Bering Strait. I could raft to an island. I could go around the world on the fruits of the land. I started to run. I got as far as the gorge and turned back. I wanted to see Dad.

I walked down the mountain to greet him and to face the people he had brought from the city to photograph me, interview me, and bring me home. I walked slowly, knowing that it was all over. I could hear the voices of the other people. They filled my silent mountain.

Then I jumped in the air and laughed for joy. I recognized my four-year-old brother's pleasure song. The family! Dad had brought the family! Every one of them. I ran, twisting and turning through the trees like a Cooper's hawk, and occasionally riding a free fifty feet downhill on an aspen sapling.

"*Dad! Mom!*" I shouted as I came upon them along the streambed, carefully picking their way through raspberry bushes. Dad gave me a resounding slap and Mother hugged me until she cried.

John jumped on me. Jim threw me into the rushes. Mary sat on me. Alice put leaves in my hair. Hank pulled Jim off. Joan pulled me to my feet, and Jake bit my ankle. That cute little baby sister toddled away from me and cried.

"Wow! All of New York!" I said. "This is a great day for the Katerskills."

I led them proudly up the mountain, thinking about dinner and what I had that would go around. I knew how Mother felt when we brought in friends for dinner.

As we approached the hemlock grove, I noticed that Dad was carrying a pack. He explained it as food for the first few days, or until I could teach John, Jim, Hank, and Jake how to live off the land. I winked at him.

"But, Dad, a Gribley is not for the land."

"What do you mean?" he shouted. "The Gribleys have had land for three generations. We pioneer, we open the land." He was almost singing

"And then we go to sea," I said.

"Things have changed. Child labor laws; you can't take children to sea."

I should have glowed over such a confession from Dad had I not been making furious plans as we climbed; food, beds, chores. Dad, however, had had since Christmas to outplan me. He strung up hammocks for everyone all through the forest, and you never heard a happier bunch of kids. The singing and shouting and giggling sent the birds and wildlife deeper into the shadows. Even little Nina had a hammock, and though she was only a toddler, she cooed and giggled all by herself as she rocked between two aspens near the meadow. We ate Mother's fried chicken. Chicken is good, it tastes like chicken.

I shall never forget that evening.

And I shall never forget what Dad said, "Son, when I told your mother where you were, she said, 'Well, if he doesn't want to come home, then we will bring home to him.' And that's why we are all here."

I was stunned. I was beginning to realize that this was not an overnight camping trip, but a permanent arrangement. Mother saw my expression and said, "When you are of age, you can go wherever you please. Until then, I still have to take care of you, according to all the law I can find." She put her arm around me, and we rocked ever so slightly. "Besides, I am not a Gribley. I am a Stuart, and the Stuarts loved the land." She looked at the mountain and the meadow and the gorge, and

I felt her feet squeeze into the earth and take root.

The next day I took John, Jim, and Hank out into the mountain meadows with Frightful to see if we could not round up enough food to feed this city of people. We did pretty well.

When we came back, there was Dad with four four-by-fours, erected at the edge of my meadow, and a pile of wood that would have covered a barn.

"Gosh, Dad," I cried, "what on earth are you doing?"

"We are going to have a house," he said.

I was stunned and hurt.

"A house! You'll spoil everything!" I protested. "Can't we all live in trees and hammocks?"

"No. Your mother said that she was going to give you a decent home, and in her way of looking at it, that means a roof and doors. She got awfully mad at those newspaper stories inferring that she had not done her duty."

"But she did." I was almost at the point of tears. "She's a swell mother. What other boy has a mother who would let him do what I did?"

"I know. I know. But a woman lives among her neighbors. Your mother took all those editorials personally, as if they were Mr. Bracket and Mrs. O'Brien speaking. The nation became her neighbors, and no one, not even—" He hesitated. A catbird meowed. "Not even that catbird is going to think that she neglected you."

I was about to protest in a loud strong voice when Mother's arm slipped around my shoulder.

"That's how it is until you are eighteen, Sam," she said. And that ended it.

My Married Boyfriend

CYDNEY RAX

Kensington Publishing Corp.
www.kensingtonbooks.com

DAFINA BOOKS are published by

Kensington Publishing Corp.
119 West 40th Street
New York, NY 10018

All Kensington Titles, Imprints, and Distributed Lines are available at special quantity discounts for bulk purchases for sales promotions, premiums, fund-raising, and educational or institutional use. Special book excerpts or customized printings can also be created to fit specific needs. For details, write or phone the office of the Kensington special sales manager: Kensington Publishing Corp., 119 West 40th Street, New York, NY 10018, attn: Special Sales Department. Phone: 1-800-21-2647.

ISBN-13: 978-1-4967-0140-4
ISBN-10: 1-4967-0140-2
First Kensington Trade Edition: January 2016
First Kensington Mass Market Edition: January 2018

eISBN-13: 978-1-4967-0139-8
eISBN-10: 1-1967-0139-9

10 9 8 7 6 5 4 3 2 1

Printed in the United States of America

This novel is dedicated to the memory of the late Jackie Collins. She is an author whose books I read and enjoyed, someone who impressed me with her kindness, and a woman whose literary triumphs I wish to emulate.

R.I.P.
9.19.2015

Acknowledgments

The more I write, the harder it feels, which is why I'm so grateful for every opportunity to explore my characters and share their unusual stories. I came across a review of one of my novels that said my characters deal with painful situations. Pain is a part of life. And I hope my stories show that yes, we are flawed, yet very human.

Thanks to my editor, Mercedes Fernandez. You help to shape these stories and breathe life into them.

To the Kensington team: Lulu Martinez, the marketing folks, social media people, the book cover designers, and copy editors, you are just so marvelous!

Thanks to Lisa Benford. Thanks for the insight and reference material. And to my delightful EHLS co-workers who are always willing to answer my oddball questions. You're the best!!

To my standup comedian friend, Officer Stanley. Your input was invaluable.

Shout out to my family members who like to tell people I am their kin. Too funny.

And thanks to the folks that provide inspiration or who give me little juicy insights about men, women, and all things that are human nature.

Last but not least. My fans, supporters, readers (esp. Ebony McMillan, Michelle Sloan, Meicka Jovan), promoters, reviewers (thanks Romance In Color, etc.), book club members, libraries, and online website folks that give love to authors, I am grateful for the attention you gave to *If Your Wife Only Knew.*

Let's do it again . . .

P.S. Thank you *God,* for making my dreams come true. If you had a cheek I'd kiss it!

Cydney Rax
Houston, Texas USA

Chapter 1

The Sky Is Crying

Rashad Eason reached across the desk and handed the woman a fifteen-hundred-dollar cashier's check. She had pasty, pimpled white skin, a buzz haircut, and a thick mustache. She was very unattractive. To Rashad, she resembled a proud butch lesbian, but that didn't matter. He had extensively researched Lily Tangaro online. He admired her track record and needed a competent person to do the job.

"You think you can get me everything I want?" he asked.

Lily examined the check, then reclined in her leather swivel chair. "You're serious about this, aren't you?"

"More serious than a triple bypass."

"But it hasn't been that long since you physically separated from your wife."

"I know that. But if I don't do something fast, I may change my mind."

"I see." She paused. "We always recommend that the plaintiff think about the decision for six months."

"I can't wait that long. Thinking about this for six months would kill me."

She nodded and secured the retainer payment inside a file folder.

"Sign these documents and we will get started on your case right away."

Rashad eagerly reviewed several papers that Lily gave to him. He took a blue ink pen and scribbled his name and the date. Then he stood and shook her hand.

"Thank you, Ms. Tangaro."

"Call me Lily."

"Will do, Lily. And my son, Myles, really thanks you."

"Seriously? He's only six—"

"He's seven. Myles knows what's up. He's seen a lot, unfortunately. And this is why I gotta do this. It may be the only way I get to spend quality time with him. Plus, I don't want my son around his crazy mama any longer than he needs to be."

"Totally understandable. We'll be in touch."

"No doubt, Lily. I appreciate this."

Rashad drove away from his new attorney's office feeling more hopeful than he had in weeks.

Rashad was lucky Lily agreed to meet with him in her office to sign his paperwork, especially since it was the day after Thanksgiving. It was a Black Friday indeed on this rainy morning in Houston.

Light drops of water drizzled from the sky. Rainy days made Rashad feel depressed. But it was time to go see Myles. And spending time with his son was one of the few things he could be happy about these days.

When Rashad arrived at the designated pickup spot, which was in front of Mama Flora's house, he let the car idle next to the curb. Technically, Mama Flora could be considered his grandmother-in-law. She was his wife's maternal grandmother, and the woman who raised Kiara. She was sensible and didn't stand for drama. Rashad and Kiara both agreed that exchanging Myles for visits at Flora's place would be the best option.

Rashad impatiently drummed his hands on the steering wheel. He listened to raindrops splatter to the ground. Minutes later, Kiara drove up and parked directly behind him. He observed her through the rearview mirror.

"Damn, I can barely see her, but the woman still looks good," he admitted to himself. He hadn't laid eyes on Kiara in weeks. And after all this time, she still tugged at his heart.

He saw her mouth moving and assumed she was talking to their son, whom he also hadn't seen in a while. Within minutes, both Kiara and Myles emerged from the car. Wearing white gym shoes, the little boy ran behind the car then raced ahead of his mother. He fled into the street instead of remaining on the sidewalk. Soon he tugged at his father's locked door handle and yelled.

"Hurry up, Daddy. I'm famished."

Rashad laughed and popped the locks. He got out of the car and scooped Myles off his feet and hugged him tight.

"Really, Myles? You're famished? Where'd you learn that word?"

"The Food Network."

Rashad chuckled as he set him back down.

"Oh, so I don't get a 'hey, Daddy, how you doing? I miss you. I love you, man'?"

"Hey, Daddy, I missed you. Can we go to Steak 'n Shake for dinner?"

"Myles." Kiara interrupted as she hurriedly approached them. She was wearing a short, purple, long-sleeved dress and four-inch wedge-heel sandals. "I told you about running in the street. Are you crazy? Do you wanna get hit by a car again? It's raining and that makes it harder for drivers to slow down in this weather."

Kiara eased up next to Myles. She thumped him on his forehead.

"Ouch, Mommy."

"Don't do that," Rashad scolded. "My little man misses me, that's all. It's been a minute."

"Whatever, Rashad," she hissed. "None of that matters. He knows better than to do something reckless like running in the street. He doesn't listen."

"I do listen, Mommy." Myles mostly ignored his mother as he happily gave his father a few daps. The little boy always seemed calm and sure of himself when he was in Rashad's presence.

"You're a chip off the old block, son," his father said. He knew the danger if Myles didn't look where he was going, but Rashad didn't notice any cars coming down the street. He could tell how much his boy deeply missed him and that made him feel good.

"Damn, I've been dying to hang out with my little man. Has he gotten taller? What the hell you been feeding him?"

"That's a stupid question, and you know how I feel about those."

"I was just joking, Kiara. Lighten up."

"Ain't got time for jokes."

Suddenly the air grew tense. Rashad felt himself getting agitated.

"Look, this is the holiday season. People are supposed to be merry. But you act like you on something. You been drinking? Can't you ever be happy and just chill?"

"Lord Jesus. More stupid-ass questions. Don't start."

Kiara gave Rashad a sober look and handed him Myles's backpack.

"Lucky for you, Mama Flora is away from her house right now. At the last second, she had something to take care of and she had to leave. So we both have to be mature enough to handle this without her."

"That's cool. I got no problem with that."

"Anyway, all his things are in there: two pair of pants, some shirts, underwear, pajamas, favorite electric toothbrush, all that."

"Hmm, seeing this makes me realize I gotta stock up on some stuff for him to keep at . . ."

He wanted to say he had to buy clothes for Myles to keep at his other place, a home he recently started sharing with his pregnant lover, Nicole Greene. Weeks ago, when his wife forced him to leave the house because she got sick of Rashad's lies, Nicole instantly suggested that he come stay with her. On that short notice, he had nowhere else to go. So he took her up on her offer. And now he was adjusting to his "new normal."

Rashad mentally switched gears as he gazed at Myles.

"Damn shame we couldn't eat turkey and dressing together, and watch the Lions and Cowboys game. That's what I did with my dad every Thanksgiving when he was still alive. I was *always* with my daddy on that holiday. Sitting up in that cold-ass living room. Eating good food and talking smack. I wish we could have done that, Myles."

Rashad stared at his son but he was talking to Kiara.

"Um," she responded. "We had the whole day already planned so he wouldn't have had a chance to come by anyway. We went to the parade downtown. We ate a wonderful dinner. And then we drove down to see the Festival of Lights at Moody Gardens. Myles ended up having a *real* good time with me and Eddison, didn't you?"

"Uh huh," he said.

"Cool," was Rashad's clipped response. "I'm glad for you."

He acted like he wasn't bothered. But Rashad hated that Kiara stopped him from spending time with his child two holidays in a row. *She* got to pick his costume and take Myles trick-or-treating. And *she* got to eat turkey with him, too. What gave her the right? Just because she made him leave the house, does that mean she could enforce all her own rules as well?

Rashad fought to hide his anger as he leered at Kiara on the sly. She was holding one of those huge pink-and-black golf umbrellas in her hand. Even on a dreary looking afternoon, somehow this woman managed to appear elegant and beautiful. Her eyes were full of spunk and passion. It seemed she didn't have a care in the world.

And he hated it.

But at the same time, Rashad was strangely tempted to grab his wife in his arms and tell her that they were both acting silly. He wished they could get their emotions in check, work things out, save the marriage. He really didn't want to file for divorce, but she was acting unreasonable. He wished she could get some sense into her stubborn head. Maybe she'd listen and let him come back home, where he felt he belonged. But that scenario was a hopeless fairy tale. He knew Kiara was still pissed and he didn't want to risk getting swung at in public.

"All righty, then," Rashad spoke up, anxious to leave. "Since I have less time than I originally thought, we need to make that move right now. I will have little man back here on Sunday night around eight."

"Eight?"

"Okay, then. Seven."

"Sunday *afternoon*, Rashad. I need him here by two so I can make sure he has time to take his bath, complete his homework, and eat dinner. Plus, if we decide to go check out that new movie he's begged us to see, we will probably want him around noon."

We.

Rashad knew his wife was referring to her new man, Eddison, when she said "we."

"Back by *noon?*" he scoffed. "That means I'll barely get to spend, hell, even a full twenty-four hours with him—"

"Sorry, but that's just how it is."

"You're not sorry, Kiara. You're selfish and controlling. I haven't seen my son since God knows when. I have a right to be with the boy just like you do. And I will bring Myles back when I'm done with him."

"Wait one second here," she whispered in Rashad's ear. "I find it sooo strange that all of a sudden you are so desperate to spend time with him. You should have thought about how important he was back when you were sacrificing time with your son to go lie up and bump your nuts on that whore."

"W-what did you say?"

"You heard exactly what I said. If you hadn't done what you did, we wouldn't be out here on these streets doing this—exchanging a child like he's a drug or a piece of currency. Do you know how mad this makes me? I did everything and I mean *ev-e-ry*-thing I could to make you happy, but no, no, no. Nothing I did was good enough. You had to go get yourself a damned side piece. Her pussy must taste like Skittles."

"Kiara, you best shut your mouth."

"So it's true? Her coochie taste like Gucci?"

"I'm warning you."

She suddenly noticed that her voice grew from a whisper to a shout. She was ready to attack Rashad with more angry words, but she grew alarmed when she noticed a frozen smile gripping her son's face. He looked like he was scared something bad would happen if he moved an inch.

Kiara realized she'd gone too far. But she usually did when it came to Rashad. She hated that his whorish ways destroyed their perfect family life. She hated the fact that not only had he knocked up that heifer Nicole Greene, but Kiara had also discovered he'd been hiding a two-year-old daughter that he had with another woman who worked for her: Alexis McNeil, her own administrative assistant. Her hubby hiding baby mamas and side chicks who worked in her office was too much. Rashad made her look like a fool. The more Kiara thought about it, the crazier she felt.

She reached and grabbed Myles's hand as if to snatch him back toward her car.

"What are you doing?" Rashad asked.

"Let me be clear. I don't know if we're ready for this informal custody sharing thing. I know it's the decent thing to do, but hell, I'm not feeling very 'decent' right now. I think we need to take baby steps. So if you can't bring him back by noon, then he's going home with me right now. I'll let you have him in two weeks. For a full weekend. Promise."

"See, this is bull. I was supposed to get him last weekend, remember? You broke that so-called promise. Why you always got to be in control?"

They were still standing in the street next to Rashad's idling sedan.

"Why you always try to run shit like I'm your child? Or your employee. Huh? I'm a grown-ass man." He stepped closer to her. "Who the hell put you in charge of me?"

Kiara snatched Myles's bony little arm and pulled at the sockets so violently that he screamed, "Ouch! That hurts."

"Your crazy ass better let go of my son." Rashad grabbed Myles's other arm.

"Shut up! I don't like how you're talking to me."

"I don't like the fact that you fucked another nigga and now you're pregnant. I guess we should go on the *Maury* show to find out who the real father is."

"What the hell?" She couldn't believe Rashad would spew such venom in front of their child. "That's it. Forget this. Come on, Myles." She yanked him again.

"Mama, I want to stay with my daddy. I want my daddy." Myles inched closer to Rashad.

"I don't care what you want. He doesn't deserve you. We're leaving. Come on."

Raindrops poured from above as if the sky were crying. Kiara tried to hold her umbrella in one hand and drag away Myles with the other.

But the boy wrestled with her, pulling back from her, and tried to free himself.

"My arm. It hurts. It *hurts.* I don't like this. Let me *gooo.*"

Kiara wouldn't release Myles, but Rashad did.

He'd been taught that real men don't cry. But right then, he was filled with uncontrollable rage and a lingering frustration that made his throat swell with pain. It wasn't fair that since Kiara banned him from their house, he hadn't played with his son, hadn't looked him in his eyes, or helped him with his homework. He missed fixing Myles's breakfast and shooting hoops with him in their backyard. Little things meant a lot. And Rashad resented the legal system that granted numerous women so much power when it came to a man, his money, and his children.

He stared at his wife, almost in disbelief that feelings of pure hatred were boiling up in him and making him flush with so much anger that he started sweating.

"Mommy, I want to be with my daddy. Let me go."

"Stop all that yelling, Myles. I want you to come back home with me."

Several cars slowly drove past them, which infuriated Rashad. "Look at this. You got people staring at you like you're crazy."

"The hell with them. I'm not crazy. I'm just doing what I have to do to protect my son."

"He's my son, too, Kiara. I don't know why you seem to have forgotten that." If his wife hadn't been pregnant, there was no telling what Rashad would have done to her. He didn't want to fight, but her unpredictable behavior drove him to respond in ways that he hated.

"All I know is, it's damn near Christmas," he continued in a choked voice. "I wanted to take Myles shopping this weekend. I-I-I have all *kinds* of plans for him, don't you understand that?"

"I don't give a damn about your stupid plans. You better learn how to speak to me like you have some sense. You can't just say anything in front of a child."

Rashad felt like his wife was a hypocrite. She clearly saw his sins but was blind to her own. But he counted to ten and calmly told her, "Kiara, I apologize if it seems like I was disrespecting you. But can we let go of this argument? Please. And let me give Myles the chance he deserves to hang out with his father . . . his *real* father."

"Oh, hell no. I know you're not trying to throw shade at Eddison, who's been nothing but remarkable to us. Plus, that boy's not stupid. He knows who his daddy is."

"Mommy, you're hurting me. Please let me *gooo.*"

Kiara then realized she had Myles in a death grip. She felt his fragile bones between her fingers. She heard the pain in his voice. She released him.

"Oh, God. I'm sorry, baby. I-I . . . Please forgive me."

With tears in his eyes, Myles nodded and leaned against his father's stomach.

"Kiara," Rashad said in a gentle tone. "So you're going to let him be with me till Sunday night?"

She hesitated and reached into her purse. "Fine. I'll let him go since we've went through all this trouble in the first place. We can negotiate a fair time for his drop-off. But I want you to know that I bought him his own cell phone today. Whenever he's away from me, he must keep it on him at all times. And we taught him how to use it. In case of an emergency."

"You really don't trust me, do you?"

"No, I do not. But that's beside the point. I just want Myles to be okay. I just want him to be happy." Kiara's voice caught in her throat as she wiped tears from her eyes.

She kissed Myles's little cheeks and allowed a brave smile to brighten her face. "Bye, baby. I love you."

"Love you, too, Mommy. Come on, Daddy. My stomach is growling. Can't you hear it?"

"That's a damned shame. We'll go eat right now, son."

Kiara swiftly turned around to leave. The street was slippery and wet. In her rush to get away, her feet got tangled together. The wedge heels were narrow and clumsy. Her right ankle twisted and gave way underneath her. Her umbrella plunked to the ground. She slipped on a pothole and fell forward, but landed on her thigh. Her hand scraped the rugged, scraggly surface as she braced herself against injury.

"Ugh, ouch. Dammit."

She lay on her side feeling totally embarrassed, wincing.

Rashad wanted to ask Kiara if she was all right, but he simply stared at her.

Rain water sprayed her hair and cheeks. Her hair became a matted mess.

"I can't believe this. Rashad! Can you help me up? Are you just gonna stand there?"

He gaped at Kiara and wondered if she had just got what she deserved.

She'd made life so difficult for him recently. Rashad knew she was now seeing that man on her job, Eddison Osborne, and Nicole had told him that they'd had an affair.

Rashad could clearly see Kiara's tiny baby bump. He wondered if the baby was his, even though she'd told him that it was.

"Rashad, did you hear me? I need your help."

"Why should I?"

"Huh? I can't believe you said that!"

"I don't know whose baby you got inside of you."

"Rashad, oh, my God. How can you go there?"

"Because *you* went there—with that other man!"

"Now is not the time. Help me up, please."

He stared down at her belly. And so did Myles.

Kiara felt completely humiliated. She never wanted their son to see her like this.

"Rashad, show your *son* how to *treat* a *woman*!"

Rashad looked skeptical and remained unmoving.

"Myles, baby, please."

Myles raced to his mother and immediately grabbed her outstretched hand. His tongue stuck out of his mouth as he struggled to help Kiara. Rashad suddenly rushed to the other side of her and held out his hand, too.

Wincing in pain, she got on her knees, and leaned on Rashad as he hoisted her to her feet.

"Thank you, baby." She ignored Rashad. "You are my precious son. You must always remember to be a gentleman and help your mother. And always be good to a lady. Promise me."

"I promise, Mommy."

"Ha!" Rashad muttered.

"All right, okay. I can do this," she said to herself. "I can make it to the car."

"Bye-bye, Mommy. Don't forget to pick me up on Sunday."

"I can never forget anything that has to do with you."

She watched Myles excitedly race around to the other side of the sedan as Rashad went and opened the passenger door for his son. Kiara waited until Myles was safely inside the car. She rubbed her hip and hobbled over to Rashad.

"You didn't act concerned about our unborn baby for one second."

"I don't know whose baby that is." He paused. "How many times did you fuck that dude?"

"How many times did you fuck both your baby mamas?"

"Oh, so you hooked up with him just to get revenge? Was his dick bigger than mine? I don't care how big it was, no man could ever love you like me!"

"Oh, my God! Just be quiet with all that. I can't believe I used to love your pathetic ass. And you best believe that part of my life is gone. I'm moving on, Rashad. And you acting like a dick and trying to shame me in front of Myles is unforgivable. You'll never get this pussy again."

She turned away again, this time moving more slowly than the first time. Then she quietly limped away, hair soaking wet, but head held high.

After Kiara slid into the vehicle, she slammed her door, revved the engine, and waved her middle finger at Rashad as she drove past him.

Eason vs. Eason had officially started.

Chapter 2

A Man That Loves His Woman

Kiara drove away from Rashad reflecting on the dreadful path her life had taken. After being married for a little over ten years, breaking up with her husband was never part of the plan. Change terrified her, but she was up to the task.

After a pleasant half-hour drive, Kiara arrived in front of Eddison's house. It was an immaculate two-story dwelling located in the Wilchester subdivision of Memorial West. Marked by towering oak trees and neatly manicured lawns, the neighborhood enjoyed a country feel in the big city. Kiara drove onto the horseshoe driveway and wasn't surprised when the garage was already open.

Eddison met her inside the doorway. A beige towel hung around his neck. He was shirtless and wore a pair of mesh shorts. And his hair was longer; with his medium-length dreads, in Kiara's eyes, he was as handsome as singer Eric Benet. As soon as she stepped out of her sedan, he reached for her purse and weekender duffel bag.

"What happened to your hair?"

"Long story," she said. "I don't even want to go into it."

Kiara had stopped limping by then, knowing that she had exaggerated her physical pain in order to make Rashad feel guilty. Although her slipping and falling were genuine, she felt confident that her unborn child was safe within her protective womb. She was miffed that Rashad failed to express any sympathy for her, and his lack of concern encouraged her to forget about him and focus on her new life.

Like an airport attendant, Eddison carried her belongings inside the house. They proceeded to his first floor master bedroom. He placed the items on a chair and as Kiara sat down, he gently pulled her soaked shoes from her feet.

"Thank you, sweetheart," she told him.

"Why are you wearing this type of shoes? They're much too high for a pregnant woman. And your feet? Usually they're very pretty. But now?"

"Oh, Eddison." She tried to hide her feet. "Don't look at my jacked-up toes."

"I'm not looking." He bent down to inspect them even further. "The paint is all chipped. And you look stressed as hell." He rose up and began to caress her shoulders. "I have something in mind to make this situation better. I can't have my baby looking any old kind of way."

She was amused by the way he fussed over her and had to laugh in spite of herself.

"Eddison, I swear you're like a dream come true. I sort of wish I would have met you first, considering everything that's happened."

"Hey, I wish the same."

Ever since Kiara had kicked Rashad out of their house five weeks ago, she'd been spending more time with Eddison and she provided him updates on the status of her and Rashad's relationship.

"But, Eddison," she continued, "if I had met you first, then you wouldn't have met Nina. Now you two had a great thing going. And I'm sure you don't regret that. Being with her probably made you into the man you are now."

Nina was Eddison's late wife; she had died a few years ago. She was a golden-hearted woman who lost her life in the Middle East while she was on a tour of duty.

Eddison and Kiara met at work and had always been friends, but after Nina passed away, he saw Kiara through different eyes. He knew she was married and kept his distance. But last summer, when they had engaged in personal conversations and she'd tell him about Rashad, he recognized the cracks in the armor of her relationship. Eddison could no longer hide his true feelings. And he finally let her know how he felt about her.

"If I'd met you first," Kiara said, "Myles wouldn't exist. I can't imagine life without him. So, no, I take that back. But I'm sure you get what I'm trying to say."

"No one is a hundred percent in control of their future and how things turn out. We just have to do our best and deal with whatever fate brings us."

"I agree," she admitted. "I learned that the hard way."

"I did, too." Eddison stopped massaging Kiara's shoulders. He removed his gym shorts and got dressed in a navy polo shirt and some tan shorts. "I've never told anyone this, but at first I was very angry at God for taking my wife from me. I wondered why He let me find her just to snatch her away a short while later."

Kiara thought about her own situation. Letting go of a marital relationship was difficult, and she sympathized with Eddison.

"I know how you feel, Eddy, even though I've never been through your exact experience."

"Yeah. So, at first I was hurt, confused, and angry, but as time passed, I looked around." He heartily laughed. "And I saw all these women out here . . . lonely, smart, attractive ladies who'd *never* had a husband. And it occurred to me that I'd been blessed. At least I got to spend six years of my life with Nina." He paused in thought. "It was brief but definitely worth it."

Kiara nodded. "I believe that. And it's good to hear you open up about it and come to terms with everything."

"'Tis better to have loved and lost, than never to have loved at all," he said dramatically.

"That's a famous saying," she remarked. "Who said that?"

"*I'm* saying that."

Eddison stared deeply into Kiara's eyes until she became deliciously lost inside of them. His loving ways swept her off her feet and made Kiara's current situation easier to deal with.

Once she got dressed in more comfortable clothing, she allowed Eddison to take over. He asked her to put on some flip-flops. Then they boarded his Chrysler 3000 and Eddison drove to a nail salon located in an impressive part of Sugar Land. Kiara loved money and was used to the finer things in life, but she had to admit that Eddison was on a whole different level than Rashad.

They parked and walked into a beautifully decorated, high-ceilinged room with soothing lights, tan walls, and relaxing yoga-type music that played in the background. The entire place was brimming with women getting manicures, pedicures, and facials.

"When you first came over to the house," Eddison said, "you seemed frazzled. I could tell you had a hard day. The original plan was for me to simply run you a nice hot bath. But, baby, you're about to get pampered by real professionals."

"You're not so bad yourself." She laughed. "And I love that you are full of surprises."

Eddison marched over to the receptionist. "We want a Piña Colada pedicure. As soon as possible."

"Yes, sir." The receptionist immediately escorted them past the other customers to their chairs.

Kiara selected her nail color, a pretty teal green that was perfect for the holiday. Eddison sat beside her and decided to get a gentleman's pedicure. They were offered a complimentary glass of white wine and reclined in their shiatsu massage chairs.

"Oh, my Jesus." Kiara reacted to the massager that kicked in and helped release the tension from her shoulders and lower back. "I thought your massage was great, but, baby, this feels absolutely amazing."

"It should. You're sitting on a five-thousand-dollar chair."

"Get the hell out of here!" She laughed.

"Seriously, Kiara. You *are*. . . ."

"You used to take your wife here or something?"

"Yeah. Nina always told me it was one of the greatest stress relievers she ever had. I hope you don't mind."

"I don't mind at all, Eddy. I'm flattered. And I want to pinch myself."

"Pinch on." He grinned, happy to have made her happy.

The royal treatment felt incredible, especially after what she just went through. Kiara could have wept for joy. The more Eddison treated her with love and respect, the more she felt like she could potentially fall in love. Yet she was scared; she never again wanted to endure the pain that Rashad gave her.

Kiara reached in her satchel and pulled out a copy of *What to Expect When You're Expecting,* with the intention of reading while her toes got worked on.

Several women stared at the couple and noticed Eddison's open affection.

The glances he gave Kiara made her feel protected, desired, and as precious as a soaring butterfly.

"A man that loves his woman will love his child," a female customer told Kiara when she noticed the spine of the book she was holding.

"A man that loves his woman is worth keeping," Kiara responded.

"And yes, I love this woman. I do love her."

Kiara gasped. She wanted to slink in her chair and die. This was his first time publicly confessing his love for her.

"Mmm mm. Look at them," the lady cooed. "Your baby will have a wonderful father."

"Yes, he or she will," Kiara replied.

"So you won't know the gender till it's born?"

"I won't know a lot of things until it's born."

Eddison and Kiara heartily snickered.

At that point, she had no idea whether Rashad was the father or Eddison.

"Must be nice to be pampered in and out of a nail salon," the manicurist said in a wistful tone as she assembled all the tools for Kiara's pedicure.

"It's heavenly," Kiara answered. "He's a wonderful man."

"I wish my man was like him."

"I found out that if one man doesn't treat you right, you don't have to put up with it. You gotta trust that you will come across another man, a good one, who will treat you the way you're supposed to be treated." Kiara said this to her manicurist but she was preaching to herself in an effort to encourage her own heart. The memory of Rashad's recent behavior when she fell on the street was fresh in her mind. How could the man who once loved her do her that way? It hurt her heart to realize how bad things had gotten between them.

But Kiara grew sick of Rashad invading her mind. She decided to enjoy her pedicure and let Eddison do all the nice things he wanted to do for her. She picked her book back up, but as she read the chapter titled, "What You May Be Wondering About," multiple thoughts hammered at her:

Why are you pissed at Rashad? Yes, he cheated on you, but didn't you inadvertently help him? You know the man loves sweets; and you handed him a plate of his fa-

vorite cake with icing on top. Did you actually think he wouldn't want a piece? Why are you so stunned he slept with Nicole Greene? Rashad's a good-looking man. And since you slept with Eddison for revenge, you're no better. You don't even deserve Eddison. And once he realizes who you really are, he'll let you fall down and lie in the gutter, too.

Kiara trembled violently and returned the book on her lap. Her heart sunk, and suddenly being pampered didn't feel so good. She caught the ongoing envious stares from the women sitting near her. She knew they only saw the shell of her: the woman whom others admired because it looked like she had her life together. If only they knew the truth.

Myles, her unborn baby, and her new man were the things that made her happy. And even if the way that she ended up with Eddison was completely immoral, no one on earth wanted to admit bad things about themselves, even if they were true.

"Are you all right, sweetie? You don't look so well."

"I'm great!" she told Eddison. "I'll be even better in time."

Kiara offered Eddison an encouraging smile and tried to relax.

"Maybe a little drink will help me feel better." She allowed herself a teensy sip of wine.

"Try not to take more than that one sip. In fact, I will ask them for bottled water. Put that glass down."

She instantly obeyed him. "You really do care," she whispered.

"Your life impacts more than just you."

Eddison requested a cold bottle of water for Kiara. His take-charge attitude made it seem like he was enhancing her life even in tiny but important ways.

Right then she refused to allow negative thoughts to condemn her. She was eager to face her future, a better future, and not be mentally punished by her conscience.

Eddison was a rare man. Kiara believed it with all of her heart. But the heart can be fragile once it's been hurt.

Kiara guzzled a swig of water and asked, "Eddy, do you believe that people can have just one soul mate?"

"Hey, I loved my wife until the day she died. But she's never coming back. I know that Nina wouldn't want me to mourn her forever. And everyone deserves to have love throughout their life, not just one time. So yeah, my next soul mate . . ." he whispered. "Could be you."

"Me! That sounds wonderful but *crazy*." Kiara laughed nervously. "I-I'm still . . ." She cautiously eyed the women around her who seemed to envy her.

"You won't be in that dilemma forever.

"True, but I feel like a flop. Like, if it didn't work the first time, why would God give me another chance?"

"Because no one is perfect, Kiara. And if the Lord is good, He can give anyone who needs it a second chance. There are far too many people on this earth who didn't hit a home run their first time at bat, but they stepped up to the plate again. They forgot about their failure. They took another chance, swung the bat, and knocked the ball out the park."

"You make everything sound so easy, and doable, and possible."

"That's because anything is possible, if you'd only believe."

Chapter 3

You're My Lady Now

After Eddison and Kiara returned from the nail salon and settled inside his house, they ate a simple dinner that he prepared: baked salmon, canned corn, and a green salad. Then they cuddled and fell asleep in his bed while watching TV. But much later, when it grew pitch black outside, and when Eddison could hear the birds singing in the trees of his backyard, he glanced at the neon clock on the table next to him. He gently tapped Kiara on the shoulder.

She stirred in her sleep. "Huh? What?"

"Get up. Get dressed."

"What time is it?"

"It's almost six."

"A.M.?"

"Yes. Get up. Get dressed."

"But it's *Saturday*."

"I know that. Now come on." She groaned, but got out of bed and dressed herself alongside Eddison.

After they got in his Chrysler 3000 and looped around the circular driveway and zoomed down his street, Kiara noticed how dark it was. "Eddison, where the hell are we going at this time of the morning?"

"You'll see."

With a smile on his face, he drove until he entered I-10 going west; surprisingly, the highway was littered with cars speeding toward their destinations.

"Oh, I know what you're doing." Kiara yawned. "You must want to catch the day after Christmas sales."

He chuckled. "It's still November, woman, nowhere near Christmas You really are sleepy. I need you to wake up soon. There's something you need to see."

After a while Eddison reached the suburb of Katy, Texas. He kept going until he came alongside a large, empty field lit by several streetlights. It was a charming three-acre parcel, and the ideal location to build a country estate.

Eddison emerged from the car and ran around to open Kiara's door. They walked a few yards across the vast meadow. The firm grass smelled fresh and sweet and it loudly crunched underneath their shoes.

"Can you see this?" he asked as they came to a stop.

"Yeah. What about it?"

"What do you see?"

"Um, not much. Just a bunch of grass."

"Exactly, Kiara. And right now your life can be compared to this vast, empty field. That means the possibilities of what can be are endless. Because there's nothing but grass . . . with no tall buildings to block your vision. That's what I meant by anything you want is doable . . . if you can dream it, you can see it. And if you can see it in your mind, you can build whatever you want to build . . . when the fields are empty."

"I'm confused." Her voice trembled. "What about the baby that's coming?"

"Right now, your life is an empty field." Eddison grabbed her hand. "Whatever good you can imagine happening in spite of everything that's going wrong, it can still be yours. Don't let fear keep you stuck in the past. I had to learn that lesson myself. Just keep believing, my lady."

"All right, Eddy. I will try my best."

"Say, 'I believe.' "

"Do I really have to?"

"Yes, you do."

"It seems silly."

"Of course it does, but do it anyway."

"I believe."

"Say it like you mean it," he commanded.

"I believe, dammit," she shouted.

"Good job."

Eddison grabbed Kiara's shoulders and carefully led her a few steps away. They walked toward the east.

"Look up." He pointed.

The earth felt quiet and still. Kiara watched the brilliant sun as it mysteriously rose. The sky resembled the work of a master painter. The colors of the horizon were orange, pink, and yellow, all swirled together. Kiara had never seen anything like it.

"Amazing how something so simple can be so inspiring," she gushed in awe. "It's breathtaking."

"Yes, it is," he replied. But he was staring at Kiara when he said it. "How'd you like to wake up and see that every morning?"

"It would be like a dream . . . like heaven."

They held hands and watched the sky transform from twilight to morning. She enjoyed the country landscape. And for the first time in a long time, Kiara gained the courage to face the future. One failed relationship wouldn't block her desire for happiness. She'd make sure of that.

When they drove away from the field, Kiara settled in her seat and closed her eyes so she could snooze and fantasize about babies and love and family. And Eddison wrote down the phone number depicted on the large "For Sale" sign that stood in front of the grounds near the sidewalk. It was a property he'd viewed before, and he was happy to know it was still available.

By the time they got back to his house, and he started making her a breakfast of eggs, toast, and turkey sausage, Kiara started singing.

"This is no ordinary love," she sang.

"No, it's not," Eddison replied as he took time to smack her on her butt.

"You are very romantic, Eddy. Now I understand why the women at work throw themselves at you and the women in the grocery stores try to force themselves on you."

"I wish I hadn't ever told you that."

"I'm glad you told me. What woman wants a man that nobody else wants?"

He could only laugh and blush, which made Kiara feel horny with desire.

Following breakfast, they showered together. Afterward, they dried each other off with large towels and crawled into his bed. They stretched out facing each other, and when Eddy began kissing Kiara, she eagerly responded. She thought he was so sexy, and kind, and manly. Plus his lips were luscious and hot. She liked the feel of his hands on her breasts. He aroused her even in her pregnant state.

Whoever said sex ended when pregnancy began didn't know Kiara and Eddison.

He got behind her in a spooning position, then quietly entered her. She wanted him to.

"I feel like I'm hurting you."

"Eddison, you can never hurt me." Kiara's tone was serious. She relaxed and had to admit that she loved having sex with Eddy. She thought it was fun to make love and have full conversations with him. "But I know one thing," she said as he was stroking her from behind with his chest against her back. "When this breaking-up mess is over with, and when I can fully give my heart away again, I vow to never be hurt through a man's actions. I'm going to protect my heart like it's Fort Knox."

"That's noble, Kiara, but not entirely preventable. Things happen. Life and love may hurt sometimes."

"Yeah, well, I definitely want to love again, but I'll be very careful next time. Oh, God, mmm, that hurts yet it feels so damned good." Her eyes rolled in the back of her head as Eddison made love to her. "Jesus Christ Almighty. I-I've got too much other stuff to deal with."

"You're so cute when you're determined."

"I gotta be determined." Kiara enjoyed the feeling of Eddison rocking her from behind, cupping her breasts. "You want to hear my weekday schedule? Alarm goes off at five. Take shower. Wash face. Brush teeth. Put on makeup, comb hair. Get Myles up. Make him wash his face and brush his teeth. Make him go find his backpack and his Chuck Taylors, which I know are lost somewhere in that big old junky closet he got. Get him out the door in time so that he can eat breakfast at the fancy school he goes to. Ooh, that feels good. Keep going. Then I, I, I answer his thousand questions during the ten-minute ride. 'Mommy, why this' and 'Mommy why that?' Drives me crazy. And then, ouch, ugh, mmm. And then I drive my son's hyperactive ass to the drop-off circle. Then I say bye to him, and floor it so I can beat everyone to work before they get there because I'm the HNIC. I'm making big paper and I gotta be the ex—uh, oooh, mmm yeah—I gotta be the example. Ouch, that feels so good. Keep going, baby. Then I. Then I log onto my computer." She gritted her teeth. "I-I review my calendar. Move money around so the budget stays right. Deal with these messy-acting employees all day long. Ignore the daggers I get from that skank bitch Nicole. I go to meetings. Oooh, baby." She shuddered and felt like she wanted to faint even though she was already lying down. "I-I-I go to one meeting after another meeting and I—"

Eddison thrust into her one good time and she screamed at the top of her lungs.

"Kiara! Why you getting all wired up while I'm trying to give you a tune-up?"

She moaned and shuddered, then burst out laughing. Eddison happily kissed her neck and squeezed her nipples. His touch felt magnetic and gave Kiara tingly goose bumps. She loved how good he was at making her forget the bad stuff.

Kiara quickly ducked underneath the covers and made sure to do everything she could to make her man feel as good as he always tried to make her feel. But while she was trying to love him, her thoughts centered on someone else.

What's he doing? Who is he with? What would he do if he knew I was fucking Eddison and loving it? Who gives a damn?

She mentally regrouped then climbed on top and rode Eddy's dick for a while, till it felt good and hard. Painful yet pleasurable. And it amazed Kiara that her husband's past actions had turned her into a bit of a slut. Prior to getting married, she'd only been with one other lover. Then she met Rashad and she assumed he'd be the last man she'd ever be with. But these days, Kiara boldly explored her sexuality. Now that she was in her mid-thirties, she felt like she was at her peak. She and Eddy did it so many times the past month that she'd lost count.

After they both climaxed, they continued to enjoy each other. All that weekend they went shopping, ate at cozy restaurants, and explored each other's bodies. It almost felt like a honeymoon.

By the time Sunday morning rolled around, Kiara knew she needed to return to her own house and take care of some legal business. Eddy was spoiling her and she loved it, but there was another part of her life that had to be dealt with—alone. She had gathered all her belongings and had just settled into her vehicle and was getting ready to back out of his garage. But before she did, she waved him over to her car.

He leaned in and kissed her on the lips.

"My weekend was great, Eddy. But you wore me out."

"Good! And you're welcome."

She laughed. He kissed her again.

"I enjoyed being with you, too, Kiara. We felt like a family. We are family."

She pondered his words. Kiara cared deeply about him, and as much as she didn't want to be hurt by any man again, she really didn't want to hurt Eddison, either. She was always told a man should love a woman more than she loves him, but did that mean that he'd end up disappointed at some point?

"Eddy, I love the way that you love me . . . but again, what if this baby that I'm carrying isn't yours? I-I couldn't bear what would happen if you give me this wonderful type of attention just to find out things haven't turned out like you want . . . I want to make sure that you get everything you want, too."

And just that quick Kiara went from feeling warm and happy to tense and emotional. Her eyes blinked back tears and she thought she was about to have a panic attack.

"It's all right, my love. Try not to worry about it. We will cross that bridge when we get to it. But no matter what happens, I will always think of that child that you're carrying as my own."

"But what if it isn't? What if DNA proves otherwise?"

"Do you plan to stay with him . . . if the kid is his?"

"No. No way. That's not happening."

"Then it's settled. I *can* be that child's father. We can be together. And you will never have to worry about me not treating you well. You're my lady now, Kiara."

"Okay then," she whispered. "I'm your lady."

She waved at him and drove off in a daze.

Love could be beautiful but wasn't it also risky and unpredictable? Yet Kiara needed love. She told herself not to be afraid, and to get to know Eddy on an even deeper level; because in spite of her reservations, she could picture herself falling deeply for him. And if that happened, she would have to conquer her demons and claim him as hers before another woman did; for she definitely didn't want him to be the one that got away.

Chapter 4

Coming with the Territory

All Thanksgiving weekend, while Kiara hung out with Eddison, Nicole Greene was determined to bond with Myles.

When Kiara first banned Rashad from their house, he stayed at the Hampton Inn for a couple of weeks. It cost over two grand, and even with a forty-two-inch flat screen and free wifi, his room felt lonely, freezing cold, and sterile, and he wanted to punch holes in the walls. So when Nicole told him he was crazy for staying at a motel and assured him that she'd cook his meals, wash his clothes, and save him a lot of money, he quickly took her up on her offer.

Rashad was now shacking with Nicole in her rented house on the west side of Houston. It felt good for her to wake up with her future baby daddy in her bed, something she planned to experience permanently. And early on Black Friday, instead of shopping at the mall, Nicole had spent hours cleaning the entire house until it was spotless.

Mid-morning, when the little boy arrived with his dad and stepped inside the corridor of Nicole's home, she graciously welcomed him as if he were the Prince of Wales.

"Well, hello there with your little handsome self." She warmly greeted him and practically curtsied. Myles gave her a curious stare then strutted into the house, eyeballing everything.

Nicole followed him and anxiously held her breath. It would be his first time staying overnight with her and Rashad and she wanted everything to go well.

When Myles had been shown to his room and began to unpack his overnight bag, Nicole wrung her hands and could barely keep still. She already knew Myles was very observant and outspoken. Even though she was the adult, she felt she had to be on *her* best behavior.

"How's it going, Myles? I hope you like the room you're staying in," she said to butter him up.

"I'm good." He tossed his clothes on the bed. "I'm sure I'll like it."

"Okay then. If you need anything, be sure to ask me or your father."

"I know that already."

"All righty then." She grinned so hard her cheeks hurt. Myles abruptly raced from the bedroom and went to look for his father, who had carried into the house a kids' plate meal from Steak 'n Shake.

"Take your shoes off please," Nicole called after Myles, but she wasn't sure he heard her.

"In time," she assured herself. "This fairy-tale type of shit takes time."

A couple hours later, Myles screamed that he was hungry again. Nicole was about to remove the half-eaten turkey and a container of dressing from the refrigerator. But Rashad informed her that he was sick of holiday leftovers. She dropped everything she was doing and rushed out the door on a fresh grocery run. She returned home and made Myles a grilled cheese sandwich to tide him over. Then she baked some chicken and prepared fresh cauliflower and broccoli and wild rice.

Once she fixed all of their plates, everyone sat at the long table with the fancy orange tablecloth, about to eat off chinaware.

Nicole happily beamed; she felt she could get used to this scenario, with her and Rashad sitting at the opposite ends of the table and with Myles seated nearby. Plus their new baby that was on the way would eventually sit in his or her high chair across from Myles. She couldn't wait for all of them to be together, enjoying one another the way families were supposed to do.

That's all Nicole wanted: to be Rashad's woman, bear his children, and spend her life with him. She wanted to prove to her family back in Alabama that she had what it took to live in holy matrimony.

Feeling proud of herself, Nicole picked up her fork, severed a piece of meat, and took one hungry bite out of her perfectly baked chicken breast. But she got interrupted before the flavor could sink in.

"Yuck," Myles said at the carefully arranged food on his plate. He took one look at his vegetables and announced, "I hate cauliflower. Just hate it. It has no taste. None!"

"Myles, baby." Nicole laughed nervously. "It's actually good. I seasoned it well. And there's some cheese sauce waiting on the stove if you want to cover your veggies."

"I love me some cheese, but it doesn't matter," Myles answered in a firm voice. "I ain't eating it."

Nicole hopped up from the table as best as she could. She got a spoon from the kitchen drawer, then stormed over to Myles. She carefully slid all the white vegetables off of his plate onto a napkin.

"Nicky," Rashad said as he watched her in action. "That ain't necessary."

"Yes, it is."

"Myles is not too good to eat what you cook. He doesn't have a choice."

"It's no big deal, Rashad. I'll just have to learn what he likes and doesn't like. From now on, cauliflower is off the list."

"Are you serious?"

"I am. The most important thing," she said nobly, "is that you're spending time with your precious little boy."

She went and flung the napkin filled with veggies into the trash compactor.

Myles smiled to himself and figured he'd scored major leverage.

Later on, when Nicole knew Myles was exhausted after play-wrestling with his father, she presented the boy with a two-layer chocolate cake.

"Wow." He jumped up and down. "My favorite. How'd you know?"

Nicole merely giggled. She didn't want him to know that after they finished eating dinner, she had secretly pulled Rashad to the side and asked him a series of questions:

"What's his favorite color?"

"Purple."

She nodded. "Favorite dessert?"

"Cake. Anything sweet."

"Icing?"

"Chocolate."

"Got it. What's his favorite kind of toys or other interests?"

"Reading books. And he loves things that fly, and animals. Myles is a lion, elephant, and bird fanatic. He begged me to take him to Botswana one day. I told him a season pass at the Houston Zoo is much less expensive than an African safari camp. He actually told me the zoo animals there are clones and not the real thing. Can you believe that?"

"Oh, really? It's like that? Hmm! Noted." Nicole opened a memo app in her smartphone and recorded everything he told her.

And while Rashad played and talked with his son, Nicole whipped up the cake from scratch.

She watched Myles bite into his first slice; a warm, cozy feeling poured over her when she saw his eyes widen. He moaned in delight. "Yummy, this is the best cake ever. Even better than my mommy's."

Nicole went to bed that night feeling happy and more confident.

On Saturday morning, Rashad and Myles were outside kicking a soccer ball when Rashad received an unexpected phone call. Rashad was informed that a raw materials delivery, which had been delayed several days previously, had just arrived in

Houston. This was critical because he needed the goods for a major contracting job that his firm, Eason & Son, was about to start. He decided to go check on it and asked Nicole to watch Myles for him.

"Instead of having little man tag along with me, I think he'd have more fun by staying here with you and bonding or something, okay?"

"I thought you wanted to spend as much time with him as possible."

"I do, but this won't take long. Plus, he needs to adjust to being around you, right? Can you do that for me, please, pretty lady?"

"Oh, sure, babe. I'd be happy to do that."

"I'm sorry this is so last minute. But get used to me having to run and take care of business," Rashad told her. "As a warning, it comes with the territory."

"No problem. Do your thing. I'll hold it down for you here at the crib."

He told her thanks. Then he asked Myles, "You know my phone number, right?"

"Yes, Mommy put it in my cell phone and showed me where my address book is."

"Good. Get your phone and call me right now so I will have your number, too." Kiara had bought Myles his own cell phone that morning, but Rashad was just now asking for the number.

"Okay, Daddy. I will call you. Don't leave yet. Make sure I do it right."

After Myles did exactly as he was instructed, Rashad felt his son was in good hands. He gave him a loving pat on the head, told him to be good, and left to go to check on his delivery.

Myles immediately kicked off his gym shoes. They made a loud whack when they hit the wall.

"Ahem." Nicole cleared her throat and slowly walked with her hands clasped behind her back. "You, young man, should probably to learn to take off your shoes . . . more quietly."

"Okay, I'm a have to get my daddy to show me how to do that," Myles said and burst out laughing. He was a charming and handsome little boy whose mischievous ways reminded Nicole of Rashad.

Myles settled on the living room floor. His complete attention was on the television. He inserted the *Tarzan: The Legend Lives* DVD that his dad previously arranged for him to watch.

Nicole sighed but went to pick up the boy's shoes and place them neatly on a rug near the wall. She turned her attention back to her future stepson. She sat down and watched him concentrate on the animated flick.

"Hey, Myles, come over here and sit next to me on the couch."

Nicole rubbed her hands together and thought about what she wanted to say; she didn't know if Kiara had told him a bunch of nasty things about her.

He perched on the edge of his seat and stared at her.

"Hello. Um." She took a deep breath. "Do you know who I am?"

Myles appeared baffled for a second. "Aren't you Ms. Nicole?"

"That makes me sound old, but yeah. You may call me that. Or if you want to, you may call me Mom. That's only if you want to."

"Mom? Like you're my mother?"

"Um, well, yeah. Because, you know, one day it'll be official, but right now you can just call me Ms. Nicole."

"I already have a mom."

"Look, Myles. You're a smart boy. I can tell. I'm sure you know what's going on between your parents."

"I know they fight a lot. A whole lot."

Nicole hungrily licked her lips and leaned in closer.

"You say they fight? Like he actually punches your mom? With his fists? Like in her jaw?"

"Nooo. He just yells and curses. Like a grumpy old person."

"Oh, okay. My goodness. I wonder what that's all about." She smiled like she wished she had a front row seat at their fights. "Anyway, I think that is one of the main reasons why your dad now sleeps over here. So he won't have to fight with your mom all the time—at that other house. So now that he's living here, I'm sure you'll be visiting us a lot. This will be your second home. And I think it's perfectly cool if you wanna call me Ms. Nicole for now, even though I'm not that old. But 'Mom' will come later on for sure."

"You look kind of old, but exactly how old are you?"

"Take a wild guess."

"Umm, forty?"

"You gotta be joking." Nicole nearly punched him. "On second thought, you don't need to know my age. It really doesn't matter. I'm a grown woman old enough to be your mama. Put it that way."

"Oh, all right." Myles shrugged with an unbothered look. He suddenly yelled like Tarzan. Nicole raised her eyebrows. The boy attempted to continue watching the movie but she gently took the remote from him and reduced the TV volume.

"Myles, I'd just like to say that I'd like nothing more than for you to feel completely comfortable over here. I want you to treat this house just like your own."

"You mean I can leave my room real messy, and eat Cheetos in bed, and not make my bed in the morning?"

She laughed along with him, even though she wanted to frown and shudder and spit. "Well, I just think you'd want you to be neat as possible, right?"

"Ms. Nicole, I hate making my bed. It's stupid. All I'm gonna do is get right back in it later that night. What a waste of time and energy."

"Being neat is a waste of time?"

"And energy," Myles reminded her.

Nicole was momentarily stunned and wondered what the hell she'd gotten herself into.

It comes with the territory.

"Anyway, like I said, this place right here is going to be your home away from home."

Myles observed his surroundings. "It's smaller than my real house. My other house has two floors and a lot of rooms. And the backyard is huge. You should see it."

She gritted her teeth. "Um, yes, my house is smaller. But that doesn't mean you still can't have fun, right?"

"I thought bigger was better."

"I cannot believe this," she muttered under her

breath. "Bigger isn't always better, Myles. You have to use your imagination. I'm sure you are good at that. And you can pretend like this sweet little house that your dad and I live in is as big as a castle."

"Mmm hmmm."

"And in this castle you have been privileged to have your very own room. It will be the room you slept in last night."

"Oh, yeah? I was scared, though. I thought a cockroach was going to crawl on me. I love animals but I hate insects."

"Um, excuse me. We do *not* have roaches."

"Then what was that long, brown creepy looking bug that was crawling on the floor and across the wall making that *chi chi chi chi* noise? It sounded so *scary*. I pulled the blanket over my head and tried to fall asleep, but the lights being on didn't help."

"Y-you left the lights on *all* night?"

"Yeah. I told you I was scared to death."

"Oh! You love lions but you're scared of a little bug?"

"African elephants are afraid of mice, ducks, and honey bees, Ms. Nicole. Google it."

"Coming with the territory, my ass." she whispered.

Nicole had had enough of this kid. She stood up and placed her hand on her hip.

"Never mind all of that, smart guy. You do realize that running electricity all night costs a lot of money, right?"

"I ain't got no worries. My dad has plenty of money. He can pay the bills, Ms. Nicole."

She stared curiously at Myles. "How much money is plenty of money? Is he . . . is he like, a millionaire?"

"Yep. My dad is rolling like Dr. Dre."

"Dr. Dre is a billionaire, though," she said, proud that she knew something that Myles didn't. Even though she doubted the boy knew exactly what he was talking about when it came to Rashad's finances, she handed him the remote control. She told him, "Excuse me." She ran to her bedroom and closed and locked the door. Nicole powered up her laptop and did a Google search on Eason & Son Contractors. She found out Rashad was listed as a HUB, a historically underutilized business for small, minority, and women-owned businesses. He also was a member of the National Association of Minority Contractors. She learned that the firm had been in business for well over thirty years and had been founded by his father, the late Derek Q. Eason. It wasn't the biggest company in the city, but Rashad had been awarded several lucrative contracts. Apparently, he'd garnered some reputable clients, including a few government contracts, and his staff was growing. Nicole then realized that when he oversaw the renovation work at her house last summer, it was because he wanted to be there and personally handle the job. She knew he could have sent his staff, but he didn't.

Nicole continued to research a list of Rashad's completed projects. He even had an impressive website with video clips of him participating in ground-breaking ceremonies and grand openings. She licked her lips and mentally calculated some numbers.

With the way things were going, she assumed that he and Kiara would split up and that the woman would probably demand fifty percent of all his assets. They had just made ten years of marriage, which bettered Kiara's chances for a nice settlement and a share of his pension.

"At least she was conniving enough to wait ten years," Nicole said to herself. "She's about to get paid. But I can't allow that. Those are *my* coins now. She doesn't deserve half. She slept with her coworker, which makes her an adulterer. And a female adulterer is way more scandalous than a male one. She *had* to be in love with that redbone man to sleep with him."

Nicole began compiling information about both Kiara and Eddison. By the time she was done, she was ready to help Rashad win his case in any way she could.

Nicole glanced at her watch and realized Rashad had been gone for hours. The length of time made her feel uneasy, but at least he had given her a heads-up about where he was going and what he was doing. When Rashad returned from his errand, Nicole gave him a questioning look.

"Hey, cutie. Don't be mad. This task took longer than I thought."

She let go of her annoyance at how long he'd been gone and told him she'd be right back. She drove over to Kroger and bought a triple pack of ant and roach spray that she tried to sneak into the house. But Rashad saw her when she returned.

"What's in the bag? More food?"

"Oh, it's just a few items I thought we could use to make your son's stay as comfortable as possible."

He simply grinned in amazement at her and

felt grateful that she was going out of her way to be the perfect host.

Later, when Rashad was showering, and Myles was in the living room watching television and eating snacks, Nicole retrieved one of the cans and made sure to lightly spray the boy's room.

And hours later, after he went to bed, Nicole went and got Rashad, who insisted on sleeping on the couch so as not to let Myles know that he and Nicole were lovers.

"Come to bed, babe." Nicole turned off the TV and dragged Rashad by the hand into their bedroom. They crawled in the bed and Nicole immediately started peppering his neck with lustful kisses.

"You sure are horny tonight."

"Tonight?" She mounted him and pulled his wife-beater over his head. "Baby, I want you every night."

"I see." He laughed as Nicole gently pushed him until his back was pressed against the headboard. She leaned forward and began sucking on his nipples. "Um," he moaned. "You are a good woman."

"And don't you forget it."

"How can I forget? You do just about everything I like."

Nicole melted inside. All she wanted to hear was that as a woman, she was among the best.

"'Just about' is cool, but that means I could do better," she said and moved from his nipples to his dick. "Babe, what is something that I don't do that you wish I did?"

Before he could get any words out his mouth,

Nicole pulled on his penis and started sucking and licking the tip until finally Rashad came all over.

She laughed and made sure to *ooh* and *ahh* so Rashad would see that she was having a good time. They entangled their legs around each other as Rashad slapped her from behind. She gritted her teeth and enjoyed how good he felt inside of her. She moaned and shuddered as her orgasm took over her entire body. She was sticky and sweaty, but she didn't care.

This is it, she thought to herself. *There is no other man on earth that can give me exactly what I want except Rashad Eason.*

After they both were worn out from making love, Nicole gave Rashad five minutes of rest before she started in on him.

She placed her head on his chest and sighed with contentment.

"Hey, babe, you were great," she said.

"Thanks, you were—"

"May I ask you something?"

"Yeah, Nicole. What's up?"

"How is the divorce coming along?"

"It's in process."

"When do you think it'll all be over, Rashad?"

"I don't know. These things can take time. It depends on if we can come to some agreement. If Kiara gives me a hard time about splitting assets and wants to contest anything, that'll delay the process. But from what I've been told, once everything is agreed upon, it'll take sixty days for the divorce to be granted."

"Hmm, sixty days. All right." Nicole mentally calculated whether she could get him to marry her before the end of next year; preferably a late summer wedding. Or maybe they could wed soon after she gave birth and once she lost all her baby weight. Her baby was due on June eighth. It was important for her to look sexy and fit and trim for her man if she wanted to keep a permanent hold on him.

Nicole paused, then kissed Rashad on his bare chest. "Question! How much is your McMansion in Fresno worth?"

He moaned with pleasure when she flicked his nipple with her tongue.

"How much?" she demanded again.

"Shit. In this current market, if I am lucky and get the right buyer, it could sell for a good half a million."

Nicole already knew the house's market value, because she had gone on the appraisal website to see how many properties he owned. In addition to the house, she discovered that he'd purchased four small parcels of undeveloped land. She loved that her baby was doing more with his money than buying Escalades and Rolexes.

"Damn, that crib is worth *that* much?" she asked, feigning surprise. "So if she buys you out—?"

"I doubt it. She doesn't have that type of money."

"But what about that money she had been stacking up and hiding from you? How much did she build up?"

Rashad had informed Nicole how he discovered his wife had maintained secret savings. Kiara quietly pilfered money from his contracting business and placed it into her own accounts. And on the day she got sick of him, she threw receipts in his face to let him know what she was capable of whenever he pissed her off. Rashad was stunned. It made him feel she knew their marriage wouldn't last; like she didn't trust what they had, even though she fought hard to have it.

"I don't know how much she built up; which reminds me. I gotta tell Lily to make sure and research any hidden assets Kiara has. That shit pisses me off."

"Who the hell is Lily?"

"My ugly-ass divorce lawyer. She likes pussy as much as I do."

"What?" Nicole shrieked, but she calmed down after Rashad explained that his attorney had a strong appreciation for females.

"Oh, okay," she remarked, feeling relieved. "But you *used* to call her Ms. Tangaro."

"She told me to call her Lily, so that's what I'm going to do. Is that all right with you, my crazy little Birmingham girl?"

Nicole giggled and felt happy that out of all the places this man could be, he chose to be in bed with her. The more she thought about how much of a catch Rashad was, the more determined she was to make him hers. Nicole whispered in his ear, "Call her Lily. It doesn't matter. I love you so much. We're going to have it all." Then she began sucking every part of Rashad. She sucked him till he forgot about divorces, alimony, assets, and secrets, and remembered every good thing he could have from being with Nicole.

Chapter 5

Nicole Takes Charge

That Saturday evening, Alexis McNeil had just finished eating dinner. She and her new man, Varnell Brown, had been invited to spend time with his sister, Carmen Foster, and her husband, Forrest, at their home in Missouri City. Alexis's daughter, Hayley, was with her mom, Mona Hooker, and Alexis felt satisfied to enjoy an evening away from her house.

Forrest had prepared an Asian shrimp-and-vegetable soup that they all devoured. Once they were done, Carmen suggested they kick back and relax.

They were seated at the dining room table. Forrest just dealt a deck of cards. He and Varnell were partners and were sitting across from each other. Alexis was on Varnell's right.

"So," Carmen said to Alexis as she scooped up

and organized her cards, "how long you and my brother been kick-ing it?"

Forrest jumped in. "What she's trying to ask is how long you've been giving Varnell some stankie on the hang-down?"

"Giving him some who on the what?" asked Alexis.

"C'mon, y'all," barked Varnell. He was normally a calm-natured man who never sweated the small stuff. But taking a big step like bringing Alexis around his family made him somewhat anxious.

"Don't start, Carmen. It ain't even like that." Varnell turned to Alexis. "My nosy sister loves to try and get in my business. And yes, she wants to know how long we've been . . . you know."

"Oh, I see," Alexis coolly replied. She was accustomed to the judgment and curiosities of others and she prayed she could handle herself so as not to embarrass herself or her man.

"I'm not sure why you'd want to know something like that," she answered. "But for the record, nothing like that is going on. And even if it was, we probably wouldn't tell you."

"Yeah, right," Forrest yelped. He discreetly examined the beautiful Alexis McNeil up and down. Alexis had a reserved yet fiery demeanor, partially because she was extremely pretty and was accustomed to men groveling around her. She wore a twenty-two-inch weave, had pouty lips, and could have passed for Paula Patton's identical twin.

"My brother-in-law is a saint," Forrest said in a loud voice, "but hell, even he can't pass up having sex with a younger Halle Berry. Even if she is crazier than a shithouse rat."

"Hey, that's enough." Varnell slammed his cards

on the table. "Alexis, you shouldn't have even dignified that idiotic question with a response. Forrest needs to worry about his own household. And I apologize for his behavior."

"It's all right, Varnell," Alexis pleaded, not wanting to make the situation worse.

"We point blank crazy," Forrest told her. "You need to know that from day one."

"I kind of figured . . ." Alexis said with a wink. She hoped they meant no harm and decided not to overreact.

"Crazy or not, you two need to know this is a respectable woman," Varnell insisted. "The fact that I brought her around you two lets you know everything you need to know. And, not to go deep into it, but she's been through a lot in her past relationships. I'd like the chance to offer her something different, if you two could just chill out and act civilized."

"Awww," Carmen said in a babyish tone. "Yep, my brother is feeling this beauty queen. Isn't that special?"

Varnell rose to his feet, clearly frustrated. "Come on, Alexis. We don't have to put up with this type of disrespect."

"Brother-in-law, sit your Russell Wilson–acting ass down and let's get it on with these spades. Some people are just too sensitive. It was meant to be an icebreaker. Damn!"

"C'mon, Varnell, lighten up," said Carmen with a laugh. "You know I don't get to hang out with you that much. So have a seat and take it like a man. If you are treating her right, that means she will be around for a long time. And if she does, she needs to know how Forrest and I roll."

Varnell reluctantly sat down and picked up his cards. He slammed one on the table.

"Take your ass whipping like a man," he yelled.

"Uh oh, partner. *That's* what I'm talking about," Forrest said. "When a man ain't getting any, he gotta let out his aggression one way or another."

Alexis smiled. "I like you two. Yeah, you are and your wife is crazy, but you're real. I actually hate pretentious people."

"They make me itch, girl," Carmen replied and she wildly threw out a card.

They resumed the game, throwing friendly shade and cracking obnoxious jokes. After the men thoroughly beat the women, they took a short break to use the restroom and get more refreshments from the kitchen.

The moment that Forrest and Varnell left the room, Carmen leaned across the table. "I know my brother, and I can tell he honestly likes and respects you. That's important in a relationship. Me and that silly teddy bear I got have been through relationship hell. Our marriage was rocky for a hot minute. I'm sure you couldn't tell," she said with a facetious smile, "but this handsome fella was so charming and generous that it forced me to deal with side chicks. Women love my man, if you know what I mean. So a lot of really crazy shit went down in our marriage. Long story short, I can't believe I'm still married to him. But I am. The love is still there. We are going to make it to the finish line. But I have to constantly keep his ass in line."

"Thanks for sharing that. I-I think I know what you mean."

"Are you telling me you've dealt with side chicks in your past?"

Alexis looked Carmen dead in the eye. "I know the side chick life. I've been one. I was the queen and the princess. But I turned in my tiara, or crown, or whatever you want to call it. It's time to do something different. And I really believe that this is where Varnell comes in."

Carmen stared at Alexis with new curiosity. "Hmm, we need to get together and talk. Does my brother know this? He normally doesn't like skanks."

"Excuse me?"

"I'm sorry, Alexis. I guess this proves I still have issues." Carmen laughed, then grew serious. "But this isn't about me. Just treat my brother right and you will never regret meeting him. And if he is saying no to sex, yeah, that is Russell Wilson in the making. So hold onto him and you can kiss the side chick life good-bye. We need to get together one Saturday when I don't have my two daughters. You like crawfish? Like with that suicide seasoning?"

Alexis told her she'd loved crawfish. They made a promise to meet up. And deep inside, Alexis agreed that if she had it her way, she would never relive her old ways again.

Sunday morning, Rashad woke up to the lovely aroma of French toast, crispy bacon, and fluffy scrambled eggs. He sat up in bed, noticing that Nicole wasn't lying next to him. He wandered into the kitchen and was met by a surprise.

Nicole stood in front of the sink wearing a red apron. She had learned that red was Rashad's favorite color; red was also the color of sex, passion, and love, and she planned to wear lots of it.

Myles stood on a tiny stepstool by the counter that stored the hearthstone canisters. One by one, he dropped lemon slices into a glass pitcher. Rashad saw the big metal spoon, a measuring cup filled with sugar, and six teabags that were sitting in a pot on the stove with steam rising over it.

"Homemade sweet tea?"

"I'm a Southern girl. You know how we roll."

"Aw, man, that's what I'm talking about." Rashad yawned and stretched. "I tried to enjoy my sleep, but all the noise in this kitchen plus the good smells wouldn't let me."

"And it's about time Daddy woke up, right, Myles?" Nicole asked.

"He's a lazy bum."

"Hey, watch that, son! Why y'all teaming up on me? I work *hard.* I deserve to sleep in once in a while."

"If you had slept any longer, you would've missed all this good food. And I know how much you love to taste my stuff."

"You damn sure right about that." Rashad took a hard look at Nicole. She was getting her sexy on by wearing a pretty dress underneath her new red apron. She looked so beautiful that Rashad imagined she was naked, even though she clearly wasn't.

He enjoyed watching Nicole cook for him. The way to his heart was definitely through his stomach, among other things. Rashad learned the hard way that most women want to be valued. He wanted to do the right thing with this lady. So he came and gave Nicole an encouraging hug. She moved her face near his lips for a light kiss, but he shook his head as a stern warning.

"Why you trying to hide our relationship?" Nicole asked. "You know I'm hot for you whether little man is in the room or not."

"Yeah, but—"

"In my opinion, if you are happy and you're doing what you want with the chick you really want to be with, ain't no need to hide it, right?"

"Can we eat now and talk about this when the time is right, babe?"

"Stop avoiding important issues, Rashad. Now *is* the right time to talk about it."

Nicole called on Myles. "Hey there, son. Remember the conversation we had yesterday when your dad ran his errand?"

"Son?" Rashad muttered under his breath.

"Yeah, Ms. Nicole. I remember. What about it?"

"Um, like I already told you, whenever you come over here you'll be sleeping in your own room." She lovingly placed her arms around Myles as she talked to him. "And the truth is your daddy sleeps with me in the bed that's in my room. I mean, in *our* room."

Rashad cleared his throat. But Nicole ignored him.

"Yeah. You see, last night Daddy tried to sleep on the couch, but doing that isn't healthy for him. It hurts his back. And if his back is hurting, he can't work. And if he can't work, he can't make money. And if he can't make money, he can't afford to buy you all the helicopters you like to play with. And without enough money, he won't be able to buy you the foods you like to eat. And he definitely can't take you on a safari. That's why Daddy needs to sleep on a nice, firm mattress. You understand what I'm trying to say, Myles?" She released the little boy. She then winked at Rashad and walked over to him and physically closed his open mouth with her fingers.

"Oh, okay. I get it! To get all the stuff I want, my daddy gotta make his money."

"Exactly. And your daddy sleeps with me on a nice comfy mattress and not on that couch, unless he's taking a nap!"

"Nicole?" Rashad shouted a warning.

"Babe, chill. He needs to know. Trust me on this one."

Nicole poured the hot tea in the glass pitcher and let Myles dump in the sugar.

"Do you really get what I'm saying, son?"

Myles stirred the sweet tea and avoided eye contact. "Yeah, I get it. Why are you telling me that?"

"Because I don't want you to be alarmed and wonder where you daddy is. He'll be with me. I'm going to take good care of your father and of you whenever you're here. You'll be like my child."

"Mmm hmm."

"And after I have my own baby," she pointed at her round stomach, "you will have a new brother or sister. Isn't that exciting?"

"Nicole—" Rashad yelled.

"Now, babe, I know you wanted to wait to tell Myles about our baby, but as the firstborn heir of Eason and Son, he really needs to be aware of these things. Stop treating him like a kid. Your child is intelligent. He sees things. He *sees* this." She rubbed her belly. "Although Myles is seven, he shouldn't be kept from the truth forever. It's a cold, cruel world out there."

Rashad nodded and tried to calm down. Nicole's pushiness annoyed him, but on the other hand her forcefulness helped him to deal with his truths.

"Yep, Nicky. You're right. I have been holding off on some topics when it comes to Myles. We ought to have more man-to-man talks. Thanks, babe, for taking on the reins . . ."

"No problem," she answered, sounding self-assured. "That's what I'm here for."

"Wow, that didn't turn out as bad as I thought." He focused on Myles.

"Whaddup, my son? How'd you make out yesterday after I left the house? Oh, and sorry that it took longer than I thought."

Rashad was gone so long that Nicole had considered baking the child another cake but thought it would be overkill, since there was still dessert left over from the day before.

"I felt good, Daddy. After you left, I had so much fun. We watched a movie and then Ms. Nicole helped me put together my Getaway Glider robot."

"Did she? Man, that's cool. Thanks, Nicky."

"Oh, it was nothing. I had a great time with him. He's a good kid."

Rashad felt relieved that Nicole tried her best to bond with his son. He knew she couldn't stand Kiara and often wondered if she could ever manage to leave her ego at the door and treat Myles with respect.

Nicole resumed cooking breakfast, "Have a seat, my king. No. Wait. Wash those hands first. I can't forget where your hands were last night."

Rashad blushed and went to wash his hands. He knew Nicole was referring to all of her parts he touched last night when they made love. He sure hoped she wouldn't give his son those details; he prayed she'd keep that to herself.

When he returned to the kitchen, neither Nicole nor Myles were there. He heard their voices in her small dining room.

She was setting up the nice dishes and tall glasses and cloth napkins.

"Damn, all this? Just for a basic breakfast?"

"Nothing is basic for us. We will go all out for all our meals."

"But why?"

"Rashad, you just don't understand. I-I-I've wanted this—a family—for a *long* time. I always wanted to be with the people I love, in a house that we share, eating meals together, cracking jokes, playing board games, and watching movies just like we've been doing ever since Friday. This is my dream. I'm on the cusp of living my *dream.*"

"Damn. I see."

She made Myles go and clean his hands, too.

"Anyway, Rashad, I told you about my ex, Ajalon, and how he blew a ton of smoke up my ass about getting married just to get himself arrested for dealing drugs. I don't mess around with felons. That fool stole all my dreams." Nicole shuddered at the memory. "And that's why it's been so hard for me to trust a man."

"Aww, boo," Rashad said. "That's what you get for fucking around with broke niggas."

"But see, I honestly learned my lesson. I am so grateful that we met and you're helping me to believe in love again."

He gently patted her on the shoulder. The more she opened up to him, the more he wanted to try to be a decent man; he was certain he could do better than her ex.

Nicole dabbed at a tear in her eye. "And once our baby gets here, it's going to be an even bigger dream come true. I cannot wait. Moving to Houston was the best thing that's ever happened to me."

"Yeah. Right. Hmm."

Myles returned to the kitchen and settled back in his chair.

Rashad stood near Nicole and reflected on all that was going on. Her optimism was great, but he felt caught between two worlds. On one hand, he knew that Nicole loved him. She understood he was still tied to Kiara and that it would take time for that relationship to legally end. He knew she'd wait. Yet, a tiny part of him wished he could still be with Kiara. They'd built so much together, and she really was his day one woman. She wasn't such a bad wife. In fact, Rashad had to admit that Kiara had been an excellent partner. He agreed with her when she said she gave their marriage her all. But he hated that she had an affair with Eddison. It was a swift kick in his teeth and he didn't like it, but he figured she only did it as revenge. She wanted him to feel her pain. So maybe their situation was his fault.

"Have a seat, babe," Nicole said, noticing the faraway look in his eyes.

Every time Rashad appeared as if he was in deep thought, Nicole felt anxious. She knew she couldn't control him, and he would always do what he wanted to do, but she could spot the look of a man traveling back down memory lane.

"What were you thinking about just now?" she asked Rashad.

"What type of question is that? Nothing."

"Mmm hmmm. I hope you're thinking about what you ought to be thinking about, I know that much."

Feeling satisfied, Nicole took extra care to arrange all Rashad's food on his plate. She poured him a generous amount of sweet tea in a glass filled with ice cubes and handed him a fork and a knife.

Nicole did the same for Myles. Rashad watched her very carefully, noting how she treated his son like a little prince. Maybe she would treat their baby like royalty, too. At times Rashad couldn't believe that he'd fathered several kids: Myles was his firstborn with Kiara. Then he had a toddler daughter named Hayley by his former mistress, Alexis. Nicole was pregnant with his baby. And it was possible that his estranged wife was going to have his kid, too.

"Finally," Nicole happily exclaimed when their breakfast was ready to be eaten. "Let's dig in."

"Nicole, I want to say it seems you've adjusted to Houston since you relocated."

"Um, sort of, but I meant to tell you that the holidays sometimes make me feel very sad. So if I act kind of moody, you'll know why." She paused in dramatic fashion. "A few months ago, I was scared that I'd be all alone during Thanksgiving. But the way things turned out, I worried for nothing. I don't feel lonely at all. And I have you and Myles to thank for that."

Perhaps fate did have a weird hand in bringing

them together. Nicole had been by herself in a strange city, but now she was with him. He had been in a marriage that was on life support—now he and Nicole were supporting each other.

Lately, life was hard for him. But in the meantime, Nicole's energetic take-charge attitude helped him to cope.

They spent time talking and enjoying their meal. Suddenly, Rashad's watch phone lit up. It was Alexis. Lately she'd been paying him dust. A woman who didn't give a damn about him always challenged Rashad, for he was a competitive man.

"Sorry, Nicky." He apologized. "I gotta get this."

"Who is it?"

"It won't take but a minute. Excuse me, y'all."

He rushed out the front door to take the call, and closed it behind him.

"Hey, you," he said. "Is everything straight?"

"Oh, yeah, everything is fine. Why wouldn't it be?" He told her that he was at home eating breakfast. Then he asked. "How is my baby girl?"

"Hayley is good," Alexis told him. "Lately she's been sneaking into my closet and trying to wear my baddest shoes. Have you ever seen a twenty-four-month-old in high heels? It's hilarious."

"She can never fill your shoes."

"Why do you say that?"

He looked behind him to make sure the front door was still closed.

"Easy. You're one of a kind. They don't make 'em like you anymore."

"And what's that supposed to mean?"

"You know exactly what it means . . . I can't forget all the fun shit we used to do."

Alexis was repulsed but unsurprised. Most men

never forgot the woman that they cared about and with whom they shared great sexual history. And if the woman would let them, they'd always try to get some again.

"Oh, Lord, I know for a fact you are talking to me behind a closed door or something because you would never ever say that in front of that crazy-ass female Shrek you're living with."

"That's cold, Alexis."

"So you *are* living with Shrek?"

"Um, yeah."

"Thanks for admitting the truth for a change."

"Anyway, I'm outside right now."

"I figured that."

"What else do you figure?" he said, trying to be flirty.

"Dude, please. Anyway, I wanted you to verify your *temporary* address."

"Why?"

"Because your *roommate* still hasn't updated her physical address at the workplace. She's been living there since, what, last June? It's now November but she still has this old-ass address taking up space in the HR system. And we need to know the current location . . . in case of any emergency."

"Why don't you just ask Nicky for it? I can hand her the phone right now—"

"No. Rashad! Don't do that. She'd just curse me out. I don't want her to know I've even asked you for this info."

"It's a damn shame y'all two can't get along."

Rashad knew full well that his sleeping around with three women who worked at the same office would create some problems, but at the time he thought he was slick enough to get away with it.

"Don't blame me for us butting heads," Alexis replied. "Nicole acts so possessive of you. And it's sad because it's not like you're even married to her. I don't have time for that drama and I barely want to deal with her at work, let alone away from the job. So, Rashad, be a sweetheart and give me that info."

He relented and quickly gave Alexis the address. Alexis would then pass it on to her boss, Kiara.

Even though Kiara already knew where Nicole and Rashad last lived, Alexis knew Kiara had obtained the address through scandalous means when she hid a cell phone in Rashad's ride and tracked the location through her iPhone. Now that Kiara was ready to start divorce proceedings, she'd asked Alexis to intervene for her. Kiara knew he'd originally checked in at a motel and she wasn't sure if Rashad and Nicole were together or if they've even moved to a new place; she wouldn't dare ask her husband for the info, and Alexis was happy to verify the address.

"Thanks, Rashad. You have no idea how much easier you made things by doing this for me."

"Whatever." He paused. "Hey, I gotta go now. She just opened the door and now she's looking right at me."

He waved at Nicole and smiled. She smiled back and suddenly clutched her stomach as if she were in pain. She glared at Rashad then disappeared inside the house.

"Yeah, something is up with her. I need to hang up from you."

"Poor thing," Alexis murmured. "I can only

imagine how awful it is for you to live the life of a sex symbol. You remind me of Dwight Howard."

"He's worth a hundred million. I wish I had Dwight Howard's money."

"Hmmm, I'll bet someone else wishes you had his money, too."

Rashad chuckled and hung up. Once he got back inside, he found Nicole had returned to the kitchen.

Myles was carefully placing dishes into the sink, which was being filled with running water and dishwashing liquid.

Nicole was wiping the counter and stopped to face Rashad.

"Hey, I saw you holding your belly. Is everything okay?"

"Not really."

"What's wrong, Nicky?"

"Who were you on the phone with that you had to leave the house to talk?"

Rashad was momentarily stunned. "Oh, so you were faking an injury? Pretending to be hurt?"

"I *am* hurt! Who were you holding secret conversations with on the phone?"

"Damn. That was Alexis, all right? You need to know that she will be calling me at times."

"Okay, fine. I get it. You two have a child. That's not my concern. I just don't understand why you couldn't talk to her in front of me."

"Because . . . I wanted privacy. *That's* why." Rashad was firm with Nicole, not wanting her to assume that she could completely run over him.

"Privacy, huh? Well, I ain't tripping. I was just asking."

"I understand that. But it was business that I needed to take care of. Stop stressing."

Nicole backed down and began hand-washing the dishes. She regretted questioning Rashad. She didn't want to seem so insecure, especially when it came to his other kids. But this wasn't about the child. She wondered whether Rashad was completely over Alexis. Did he still have feelings for the woman who bore his daughter? Nicole certainly hoped not. Besides, she didn't trust Alexis. And as she thought about it, she knew that she had to set the ground rules with her man.

"Rashad," she said in a gentle voice, "if we intend to share a solid relationship, I just think we should be able to talk about all kinds of topics. Nothing should be off limits, no secrets. I know you care about me, but I need you to show me that you have nothing to hide. All right, babe?" Her voice was pleasant and nurturing. She prayed that he understood.

Rashad listened and nodded.

"I'll take that as a yes and I appreciate your wanting to try and work with me on this area of our lives." She shifted gears. "And now that we've been well fed, I guess it's time for Myles and me to finish up all these dishes, right, son?"

"Right, Ms. Nicole."

She snatched a dish rag off the counter and began to vigorously clean the drinking glasses and filthy plates.

Rashad let her act as domesticated as she wanted to be. He knew Nicole was opinionated and passionate about the things she cared about. It is what he loved about her.

Rashad retreated to the living room to watch a show on ESPN.

He kicked back and focused on the broadcast for twenty minutes until the doorbell rang.

Myles yelled that he'd go get it. When Myles returned to the living room, he was leading Alexis by the hand. Hayley was perched on her mom's hip. She wore a pink-and-black-striped fleece dress decorated with a big white bow. A cute floral hat topped her braided hair.

"Dada," Hayley shrieked.

Rashad couldn't believe his eyes.

He rushed to lift his daughter from Alexis's hip and gave the girl a kiss.

"What are you doing here?"

Rashad set her down and Myles led Hayley to the corner of the room; she eagerly watched him while he showed her his video game.

"It's your turn to watch Hayley," Alexis replied. "Remember, you said that starting this year, you'd want to keep her during part of the Thanksgiving holiday. I guess you were so busy, you must've forgotten." Alexis casually strolled through the living room, checking out the furniture and decorations. She openly leered at an empty wedding photo album displayed on the coffee table. Then she noticed a large canvas painting on the wall; it was a sketch of a lion, a lioness, and a baby cub snuggling together in the grass.

Someone had taken a black marker and written "Nicole" under the lioness and "Rashad" under the lion. "TBD" was scrawled next to the cub.

"How utterly tacky," Alexis said with a laugh. "What's all that about?"

"It's about me and my man's business," Nicole

answered as she quietly appeared in the room. "And I suggest you mind your own."

"Actually, what's in this room *is* my business. Rashad is supposed to hang out with Hayley," Alexis explained.

"How'd you know where I live?" Nicole demanded.

"That's between me and Rashad."

Nicole quickly eyed the children and suggested that Myles take Hayley to his room. When the kids were out of hearing range, Nicole addressed Alexis. "When it comes to a chick rolling up into my house uninvited, you are treading on dangerous territory." She left the room and soon returned, waving a forty-caliber like it was a flag.

"First thing someone told me to do when I moved to Texas was buy a gun."

"Nicky, what the hell are you doing?" Rashad asked. "Why do you have that?"

"Don't worry, it's just for show. But if I have to use it, I will."

"You don't have that gun for show," Alexis replied. "There are only two reasons people obtain a gun: to kill an animal or to kill a human being."

"Guess which one you are."

"Nicole, one thing people should have schooled you on about Texas," Alexis said in anger, "is that you cannot wave or point weapons at anybody. Not jokingly. Not even for show. You're about to catch a case."

"And you're asking for trouble rolling up at me and my man's place unannounced, especially when everyone knows you and I have had beefs. I don't care if you do have a kid together. It's all about respect."

"*You* want respect?" Alexis set her purse down on the couch.

Nicole lowered the gun to her side. "I know how to get respect."

"Crazy-ass woman. Put that thing away. Don't play like that."

"I'm not playing," Nicole said. "Trust me."

"I'm not bothered," Alexis replied. "Trust me."

"Wait, hold up you two," Rashad said, stepping in between them. "We need to seriously sit down and talk. We have kids; kids that I love, with more on the way. I-I blame myself for not handling my business like a man. And I apologize, Alexis. I did forget about the visitation."

"I guess this is another thing that comes with the territory?" Nicole said to Rashad mournfully. She loved him so much and was afraid of anything that could come between them.

"You already know I have a daughter and I'm serious about having a relationship with her."

"Yeah, you've told me," Nicole admitted woefully.

Rashad wished there wasn't so much conflict regarding the women and the kids. And Alexis's brave front didn't fool him.

Just then little Hayley reentered the room. Alexis gasped and immediately ran to her daughter. Her slender hands trembled as she tried to shield Hayley's eyes from the woman with the weapon. The air in the room felt tense.

"It's all right, baby girl," Rashad said in a gentle voice. "Nothing bad is going to happen." Even though Hayley's eyes were covered, Rashad gave her a protective squeeze. And right then knew that he would never want anything to hurt the people he loved. He calmly turned to Nicole.

"Babe, don't do this. I know you don't mean what you said about using that thing, and I won't let any accidents happen around here. You're my girl, my kids are here. Hell, as the man of the house, I'm telling you we are *not* about to handle grown folks' business like this. Now go get rid of that gun right now or I will do it for you."

Nicole felt humiliated. She was shocked that her jealousy would cause her to act so recklessly. She carefully withdrew the gun. "I-I'm sorry. I was just kidding."

"Don't play like that. You ought to know better," Rashad told her.

Looking sheepish, Nicole hesitated, then quietly departed.

Alexis trembled at the thought of what could have happened. Even though she didn't love him anymore, she felt concerned for Rashad. "Look at what you've gotten yourself into. And guess what? I doubt that it's going to get any better."

Alexis glanced around. "I don't care how many hopeful-looking wishful-thinking paintings that were nailed to these walls. I'm not sure what you see in her, but Nicole is trouble. And that's all you're going to have from knocking up a woman like her: a life of trouble."

Nicole came back into the room followed by Myles. She felt more self-conscious with the boy in the room. She certainly wouldn't want to make a horrible impression on him. And she felt a little sorrowful about her actions. She quietly observed Myles and then glanced at Hayley. It had been a while since she'd seen the little girl; her legs were longer, her cheeks fuller. She was growing up. Like it or not, Hayley was Rashad's child and Nicole needed to face reality.

"Sorry about that," Nicole said with all sincerity. "I actually meant no harm."

"It's okay," said Alexis.

On the spur of the moment, Nicole playfully forced Myles to stand in front of Hayley.

"Do you know who this cute little baby is?" she asked him.

"Nicole—" Rashad interrupted.

"If we all are going to be around each other in the future, then it has to be done," she answered. "Myles, this darling little girl is your baby sister. I guess that makes me her future stepmom."

"Hey, wait a minute," Alexis protested.

"That's the problem," Nicole continued. "There is too much 'waiting' and not enough 'doing' when it comes to this situation. Now I may not necessarily like that my man has a bunch of kids. But it is what it is. And at this point no one should give two squats about how this baby got here. The issue is that she exists and if people don't like it, they can kick rocks."

"Nicole," Alexis said, her voice shaking. "It wasn't your job to do something like that. I don't need you to do that."

"I know. But if the people who are supposed to do their job don't, it gets delegated to someone else—someone who's not afraid to tell the truth." Nicole ignored the vicious stare Alexis gave her. Then she bent down until she was eye level with Myles.

"Did you know Hayley was related to you, son?"

"Um, a little bit. I heard about her but never really got to meet her."

"Well, this is your opportunity to get to know her. I think you should know who all your siblings are," she said and went to sit down. Facing the truth definitely could hurt, but Nicole wanted no pretense in their home life.

Suddenly she felt exhausted from all the activity. "Dammit, my feet hurt. Anybody wanna be nice enough to give a pregnant woman a foot massage? Rashad? What are you standing there for? Please go and get some lotion and take care of my aching feet. Geez, do I have to take control of everything around here?"

Rashad could only do what his lady asked of him. And Alexis, too stunned and frustrated to move an inch, felt that her prediction of Nicole Greene being nothing but trouble would not only hurt Rashad, but could hurt her, too.

Chapter 6

Something to Talk About

It was December first, the Monday following Thanksgiving; Kiara and her employees returned to work at Texas South West University. She held the position of senior manager in the communications department and Alexis served as the administrative assistant. Nicole had been hired last summer and now worked as a communications coordinator. The whole gang was employed in the same office and there was always something to gossip about, since this was the location where Rashad expertly handled illicit relationships between his wife plus Alexis and Nicole.

That morning Shyla Perry, the social media coordinator, was standing in the break room fresh from her delayed honeymoon exploring Central America. Everything went off without a hitch. Now she wanted to be known as Shyla Perry-Fallender.

With her short hair, big brown eyes, and wide mouth, she was a standout in their department.

"Hey, ladies." She warmly greeted a couple of female coworkers who entered the room to make themselves coffee. Shyla loaded two bagels into the toaster.

"There goes the new bride," said Taylor, one of the communications coordinators.

"Look at me, because I am a changed woman." Shyla laughed.

"I'll bet you are," Taylor remarked, being facetious.

"How was your holiday?" Shyla asked.

"Mine was good," said a tall, big-boned woman named Aisha. "My man came by and I cooked and we ate and—"

"Well, I think it's a shame that a woman who works at this college tries to pretend like she's one thing when actually she is another," Shyla continued. "She acts if her relationship is so intact, yet she's one of the main people getting her freak on with someone else that works on this campus. And they spent the holidays together."

"Wait. What?" Taylor said. "Didn't you just return from *your* honeymoon?"

"Yeah, what about it?"

"I'd think you'd be giving us details about your *own* rendezvous instead of spilling the tea about other people."

"I was just thinking the same thing," remarked Alexis, who'd been hovering nearby and decided to pop in and join the conversation.

"Oh, but what happened on my honeymoon is nothing compared to all the extramarital humping that's going on at the university."

"Shyla, you ought to be ashamed of yourself," Alexis told her. "Why are you tearing down another woman? Marriage hasn't changed you at all."

Even though Alexis did have an affair with Kiara's husband, she wasn't proud of her actions. Not anymore.

"I'm not tearing down anybody. I'm just telling the truth, something you have always had a problem doing," Shyla responded. "I'm just saying. I don't like working in an office where coworkers are fucking work husbands, and folks are getting pregnant by people on the job. That brings way too much drama."

"Are you trying to tell us something, and if so what?" Aisha asked

"What you think?" Shyla smirked. "I'm talking about someone that works in this department, the one who wants everyone to believe she had such a great marriage and a wonderful man. Well, he ain't that wonderful if she gotta creep behind his back."

"Nooo, not Kiara Eason," said Aisha, reaching out to touch Shyla with her long fingernails. "Who is she screwing?"

"Oh, I can't tell you that."

"Why not spill all the tea?"

"Well, it's like this. I *do* need my job."

"But if she's humping a man on campus, I'd want to know exactly who it is," Aisha replied. "Mrs. Eason has it going on. She can hook up with whomever she wants—but I need to make sure she ain't messing around with *my* boo."

"What? You got a lover on this campus, Aisha?"

"Mmm hmm. And he's tied to me like Super

Glue, but still, you never know." Aisha paused. "You don't know who I'm sleeping with, right?"

"You'd be surprised whose business I know around here." Shyla replied. "And I don't really tell all of it even when it is good and juicy."

Like clockwork, Nicole entered the kitchen. Alexis took one look at her and immediately left.

Nicole gave Shyla the look. She snatched her by the arm and dragged her from the kitchen, down the hallway, to her office.

Nicole slammed the door before she twirled around.

"Shyla Perry, are you out of your damned mind?"

"It's Shyla Perry-*Fallender.*"

"Girl, I don't care about your hyphenated name. You need to chill on that gossiping."

"What gossiping? What you talkin' about?"

"I thought you were my girl. But I see how you do a sister when you think her back is turned. I heard everything you said. Your voice carries."

"Oops, my bad. I guess I was overly excited."

"You need to watch that. I want to know who my friends are around here, as well as my enemies."

"Girl, stop! I am Team Nicole. We're good. We'll always be good," she said, even going out of her way to give Nicole a comforting hug. "I know you don't want everyone in your business. But I just really hate that you got knocked up by the boss's husband."

Last summer, when Nicole had first come on board at the university, Kiara found out she was living in a house with minor contracting issues. In an effort to be hospitable, Kiara recommended that Rashad help Nicole out since she knew his business oversaw renovations. Once he started working at Nicole's place, they quickly developed a friendly bond that eventually turned into a full-blown affair. Then Nicole became pregnant. And she fell in love.

"I somewhat hate that it happened, too. My mother had a fit when she found out."

Nicole always felt the need to impress her doubtful family. And she was determined to prove them all wrong.

Nicole continued. "My mom thinks it's shameful to have sex with men that are already taken."

"It *is* shameful."

"Look, Shyla, things happen, okay. I did not go out of my way to be with Rashad. But after we started kicking it, I could tell he was feeling me. And of course, I developed feelings for him, too. I mean, he told me his wife wasn't satisfying all his needs in his marriage."

"He could have been lying."

"But what if he was telling the truth?"

"Even if he was, it wasn't your job to fulfill his needs. That was between him and Kiara."

"Then why would she send him to my house to help me out with my renovations? It's not all my fault."

"You sound like you're suffering from guilt."

"Maybe. Maybe not. All I know is that you cannot change the past. I'm not trying to sound unsympathetic, but it's safe to say those two will never get back together again. And if he is free and available and I am, too, why not be with him? We now have history."

"And a future," Shyla said, and stared at Nicole's belly.

"What's done is done. More importantly, I can't forget that I made an agreement with Kiara not to tell her secret."

Nicole wanted to run and tell everyone the news after she overheard Kiara and Eddison discussing her pregnancy. So after Nicole found out about Kiara's dirty deeds, she didn't feel so bad about the sex she was having with Rashad

"Shyla, you know that Ms. Perfect agreed not to fire me if I swore not to tell anyone about her and light skin," she said, referring to Eddison.

"I know, but at this point, even if I didn't spread Kiara's business, it's obvious she can't front anymore. She's just making herself look like a fool."

"Check this out. And you better not tell a soul."

"I swear to God."

"Anyway, Rashad filed on her. I know it sounds crazy, but once this is over, we could potentially have a divorce party, an engagement party, and a baby shower, all at the same time."

Shyla began laughing. It *did* sound crazy. "Are you serious? That's so scandalous. Yet you're the type who'd do something over-the-top like that."

Shyla didn't realize it, but she was right. Because little Nicole from Alabama always wanted more out of life than just going to school, getting a job, and visiting her cousins every other weekend. No, Nicole wanted to drive a car that drew envious stares and she wanted to have cute babies that she could dress in the latest designer fashions. She knew that by capturing Rashad's heart, she was one step closer to fulfilling her dream.

"I want what I want and I know just how to get it."

"Whoa, girl. Your life is more amazing than mine." Shyla eagerly listened as Nicole spilled more details about what had been going on over the Thanksgiving holiday.

"And I know you're dying to tell the world about these amazing events," Nicole said, "but it's me we're talking about. I am not Kim Kardashian, so you cannot try to break the Internet with my business, you hear me?"

"Okay. I'll keep my mouth shut from now on. But you know that people are talking."

"Let 'em talk."

Shyla was referring to how the whole office was gossiping about the identity of the father of Nicole's baby. Starting a few weeks ago, every time Nicole left the building for lunch, a few women would discreetly follow her to the parking lot to see if a man was picking her up in his car. But they never witnessed any such thing.

"Think of how they're going to react once I get that ring on my finger," Nicole replied. "After Rashad is officially divorced, we'll give it a little bit of time. But then I am going to want to shout it to the world. I will be so happy and I won't care who knows it. Whether folks can handle it or not doesn't matter. I plan on having the baddest wedding Houston has ever seen."

"Oh, really? That costs a lot of money."

"Money won't be a problem." Nicole squealed and hugged herself. "Shyla, I shouldn't be telling you all this, but I've hit the jackpot. This man is loaded."

"Shut the fuck up!"

"But see, I can't help it. I'm finally getting to be happy . . . just like in a Terry McMillan novel."

"Baby, rich man, and nuptials worthy of a reality

show. You're living the dream, Nicole. Make sure and invite me."

"You *are* invited. Just keep your damned mouth closed until I tell you when it's okay to pour that gasoline and strike that match."

After they both laughed, Shyla told Nicole she'd talk to her later. They'd been chatting for a good twenty minutes and both needed to do some work.

A little while later, Nicole was in her office typing a press release. Their department had recently been awarded a two-million-dollar endowment and her job was to spread the good news. Nicole was concentrating on her document when she heard a rapped knock on her door. She glanced up from her computer.

Two uniformed officers stood there. The young cop had freckles and bright red hair; the older gentleman wore a nametag that read "Sims."

"May I help you?"

"Do you have a Nicole Greene that works here?" asked the freckle-faced cop.

"Who wants to know?"

"Ma'am," he continued, "we are looking for Nicole Greene. We've been given a photo and need to positively verify your identity.

"I, um,"—her voice quivered—"I'm her."

"What's your date of birth?" asked Sims.

She replied August second and handed over her driver's license when requested.

"This isn't the same address as your current residence," said the younger cop. He and his partner both closely inspected her license.

"No, it is not."

"You will have to take time to update your license, ma'am." That was Sims.

"I could go to the DMV right now if—"

"Later for that; first things first," snapped Sims. He returned her ID. "Nicole Kelly Greene, you are under arrest for disorderly conduct and aggravated assault with a deadly weapon."

She tried to not make any sudden moves while she got patted down and then handcuffed.

"Ouch, that hurts."

"Have you ever been cuffed before?" asked freckle-face.

"Never," she said. "I'm not a criminal."

"If I had a dollar for every time I heard that, I could retire," remarked Sims.

"This is nuts! I don't believe this. That stupid gun wasn't even loaded. I was just—"

Sims continued his spiel. "You have the right to remain silent."

Silence.

Nicole felt that was exactly what was happening to her. She thought Alexis would do anything to silence her, shame her, and get revenge—only because Rashad was with her now. Nicole fumed as she was escorted out of her office, down the hallway, past Alexis's empty desk, and through the exit doors of her work facility.

When she bumped into Shyla, who was trying to come into the building the same time that she was going out, Nicole yelled, "Follow us."

"Girl, what happened? Why are you in handcuffs?"

"I need you now more than ever. Please follow us."

"I got you," Shyla promised and she raced for her vehicle.

The officers placed Nicole in the back of a squad car. They made some notes and eventually drove off with Shyla right behind them.

Nicole's mind raced in several directions. Would they make her stay overnight? How could Alexis be petty enough to actually call the cops? Was Nicole about to follow in her ex-boyfriend's footsteps and experience the isolation he felt when he was put away?

Karma is a bitch, she heard her mother's haunting voice whisper in her ear.

And for the first time since she'd been in Texas, Nicole felt genuine fear.

After she was brought into the station for questioning, the cops gave her more information. Alexis McNeil had filed a police report the day before. She came into a local police station and said a woman pulled a gun on her and she felt her life was threatened. Alexis gave a sworn statement of what happened and when she was asked if she wanted to file charges, she said she had no other choice.

Sims continued to question her. "How do you know this woman Alexis?"

"Through a case of very bad luck," Nicole said.

"We'd appreciate straightforward, factual answers please."

The officers got her statement. The more she thought about Alexis, the more she hated the woman. She felt she should have shot her when she had the chance. But then if that would've happened, she'd have forfeited all her dreams. And nothing could come between Nicole and everything she wanted.

"So I'm really being charged?" Nicole finally asked as she went through the booking process. This time she was alone with Sims and although being with him scared her she couldn't stay silent.

"Yes, Ms. Greene, you're being charged."

"I now have a case?"

"Yes, you do."

"But what if I lose my job behind this crap?"

"Sometimes that happens."

"That's not fair."

"Life isn't fair when you choose to wave loaded weapons at people."

"That's the thing. It wasn't even loaded. So this is all a big mistake."

"We will investigate that claim, too."

"That's bullshit."

"Watch your language, ma'am. And get a good lawyer."

Nicole stopped bumping her gums, knowing that opening her mouth could add fuel to the fire and possibly end her life in more ways than one. She was petrified when she was placed in a holding cell. It felt like the end of the world. Flashbacks shattered her mind and squashed her faith. Even though she was in Houston, she felt like she was still in Birmingham. Legal issues, dread, people in authority who could tell her what to do. No freedom.

By the time Nicole was released and bonded out by Shyla, it was several hours later. The first person she called was Rashad. She had tried to phone him from jail but her calls went straight to voice mail.

Shyla drove while Nicole tried him one more time. She wanted to cry when he finally picked up.

"Hi, babe," she said. "I-I'm so glad to hear your voice. You'll never guess what just happened to me!"

"What?"

"Does your attorney, Lily, handle criminal cases?"

Nicole proceeded to tell Rashad everything that Alexis had done to her and everything she wished she could do to Alexis.

"You think that I hate her, but I've never done anything to the chick except talk shit. That's not a felony. The woman can't even take a joke. She's more trouble than I am and now there's no telling what I will to do to her when I see her at work again. I know one thing. She can't come to our house anymore, and I mean it."

"Y'all gonna have to stop with the pettiness and act like you have some sense. Work out your differences and act like adults. Maybe you can even be friends one day."

"Rashad, who the hell are you kidding?" Nicole said. "How can I be friends with someone I don't even trust?"

When Nicole and Shyla returned to work, Aisha, who'd seen what happened, informed Kiara that Nicole was back. Kiara requested that Nicole come to her office right away.

Nicole got butterflies in her stomach whenever Kiara wanted to see her but she went down to her boss's office and shut the door.

"Nicole, I want to hear from your own mouth what happened today. I've heard many rumors around here from other people."

"All I can say is that it was a mistake."

"A mistake in that they arrested the wrong person?"

"No."

"So what was the mistake? The fact that you pulled a gun on my administrative assistant in front of my fucking son?"

Nicole gasped.

"Don't look surprised. Do you really think I'm going to be happy about what you've done? And that I had to hear about this ridiculous and reckless behavior through Taylor and Aisha?"

"How did they find out?"

"They looked up the arrest record."

"Oh, I'm shocked that they told you. So even your precious Alexis McNeil left you out of the loop?" Nicole hated that Alexis and Kiara got along fairly well, considering the woman had a baby with her husband.

Kiara quietly studied Nicole. "Actually, Alexis was wise enough to give me a heads-up earlier this morning. She told me she thought it was very possible that the police would arrive today since you probably wouldn't be home when they came to get you. Alexis told me everything. She showed me a copy of her statement. I was so livid I couldn't think straight."

Nicole bowed her head.

"Well, let's hear your side of the story."

"You already know I've had problems with this woman in the past and she came over to my house unannounced. She can be unpredictable. I felt I needed to protect myself. And I was scared."

"You were scared?"

"Yes. I was. But, um, nothing happened. I put away that little gun. I never threatened to kill her or anything. I don't know why she made a big deal about this."

"Maybe it's because you did by bringing out that deadly weapon."

"Well, geez, I'm sorry, Kiara. I-I didn't know it would upset her so much, but she upset me, too, by coming into my house uninvited, popping off at the mouth about me and Rashad's busi—"

"You and Rashad's what?"

"I-I feared for my life," Nicole replied, not wanting to bring Rashad into this.

"Nicole, regardless of how you felt about her bringing their child over there, you seem to forget that children, *my* child, was there, too."

"I know. I'm so sorry."

Nicole tried to persuade Kiara that it was just a tiny misunderstanding and that she was confident everything would work out. Kiara told her that she would be reviewing the public arrest record.

"After hearing everything I've decided that you, young lady, are on suspension."

"What? You have no legal grounds to do that!"

"Hold on. No, I cannot fire you just because you've been arrested, but I think all this criminal activity and interruptions of my department deserves some type of leave of absence for you while you ponder your next course of action concerning your case."

"That's crazy, Kiara, you're going too far—"

"No, Nicole." Kiara stood up and pointed a finger. "Going too far would be to fire you like I wanted to do last month. But *you* went too far. Don't you ever do anything so reckless around my child again! You may have intended to scare Alexis, but who's scared now?"

"You're treating me like the silly thing I did to that chick is what I've done to you. I've done nothing to you. Not this time. Yet you want to punish me on a personal level. You can't do that, Kiara. Please reconsider."

Memories of Kiara's failed attempt to fire Nicole flooded her mind. The woman even backed Kiara into a wall and made her give her a raise. Kiara pointed to the door.

"Get out of my office. I can't stand the sight of you. I am going to look into you requesting three days' leave without pay. *You* will put in for it. I will approve it. You won't tell anyone else about this. You want to handle some personal business. And while you're off, you will think hard about your past actions and any future ones that you've considered. You may work the rest of today and tomorrow and be off Wednesday through Friday. You may leave now."

Astonished, Nicole backed out of her boss's office and nearly ran down the hall, but she didn't want to give any coworkers another reason to stare at her.

She took a long, slow, humiliating walk to her desk. And she quietly created her electronic leave request for three days off.

Without pay.

Chapter 7

Collecting Wedding Gowns

Ever since Kiara got pregnant, all she was concerned about was being healthy and fit. So later that afternoon on December first, she knew she wanted to hit the gym at her job's aquatic complex. Kiara yearned to relax and vent. She invited her best friend, Adina Davis, to join her.

Adina and Kiara met in middle school and remained close in adulthood. But after Kiara married Rashad, the women's friendship suffered. Years ago, when Adina was going through a divorce, Rashad felt she'd be a bad influence. At first Kiara agreed; and they lost touch. But last summer, when she realized she missed and needed a good female friend, the two reconnected.

Kiara entered the women's locker room and

suddenly felt empowered. She may have lost her husband, and had conflict with his new lover, but at least still had her old friend.

Kiara got undressed and heard the sounds of lockers slamming and other females chitchatting.

Adina walked into the locker room and saw Kiara tucking her hair into a swim cap.

"How's it going?" Adina greeted her, and inserted a key into a locker. "We haven't had a chance to talk like normal, so thanks for giving me a day pass."

"No problem. We'll do girl talk in a minute. Put on your bikini and let's go." Kiara was wearing a maternity bathing suit. She wanted to swim a few laps and then laze around the pool.

They walked toward the entrance of the pool room; Adina addressed her friend.

"How are things going, girl? You ready to make that step?"

"You're talking about the divorce and all that paperwork I've been filling out?" Kiara asked. They entered the room, which had a moderate chemical smell.

"I'm talking about hooking up with your new man, Eddison."

"Girl, I will tell you what's going on with Eddy, but first let me fill you in on the latest with Nicole Greene." Adina stood in line to pick up their gym towels; Kiara alternately sipped on bottled water and told her friend what had happened that morning.

"Some chicks have no shame," Adina muttered once she heard the story. "She is treating a man like a possession. Threatening another woman over a damned man? She will learn one day."

"Ain't that the truth. I won't even try to warn her about what's going to happen if she keeps acting desperate over him. She'll find out for herself. And she may do it from a jail cell."

The women laughed. "Okay, now what's up with your new man?" Adina asked.

"Eddy and I still see each other a lot. We always make plans to hang out, but I don't want to rush into anything. He's great, but I need to tread this road very carefully. So, basically, that means that this nookie may have to get put on lock," Kiara explained. "At least that's what I decided as of last night. We'll see how that goes."

"*You're* giving up *sex*?" Adina stared at her bug-eyed.

"You know how some people's relationship status is 'complicated'? Well, mine is a very you-won't-believe-it-if-I-could-explain-it type of complicated."

The ladies strolled to the end of the room and lowered themselves into an Olympic-size pool that had low chlorine levels. The atmosphere felt lush and serene. They waded to the corner to talk.

"Here's the deal. Eddy and I are still together but, of course, I have my own house and he has his. Even though we want to be together, girl, this stuff gets tricky. It's like that movie, *Addicted*. So much lust and deep, dark secrets; except we can't all get out of character once the director says 'cut.' "

"Tell me about it. Real shit has real consequences." Adina splashed her hands into the soothing blue water.

"With my marriage breaking up and headed toward divorce, I need time to seriously self-reflect."

"That's where I still am years after my own divorce," Adina said in a wistful tone. "And I never could have predicted my outcome."

Kiara knew what Adina meant. And it scared her. She'd wanted a successful relationship. And it bummed her out that she and Rashad had failed at theirs.

"Adina, even though it's only been a short while, I know that Eddy and I care about each other. But girl, what if I get remarried and the next one doesn't work out, either? Then what would happen? I do not want to become the butt of jokes and be the woman that people whisper about and say, 'She's on her fourth marriage. She can't keep a man for nothing. What's she doing? Trying to compete with Liz Taylor and Jennifer Lopez?' "

"Fuck what other people say. The ones that talk shit the most don't even have a man. They can't even handle their own situation."

"I know, right," Kiara said wistfully. "But I don't care about other people's situations. All I know is I don't want to be collecting wedding gowns time after time. I want *love,* not necessarily marriage. But can anyone have love without marriage?"

"Happens all the time. The gays did it before marriage was legalized all over the U.S."

"Tell me about it. But what's really funny is that now that same-sex marriage is legal, their gay asses are splitting up, too. What's the world coming to?"

"The world is changing, Kiara. But one thing that will never change is a person's need for true love."

Kiara exhaled and enjoyed the feel of the lukewarm water on her skin. "Okay, enough of this depressing talk. Let's do some laps."

"*You* do the laps. I am scared of deep water; I'll stay in the shallow end."

"Fine with me, girl."

Kiara swam and treaded water. She was exhausted but her goal to be healthy was more important than how tired she felt.

Another thirty minutes passed before Kiara had gotten enough cardio and was ready to go.

The women showered and dressed, then ventured through the building and decided to relax and enjoy some protein smoothies before heading home.

"Adina, get whatever you want," Kiara told her. "It's on me. I feel like a horrible friend. All I do is moan and groan about my problems. And I can't stand one-sided friendships."

A gleam lit up in Adina's eyes. Kiara knew that meant she was grateful but not bothered by her self-centered behavior.

"Forgive me?"

"No need to apologize, Ki. I understand where you are in life right now. I could write a best-selling book about what Marlon and I went through." Adina and her ex had been teenage lovers. They experimented with sex in the back of a Chrysler LeBaron. Adina gave birth to a baby girl at a young age. In the beginning, Adina thought she and her first "serious" boyfriend would last forever. Marlon was charming, cocky, and loved to make her laugh. He doted on their daughter, Remy, and helped with child rearing. They got married when Remy was three. But deep passion combined with Marlon's qualities weren't enough to keep them together.

"What would the title of your book be?"

"*Raggedy-Ass Negroes and the Women That Walk Away.*"

"Hmm. Make sure I get an autographed copy."

Kiara paid for their drinks and the ladies went to sit at the smoothie bar. They enjoyed an open view of the rotunda, which was bustling with students coming and going.

"Adina, I'm not so sure about that book title." Kiara murmured while sipping her protein drink. "It sounds like it's coming from a bitter black woman. And you know we gotta be careful about falling into that stereotype. Everyone thinks we're constantly angry. White folks are scared of us because they think we have this so-called bad attitude. Black men are running from us because they say we are mean and opinionated and can't keep quiet about what we want and what we believe in. It's so unfair. Why are we penalized just because we want more out of life? Why can't our ambitions be seen as strengths instead of detriments?"

"I'm still trying to figure that one out, Kiara. Maybe that's why I don't have any real dating prospects. I'm actually coming to terms with the fact that I may never remarry. Not the way it's looking. And I do worry about what will happen when I get into my sixties and seventies. What if I fall down in the house and no one is there to help me?"

"Adina, even if you do have a husband when you hit your seventies, who's to say that his old ass won't be slipping and falling around the house, too?"

"That's a damned shame. We can slip and fall together. How about that?"

"Don't worry about a man right now, sweetie. 'Cause I can remember the days when you were crying to the Lord to take away the one that you already had."

Adina could only nod. Back then she wanted

Marlon Davis gone. But long after the divorce, sometimes she missed him.

"And as far as my own case is concerned," Kiara spoke up, "I don't want to seem like I can't be happy without a man. On the other hand, I don't want to be that fiercely independent woman who thinks she doesn't need anybody—the type that scares off brothers. That's not me, either. I'm somewhere in the middle. I want and I give love. I want to be in love, but I won't be a slave to love."

"I like the way you put that: the Kunta Kinte of love."

"Everyone needs love, silly woman."

"Me and you, boo. But never give up," Adina told her. "We should always have hope. It's okay to hope, isn't it?"

Kiara thought of Eddison and smiled. "That's the only way to live."

Adina glanced around at all the twenty-something college kids leaving or arriving at the recreation facility. They gave off a vibe of happiness, energy, and zest for life.

"These kids have their entire lives ahead of them," Adina remarked. "And it's good that their little asses are in school learning something that's going to help them instead of wasting time out here in these streets. But um, let me tell you this—dates are rare for me. And that's fine because I am very busy at the hair salon most days trying to get other women pretty for their man; ain't that ironic? But when I do date, and the man finds out I'm a divorced single mom, he assumes that my kid is my number one priority. And he'll think that I won't have any room in my life for him. But that's not always the case."

Adina watched several long-legged girls shriek and run while young men chased them. They seemed carefree, something that she wished she could be.

"Looking at these kids makes me feel that this is the perfect time to bring up Remy."

Remy Davis was Adina and Marlon's only child.

"What about her?"

Adina thoughtfully sipped on her straw. "Don't judge me but—I don't know where she is half the time. The girl is only sixteen. And the attendance officer contacted me and told me Remy has skipped quite a few of her classes. And then I will log into the school's parent portal and check to see what she's been eating for lunch. And it's not much, which lets me know she hasn't been there. She's missed so many classes, she could never be able to make up the work. Kiara, I have a feeling my baby wants to drop out."

"Oh, no. Are you positive?"

"When I've driven Remy to school, she would grab her little backpack and tell me good-bye. I'd watch her in my rearview mirror. And she sure didn't look like she was headed for the main building where classes are held. I'd sit in my car looking at Remy take her sweet time, talking on her cell phone and wandering around like she didn't belong at school."

"Did you ask her why she did that? She did it every day?"

"Almost every day. And when I'd see these missed calls on the cell phone from the school district office and I'd ask her about it, Remy would act like she didn't know what I was talking about. She claimed she didn't know why they were calling. I'd press her about her classes and she'd give those shitty one-word answers I can't stand. 'Fine.' Or 'All right.' "

"Maybe she's being a typical teen, Adina. They are not the most talkative unless they're texting or doing iChat."

"Typical, my ass. I'm not even her Facebook friend. Remy is being shady. Even when I take a break at my hair salon and try to FaceTime her, she rejects it."

"Like she doesn't want you to see what she's doing."

"Exactly, and her behavior is fucked up." Adina stared at her empty cup. "She may lie to me or deny it, but my daughter is doing something with her time and I guarantee you it's not studying and going to class."

"But knowing you, you have gone and talked to her instructors, right?"

"I have. And the next step is for a truant officer to come pick her up."

"I'm sorry to hear about that."

"Girl, you know this isn't how I've raised my kid." Adina felt angry and frustrated. "I always wanted better for her. And it's embarrassing to me that as a mom I haven't had more control of Remy's life. I'm thinking after my divorce, I may have given her too much freedom, you know?"

"It's not too late. Regain control. You can get her back on her school grind. Do it, Adina. And don't be too hard on yourself. Being a mom is trial and error. We all make mistakes, especially after we have our first child."

"My daughter may think she's grown, but in my eyes, Remy is a child. And, I'm ashamed to admit this, Kiara, but if I'm dating a guy and he wants to know more about my daughter, I have to tell him these weird-ass stories about how Remy stayed out all night . . . and how I got in my car and I drove around looking for her like she's some type of crackhead, but I come home without her. What if he thinks I'm a neglectful mother who can't keep up with a sixteen-year-old? And if he thought that, it would suck because it's definitely not true. Or," Adina continued, "I could pretend like I'm a really modern, unconventional, and hip mother who lets her daughter explore her inner self. I can act like I'm the single parent version of Will Smith and Jada Pinkett-Smith, with Remy my own Willow Smith."

"Yeah, I hear that Will and Jada let that young girl do whatever she feels she wants to do and if a lesson is learned from her experiences, good or bad, they think they've done their job. Tragic!"

"Must be nice, but maybe it's risky, too. Yet the Smiths have millions of dollars for therapists and all kinds of psychiatrists if Willow goes way left. But I'm just a hairdresser trying to make it. What do I have, Kiara? Huh? What do I have?"

Right then, Adina heard a chorus of fresh, youthful laughter. She squinted and watched as some kids poured through the revolving doors of the front entrance of the aquatic facility. Adina rose to her feet and walked a couple of steps away from their bar.

"Kiara, i-is that her?" she asked.

"Who?"

"Is that my daughter?"

"That's crazy. Why would Remy be up here?"

Adina dashed toward the exit. The kids, however, were young with fast legs. And they disappeared before she could catch up with them.

Adina returned to the smoothie bar and questioned what just happened. She could have sworn the girl she saw was Remy. The girl had the same body type, but her profile and hairstyle looked different than her daughter's. Adina picked up her cell phone and speed-dialed Remy's number. It rang a few times and went into voice mail. The rejection from her flesh and blood made her feel livid as she cursed and hung up. But she put on a happy face anyway.

"Oh, well. I'm not gonna worry. I-I'm sure my daughter will casually walk into my house talkin' 'bout 'Whassup my mama.' Her dramatic ass has done it many times before," Adina replied with nervous laughter as she stared at more kids who were laughing and yelling and then exiting the building.

"Girl, I know you're worried about Remy, but she has no reason to be way out here at this college campus."

"Yeah, you're right. She can't even finish high school."

"And maybe it's time you swallowed your pride and tried to co-parent with Marlon."

"You're right again. We'll handle it; enough of my depressing talk. I refuse to RSVP to my own pity party any longer. Let's go."

When Adina left the building, she couldn't stop thinking about Remy. Lately, whenever she tried to fall asleep, she wondered if she'd get a knock on her door from the police. Would they tell her that her daughter had been arrested or, even worse, was lying lifeless in the morgue?

Adina didn't want to think about it.

Chapter 8

Not Hitting It, Just Kicking It

That weekend Kiara took Eddison up on his offer to go and buy items for the new nursery. He offered to drive her to several stores and accompanied her inside so she could get his opinion.

"I think I go with a classic design and think about neutral colors for my color scheme," she told him.

"That would be the smart thing to do," he answered. She grabbed his arm and they began to march through the showroom.

"Selecting furniture is easy, but the heart is not so smart." She leaned against him.

"I see you're struggling with—"

"I know what you're thinking and no, I am not about to change my mind," Kiara said to assure him. "Rashad and I are kaput. But I consulted with my attorney yesterday. He let me know right up front that divorces are not granted to pregnant women unless the man has abandoned her and he can't be found."

"I figured that."

"We'll play the waiting game until my baby is born. I feel like I'm in limbo."

"You are. But one thing you can count on is me."

She nodded and released his arm. They placed an order for a convertible crib, nursery organizer, dresser, and changing table.

Kiara reached for her credit card; Eddison stopped her. "I got this."

"Nope, no. I won't let you do this, Eddy."

"Why not? It's not a problem."

"Because it's something that he should be doing."

Eddison paused. Hurt filled his eyes. "Are you trying to tell me something I don't know?"

"No," she gasped. "I still don't know." She looked at the salesclerk, who stared at her in puzzlement. "Um, put the expense on my card," she said.

Once they left the store and headed for another, Kiara resumed her explanation.

"What I was trying to say is that I think Rashad should offer to pay for these types of things."

"And I think you're being unreasonable."

"You think what?"

"You don't want the man, yet you're trying to get his money. You want to have your cake and eat it, too. Why is that?"

Kiara immediately shut down emotionally. She sat in silence while Eddison drove. She loved him dearly, but sometimes she wondered if he was right. Was she being unreasonable and stringing him along? Was it fair to place Eddison in the middle of her complicated life?

Finally, Eddison spoke up. "Look, who pays for what doesn't even matter. And I won't let something as trivial as that keep us from talking. Do I make myself clear?"

"Very clear," she murmured. "And it is silly to fight over this."

"That's why we aren't going to do that. Your job is to stay healthy and keep your mind focused and positive. I'm trying to make things easier for you and the little one. I see how much you go through, Kiara, and all I want to do is help."

"Sometimes I don't want your help."

"But why not?"

"Because I don't want to feel like I owe you anything."

There. She said it. It hurt her to say it, but those feelings had been on her mind for a couple of days.

"Do you want to continue seeing me, Kiara?"

"What? Of course, Eddy, don't do this."

"Good. I'm glad you realize you do want me in your life. We've just got to figure out in what ways and how deeply you want me."

"I want you deeply. I want you truly. But I refuse to lay all my burdens on you. It's not fair to you. That's why I *had* to pay for that furniture."

"Okay, I get it. You are fiercely independent. But I—"

"You what, Eddy? What?"

"I love taking care of you. Will you just let me do that? Just try it and see how you like it?"

Kiara closed her eyes. If she could step outside

of herself and see what she was doing, she'd call herself a big fool. She'd probably tell God himself "no thanks" if he extended a helping hand. She smiled to herself. Then she laughed. She opened her eyes. She nodded. She held Eddison's hand and squeezed it.

"Just try to do things my way, please," he urged her. "And if you feel uncomfortable in any way, let me know. I will back off. I may not like it, but I will respect your decision."

"All right, Fairy Godfather. You got yourself a deal."

It was the second week in December. Nicole had taken off the past three days as Kiara requested. Now she wanted to stay out of trouble and not be at odds with her boss. So she efficiently completed all her work assignments and kept to herself. But when it came to Alexis, resentment carved its way inside her heart. She couldn't stop thinking about Alexis and the hateful thing that she had done.

That Monday morning Nicole was returning to her office from an off-campus meeting. She passed by the large administrative assistant work-station module. Alexis had been busy typing, but she stopped and waved at Nicole and tried to catch her eye.

"Hello, Nicole. Tell me something. Is orange the new black?"

"I can't believe you said that. It's not funny."

"I know it's not. Jail is very serious. And doing stupid stuff to get yourself put in jail is even more serious."

"I told you I was sorry. And I don't know why you had to go and do something so drastic."

"Maybe it'll teach you a lesson, Nicole."

"Oh, and what's that?"

"I don't want your man."

"Is that what this is about?"

"Only because *you* make it that way; for God's sake, the guy couldn't even have a private conversation with me on the phone. Even though you think of me as just a baby mama, don't forget, it looks as if you're second in line for the position yourself."

Nicole appeared stunned. She made sure no one else could hear their conversation. "Wait a second. If you are implying that Rashad wouldn't want to marry me because I'm having his baby, you're wrong, Alexis. I have nothing to do with how you two handled your affairs, but my situation promises to be different."

"Be careful what you wish for. Just ask Kiara." And at that, Alexis resumed typing and ignored Nicole.

Nicole returned to her office feeling hurt and frustrated. She stayed to herself and did her work. But at the beginning of the lunch hour, Nicole bumped into Kiara in the hallway.

When she took one look at her boss, Nicole felt like a bull. And to her, Kiara was a matador whipping around a red cape. All she saw was red.

Kiara hesitated when she noticed Nicole. Then she quickly began traipsing down the hallway, past Alexis's desk, out the door, and in the direction of the employee parking lot.

Nicole followed her and yelled at her back.

"Hey, wait up," she said.

Annoyed, Kiara asked, "What can I do for you?"

"During the past few days when I wasn't at this place, I did a lot of thinking. I-I just wanted to apologize to you again."

"Really? No need for that. You did your time. That's punishment enough."

"Kiara, I'm trying to be a better woman."

"Do you mean better than I was . . . with Rashad?"

"Actually, I meant trying to be nicer."

"If you have to force yourself to be nice to people, maybe you should just give up. A person is either good-hearted or they aren't."

"But I can be good-hearted. For real."

Kiara wasn't convinced. Once a person stabbed her in the back, she always kept alert for the knife to slice her up again. And she could never forget how Nicole flaunted the affair she had with her husband last summer. It was as if she felt proud of herself. Kiara thought arrogant side chicks were a menace to society. And she'd never believe that there could be any redemption for someone like Nicole.

"I'm sorry, Nicole, but my gut tells me you aren't sincere. Now, if you will excuse me, I have somewhere to go." Kiara was ready to go to her car, but right then a strange man interrupted them. He wore a dark colored business suit and slowly approached them.

The man stared intently at Kiara then asked, "Are you Kiara Mariah Eason?"

"Yes, why?"

"Oh, great. I have a little something for you." He handed her a brown envelope. "Can you sign this stating you received this package?"

"Huh? What is it?" Kiara opened the envelope.

She removed the paper and quickly learned that her husband intended to divorce her. The processor thrust paper and pen at her. She mindlessly signed it.

The man quietly left.

Kiara was visibly shaken as she covered her mouth with trembling hands.

"What the fuck?"

"By the beat-down look on your face," Nicole said, "Rashad beat you to it, huh?"

Nicole already knew that Rashad was planning to serve Kiara with divorce papers. And she fought to keep a grin off of her face. Now the woman knew how it felt to be humiliated at work. And Nicole finally believed her mother's warning. What goes around comes around. Nicole did her time, but she resented being forced to miss three days of salary.

"He did it. I can't believe it but he did," Kiara said out loud. Never would she have imagined that the man who wronged her would initiate proceedings.

"It's no secret that he and I are breaking up. But the reality of it, and the fact that he filed on me first, no, I couldn't have predicted this. Not here at work and in front of my employees. He's been doing some really low-down things lately, even for him. I just don't understand how we got here. Why are we here?" Kiara suddenly realized Nicole was hungrily hanging on her every word.

"You were the first wife." Nicole shrugged. "And now you're going to be the ex-wife."

"Nicole, please—"

"The first shall be last, and the last"—she pointed at herself—"shall be first."

Kiara couldn't imagine Rashad wanting to marry this woman. Most guys were hurt after a break-up, and even though he filed on her, she was sure it would take him some time to heal from their relationship before he'd rush into a new one.

"You really are delusional, Nicole."

"Not delusional. I know how these things work. Just look at the signs. Sometimes the first marriage for a woman isn't the happiest. She went in not knowing what she was doing. She rushed him to the altar because she was way more concerned about the dress and the ceremony than she was about the man and his heart. And when things don't work out as she planned, instead of bowing out gracefully, she held on like a monkey clutching a tree trunk. She got embarrassed. And she's too fucking scared to fall. Why? Because everyone can see her. So she's gotta save face. But if you missed it, you missed it. So you failed? Move on. Things may hurt right now, but see it as a blessing. Why? 'Cause your second blessing may be right around the corner. Literally." She laughed and threw back her head.

Kiara was stupefied. And offended. How dare a jump-off tell her how to respond to the shitstorm that she helped to cause?

"I don't even know where to begin with you, Nicole. But for starters, you sound like men are just temporary pawns in women's lives. Like people are supposed to get married and if they fuck up they should just give up and quickly move on to the next man. That's insane."

"I don't mean to sound like that, like a man is a pawn, but when you remove the emotional part of it, and stick to the facts, that's just how things turn out sometimes."

"Well, I don't plan to be a serial married person," Kiara informed her. "I take my vows seriously."

"You call me delusional? You're the one that's delusional. How can you say you're serious about your vows when you wasted no time hooking up with light skin, making him your work husband, and you're still having his baby, from the look of things."

"You definitely wouldn't know my business on that level. That's for sure."

"It is my business, because from what I understand, it's only because you assumed that Rashad and me was getting it in that you even got involved with Mr. Osborne. When the truth was, we hadn't even smashed just yet."

"What did you say?" Kiara asked.

"Yeah, you falsely imagined that your man was hitting it, when we were just kicking it. The fucking part didn't come till much later. So your whorish ass, Mrs. Eason, committed adultery *first* on Rashad."

Kiara lurched forward, her hands stretched out for Nicole's round neck. But just before she could make contact, Kiara pulled back.

Dozens of students and some faculty members were walking in the area. How could she let this young lady drive her to nearly snapping? She wasn't a violent criminal—at least not when it came to the other woman.

But Nicole's declaration did stun her. Could she be telling the truth? Her husband was faithful to her when she assumed he wasn't? Even if it were true, it still didn't compensate for the fact that Rashad had obviously been involved with Alexis and that he hid their daughter, Hayley, from her.

"I don't want to hurt you, Nicole. But why do you keep trying to hurt me?"

"I ain't trying to hurt you. I'm trying to help you. You are still young. You're still hot. It ain't like no other man won't want you even though you will end up a single mom with two kids. But you better hurry up while you can, because once you turn forty, your stock will drop like a brick thrown out of a high-rise window. Most men ain't checking for women over forty."

"You sound ridiculous," Kiara said, but she thought about her friend Adina, who was pushing forty.

"I may look ratchet," Nicole replied, "but I do my research. And I will not be on the wrong side of a statistic."

"Why are we out here talking about statistics—?"

"All I know is that half of all black women will never get married; these stats are very high in comparison to white women and Hispanics. And more than forty-eight percent of black men won't get married. And of those that do, some of 'em are choosing to marry women of other races," Nicole said in an emotional voice. She didn't want to make it sound as if she was desperate and afraid, but occasionally, that's how she felt. Although she put on a brave front before Kiara, in truth she knew how it felt to be wounded emotionally and feel insecure. She never wanted to display weakness, especially not in front of her boss. But at that moment it all began to hit her.

When she realized how much courage it had

taken for her to move more than six hundred fifty miles across country to live and work in a place in which she did not know one soul, her knees nearly gave in. She had relocated with hardly any money, without the support of her family, and was forced to move into a shoddy-ass rental house because she lacked the money to move into a more upscale apartment complex. She was so afraid the first night that she moved into the little house. At the time it had no curtains. So she taped newspaper over all the windows and prayed to God that no one tried to break into the home that night. She was scared but was happy to have a new job. And she was determined to work and stick it out. Not run back home to Alabama like a failure.

Nicole continued with tears in her eyes, "Do you know how that makes me feel to know that I could never get married because of what some dumb statistics claim?"

"I really don't care—"

"I'll tell you how it makes me feel. I don't know why I'm telling you this but . . . I used to have a man that wasn't a hundred percent black. He was fucking Italian mixed with black, if you can imagine that. I never intended to be with a man whose ancestors didn't come from the motherland. Yet he and I were tight like Romeo and Juliet. We fought the odds to be together because his family wasn't feeling this dark-skinned chick from the South. He loved me to death and I felt the same. I just *knew* us two rebels would get married. We were on our way, but . . . shit happens. Bad became worse. I felt lost. And then he was gone. And that's that."

For the first time ever, Kiara viewed Nicole

through different eyes. She always wondered why the woman chose to be the way that she was. When she first met Nicole, she knew she seemed quiet and a little reserved. But later she thought of her as ridiculously angry. And now Kiara knew Nicole was merely a hurt and scared little girl. Kiara didn't want Rashad anymore, so Nicole could have him. But she also wasn't willing to keep fighting with the woman over a man that wasn't worth it.

"Nicole, I'm sorry to hear about your failed relationship."

"Sure you are," Nicole sniffed.

"I'm being sincere. Being hurt doesn't feel good."

"No, it doesn't."

"I want to hear more about this guy. Why didn't it work out?"

"Oh, God. Why am I telling you these things?" Nicole paused, unable to believe that she was letting her vulnerabilities be exposed. "Let's just say that there were things about him that I couldn't deal with. At the end of the day, in my heart I knew I couldn't be with this man forever. It was too risky. Too unstable. Too painful."

"I can understand that."

"And once I realized that fact, it made me think more clearly about what I need. And what is better for me. I hate the stats, but if the stats don't lie, then they help me to stay focused."

"But you're just so . . ." Kiara shivered. "It's like you're mechanical, factual and, excuse me for saying this, like your heart isn't honestly involved."

"What? Are you serious?" Nicole felt defensive again. She never liked getting too close to a female because she knew they could turn on her with no warning. It happened to her when she was a high school senior. Her closest girlfriend, Darla Sims, the one whom she trusted with her life, blindsided her when Nicole found out she was actually secretly keeping company with a boy that Nicole liked. Nicole happened to walk up on Darla and Ronnie; their arms were entwined around each other while standing in line at a movie theater. A Friday night on which Ronnie claimed he was sick. And the best friend she wanted to hang out with had told her that she had to babysit her nieces and nephews. And on the spur of the moment, Nicole went to see a movie that she'd begged Ronnie to take her to. Nicole purchased her own ticket, walked into the lobby, and spotted her girl and her boy hanging all on each other in public while waiting to buy concession-stand food. Nicole drug Darla by the hair into the women's restroom. When she emerged ten minutes later, the scratches on her face proved that a once promising friendship had now ended. After that experience, Nicole's heart grew icily cold toward any female.

"Put it this way, Kiara, I hate that we got off to a wrong start and the way things have played out between us since then. I don't like beefing with females, but it happens. You may not like me or understand how I roll, but at least I'm one of the few women in your life that can give you some good unsolicited advice. I'm sorry that Rashad did what he did to you. I really am."

And Nicole excused herself and went on her lunch break, feeling happy that she had let out her frustrations on someone that day.

But deep in her heart, she still felt frustrated.

* * *

Carmen Foster kept her word and she invited Alexis to hang out with her. It was mid-December, not exactly crawfish season, but they still decided to check out Crawfish Heaven off of South Highway 6. Carmen actually went out of her way to pick up Alexis and talked her ear off as they traveled to get some lunch that Saturday morning.

They were shown to their table and Carmen took control. "You like raw oysters?"

"Love them."

"Good. Forrest hates them, so now I have someone to go with me when I'm in the mood for them. He says they are too damned cold and slimy. I tell him they're no slimier than those sardines you like to mess with. He can't say a thing after that."

Alexis laughed. "You don't seem like you're Varnell's sister."

"Oh, that's because he is so quiet and I'm so loud. I've been told I talk so loud that if I sat at the back of the church, the preacher could still hear me. We're talking Lakewood Church with their seventeen-thousand-seat sanctuary."

Their two dozen oysters soon arrived.

"Now tell me something. What made you get into the side chick business?"

"It isn't something that you wake up one day and decide 'I think I'll go find someone's husband to fuck around with.' No, it happened entirely different than that. I had no idea that my guy had a wife."

"Hmm. But when you did find out, did you dump his ass?"

"It took a while."

"How long?

"Years." Alexis knew she couldn't BS Carmen and there was no sense in trying.

"I will hold off on what I really want to say."

"Thanks." Alexis laughed. She enjoyed her oysters with horseradish sauce and washed them down with a light beer.

"Well, ain't none of my business, but I do hope you've given up that occupation. My brother deserves a good woman. He's looking, I know that much. And he is getting older, is unmarried, and that makes women suspect. 'What's wrong with you?' they ask him. 'No kids. Never been married. You gay?' "

"Well, I can't blame the women for wondering. But no, Varnell is a good man. He's very different than what I'm used to."

"You're used to being spoiled, right?"

"Yes."

"He's not poor but he's not rich. Can you deal with that?"

Alexis had to think. "I guess that'll be okay."

"What do you mean, you guess? Don't tell me you're one of those Kardashian types."

"I don't know what you mean by that."

"You should know exactly what I mean. Hell, you're as pretty as any of them."

"Thank you."

"But for some women being pretty isn't enough."

"Look, I'm not a gold digger."

"Good."

"But I do want security. I have a child."

"You get child support?"

"I will. I plan to file for back child support."

"How old is it?"

"It's a she. Hayley is twenty-four months."

"Oh, hell no. That baby is two years old and you've never filed? And I don't want to hear that 'it's complicated' excuse. It's not that complicated. You have a baby by a man. You file for child support."

"He's married."

"So what? File for support."

Alexis said that she would, and the two ladies enjoyed the rest of the morning talking, drinking beer, and trying other seafood items, all at Carmen's expense, and to Alexis's delight.

Chapter 9

Meet the Parents

It was almost Christmas; Nicole was headed home after running errands all day. It was a windy and hot afternoon, one that hadn't seen rain in several days. Nicole was driving in her car whose AC had recently stopped working. Her windows were ajar; she had just made a turn onto the street where she lived. Her neighborhood was an area that was home to a large population of multiple ethnicities: blacks, Hispanics, and Asians. Various street vendors lined the road with food trucks that sold tacos and other Tex-Mex cuisine.

Nicole was lost in her thoughts when she got interrupted by piercing screams.

"Somebody help. Oh, no. Look!"

Nicole pulled over to the right side of her street and parked. She clearly heard a woman's voice cry out, "Oh, Jesus. This is horrible."

Right across the street a scene was unfolding. The entire roof of a three-story apartment building was on fire. Huge flames poured out of some windows; other windows were getting melted. Nicole removed the keys from her ignition and stepped onto the street. The fire made crackling noises. Black and gray smoke steadily rose. It was a terrible inferno. Nicole's eyes began to itch. Two fire trucks had already arrived and sirens screamed in the background.

A crowd gathered. One thin Hispanic man stood on a balcony. Flames shot at him like the tongue of a rattlesnake. The man glanced at the street below; a few cars were located underneath his window. If he tried to jump, he could be severely injured.

"Hurry, move," someone yelled. People jumped out of the way so that the fire trucks could pass.

"Oh, my God," Nicole uttered. She began praying under her breath.

Water was being pumped by the firemen, but it was like aiming a water gun at a California wildfire.

The trapped man stood on the ledge while the flames inched closer; he abruptly made the sign of the cross then leaped off the metal railing that was completely engulfed. The crowd yelled and held its breath. He landed on top of an SUV and crumpled instantly. Emergency personnel rushed to his side.

Nicole couldn't bear the sight of blood. The man's body was twisted and mangled. He wailed and moaned as the paramedics attended to him. Nicole couldn't take it anymore. She turned away and her eyes rested on some children.

"Look at these kids," Nicole said. She wandered over to a group of approximately four youngsters ranging from two years old to eleven. They were standing next to a fireman. Their straight black hair was singed. Soot and ashes covered their tanned cheeks. The younger kids, a boy and a girl, only wore undershirts and diapers. The second oldest boy was fully dressed. The oldest had on gym shorts. All were barefoot.

One of the kids could be heard speaking Spanish, so Nicole assumed that English wasn't their first language.

She greeted the fireman and then decided to address the group using the few Spanish words she remembered from college. *"Donde está su madre?"*

They all shrugged. One little girl began to weep silently.

Nicole watched as two paramedics carried a woman on a stretcher. She was unconscious.

"Mama," the little boy screeched at the woman, but his mother didn't respond.

"Excuse me, sir. Is that their—?"

The fireman nodded and explained, "she ran back into the house to save the kids, but—"

The little boy shrieked again and tried to run toward the body.

Nicole quickly shielded the little boy's vision so he couldn't see his mom.

EMS brought out more bodies, which were covered by blankets and transferred into body bags.

The smell of iron was strong, the fume of death undeniable.

Someone else screamed. A woman fainted.

Grief had arrived and word soon spread.

"Mi madre. Mi madre."

Nicole felt weak in the knees as she saw fear cloud the little ones' eyes.

"The kids look thirsty," she told the fireman. "May I please give them something to drink? My car is right over there."

He responded, "No problem."

Nicole gathered all the kids in a circle. "Come with me. We aren't going far."

Nicole made them cross the street with her. She opened the trunk of her car and removed a cooler filled with pouches of flavored drinks that she routinely kept in the car in case she got thirsty. The kids eagerly sipped on Capri Suns while they waited. Nicole reached in her purse and grabbed all the cash in her wallet. Ninety dollars in all; it was the money she had intended to use to buy Rashad's mother a Christmas gift. She stuffed the crumpled bills into the oldest boy's hand.

"*Aquí.* Take it."

He held a blank look in his eyes but he accepted the money. "*Muchas gracías.*"

"*De nada,*" Nicole told him. "It's nothing."

His little brother abruptly fell down on the street and lay prostate on his back; he covered his face with his hands and wept.

It was a struggle, but Nicole sat down beside him and caressed his sweaty shirt. "It's okay, honey. I know you love your mommy." Her voice broke. She thought of her own unborn baby and loved her child even more.

Soon a Houston NBC news truck pulled up. A reporter and a camera man started interviewing witnesses. The female reporter noticed Nicole choking back tears as she comforted the children.

"Hello, I'm with the media. May I ask what happened?" the reporter said to Nicole.

"It was crazy. The flames were awful. A man almost got killed trying to jump. And these kids. They—" She bit her bottom lip, unable to continue.

The reporter saw all of the children quietly sipping their flavored drinks. She noticed the money in the older boy's hand.

"Did you help these kids?"

Nicole reluctantly nodded. The youngest, a two-year-old girl, waddled over to Nicole and stretched out her tiny hands. Nicole struggled to lift the child. She placed her on her hip while the reporter observed.

"It's obvious you care. Are you their babysitter?" the reporter continued.

"No, I'm not."

"Why did you help these children? Do you know them?"

"I dunno. I-I'm about to become a mother myself," Nicole said, and let out a sob. One of the kids came and hugged Nicole around the waist. The weight of the two kids hanging onto her made Nicole tired, but she pulled herself together as the camera man pointed his lens in her face.

"I couldn't imagine anything bad happening to my baby; my child. And I just put myself in their shoes. This tragedy will affect them for the rest of their lives. They don't deserve it."

"Will their mother be all right?" the reporter softly asked.

"I honestly don't know." Nicole kissed the little girl's smudged cheek. It felt brittle and tasted salty, but Nicole didn't care.

She was dazed as she answered question after question. The reporter noted how Nicole would alternatively speak to the kids in Spanish, other times in English. Someone came over and volunteered info about how Nicole shielded and protected the kids.

Before it was over with, the story of the inferno got carried on all the major networks, including CNN. Four people died from the tragedy. The reporter who questioned Nicole heard that that the kids' mother took her last breath while en route to Memorial Hermann hospital. Eight firemen suffered from heat exhaustion, many tenants lost everything, and a few survived with just the clothes on their backs.

ABC-13 came along. They got Nicole's name from an iReporter. They conducted a brief interview. They informed Nicole that they received official word that the children's mother had died. Nicole was visibly shaken. She told the reporter, "I relocated here from Birmingham, Alabama. And you never could have told me I'd be a witness to such a tragedy."

Soon other journalists lined up nearby; they set up cameras and waited to aim their microphones at Nicole's mouth.

After the taped segments were done, Nicole smiled gratefully when people within the community began to bring food, fresh drinking water, and clothing. They placed everything on top of a makeshift table hastily set up on the street.

"Thank you, God," she whispered as she watched the kids' stunned faces.

Nicole remained on the scene as fire personnel cordoned off the area and started their investigation. She received countless pats on the back. And some requested her name and phone number.

She gave the kids' hugs when one of their relatives arrived to take them with him. They exchanged information and she promised to keep in touch.

As soon as the kids left, an elderly woman approached Nicole.

"You're pregnant, right?"

"Yes ma'am," she said.

"You're going to be a wonderful mommy."

"I sure hope so."

Four hours later Nicole made it home.

"Oh, my God, that was so unbelievable." Tired as she'd ever been, Nicole plunked herself down on the couch and sighed. In that moment, she understood that life was precious and unpredictable, and she had to make each day count.

Every single part of Nicole's body ached. She just wanted to lie down and go to sleep.

"Where the hell have you been?" Rashad asked as he entered the living room. "Why didn't you answer my calls?"

"My phone went dead," she responded in a raspy voice. "I was at that fire down the street. It is too much to even go into. Just horrible and crazy. And trust me when I say I'm glad to be home, bae. I'm so glad to be alive."

Rashad told her he was happy she was home, too. He prepared her a quick and simple dinner of hamburger patties and mac and cheese out of the box. Then he made sure that she got adequate rest that night.

Early the next morning, Rashad vigorously patted Nicole's shoulder while she was still asleep in bed.

"Get up, Nicky. Wake up."

"Wake up? Why? I'm asleep," she yawned.

"Get your ass up, now."

"Is it an emergency?"

"Maybe. Look."

She opened her tired eyes. Rashad turned up the volume on the television.

"You're famous, Ma."

There was footage of Nicole being interviewed by a news reporter. Her name was in big yellow letters on the TV screen. When Rashad turned to a different channel, he saw Nicole again, speaking about the fire and the kids.

Her phone started chirping. Texts poured in.

She answered her phone. "Yeah, I just saw it," she told Shyla. Nicole had to sit up in bed and groggily repeat the whole story to her girlfriend. The second she hung up, her phone rang once more. This time it was a reporter from Montgomery, Alabama. She agreed to a live phone interview. By the time a couple of hours had passed, Nicole had spoken with journalists from Atlanta, Las Vegas, Toronto, DC, and every other place in between. She gave impromptu interviews that lasted several minutes. And some of the reporters scheduled telephone interviews that would take place all throughout the week.

"I can't believe this," she said as she hung up from the last call. "Someone must be playing a joke on me. I guess my communications degree from UAB came in handy." She laughed.

"I didn't know my baby was as famous as a reality TV star."

"You mean that?" she said, feeling excited. "I'm your baby?"

"You're my *baby*, baby." Rashad picked up Nicole and spun her around. He immediately started huffing and puffing.

"You've been eating like a pig and now you are as heavy as one."

"You know you're wrong. Put me down, crazy man."

He instantly set her down. Then he kissed her to let her know all was well. She loved that. She loved when he showed her how he felt about her. And she enjoyed when he did what she asked him to do; she wanted it to happen again and again.

The next morning, Nicole woke up in a panic.

Rashad immediately sensed her mood. "What's wrong?"

"It's Christmas Eve and we're meeting your mother tonight. I-I spent the money that I was going to use to buy her a last-minute gift."

"Oh, all right," Rashad said. He and his mother, Beeva Reese, didn't see each other as often as they should, but during this holiday season he wanted to make an effort and do right by her.

He pulled out his wallet and peeled off two twenties.

"Here, go find her something."

"Forty dollars? Are you serious?"

"I'm running low on cash. I've had to give Lily another two grand. I paid my people some generous Christmas bonuses. And I owed back taxes. My funds took a big hit."

"Oh, please, that's crazy, Rashad. You have so many projects going that you can barely keep up."

"True, but the money is still funny. And I'm not joking."

Nicole wondered if she should believe him or not.

"Does that mean I shouldn't expect a nice gift from Santa?"

"It means that Santa's attorney told him do not buy any girlfriends expensive presents right now. Kiara's attorneys are going to be all over my bank statements and cash withdrawals. And if I am caught buying diamonds and gold, it could be categorized as community property. Kiara doesn't play that. That's hardball, so you gotta wait till I'm single again before I can splurge on you. I can buy the baby nice shit, but not you."

The words "splurge on you" rang loudly in Nicole's ears. She heard future, she heard desire, and she wanted to be patient and hold on until her married boyfriend officially became her man.

"Hmm, that sucks," she replied, "but I hear you. Let's forget about me for right now. Somehow I will manage. But I'm mostly thinking about your mama, and with this little bit of money you gave me I'll have to do the best I can. What type of things does she like?"

It had been a while since Rashad bought his mother a decent gift. And that was because every time he did do it, she rarely said thanks so he said forget it. And the only reason he agreed to buy her something now was because Nicole insisted on it.

"Damn, I dunno. But one thing she likes is fruitcake."

"Ugh, fruitcake? Are you sure?"

"What do you mean am I sure? I know what my mama likes."

Nicole ended up buying a couple of two-pound fruitcakes from Three Brothers Bakery; she thought that if they were really the woman's favorites, she would score major points.

Rashad called Beeva Reese to get the address of where she had moved six months ago. He and

Nicole went on an hour-long drive to Bryan, Texas, late that afternoon. When Rashad rang the doorbell of the attractive brick house located on a hilly street, a man whom he'd never seen before answered the door. He had salt-and-pepper hair and was small in stature and build.

"Hi," he said. "Welcome." Then a woman appeared from behind him. She had short reddish blond hair, round, fat cheeks, and wide hips. She was a couple of inches taller than her man.

"Well, hello there," she said in a booming voice.

"Hi, Mrs. Eason," Nicole replied in a respectful soft tone. "I am Nic—"

"I can tell your husband doesn't tell you much. You know everyone always calls me Beeva Reese, but I'm about to become Beeva Murphy. And this is Winston Murphy." Her man greeted them and disappeared inside the house.

"Merry Christmas, ma'am. Here's your gift. I-I hope you like it." Nicole proudly displayed the fruitcakes.

Beeva barely suppressed her frown. "Umph. You shouldn't have."

"Oh, it wasn't nothing."

"I wasn't being modest. You really shouldn't have. I'm allergic to these nasty-ass stinky things, but it doesn't matter. We can feed them to our dogs."

Beeva grabbed the packages from Nicole and went into the house.

Nicole felt like punching Rashad. How could she make a good impression with his mom if he didn't even know a few of her favorite things?

Nicole followed the woman into the house; she

went to the left, which took her through a simple but elegantly decorated dining room. Nicole admired family photos on the wall then continued on. She found Rashad's mother in the kitchen screaming.

"What's taking you so damned long?" Beeva yelled at her microwave oven.

The sounds of kernels popping filled the air.

Rashad shrugged. "Popcorn," he said. "Beeva loves the hell out of some Orville Redenbacher. I just should have bought her eight packs of microwave popcorn and called it a day."

"Are you joking?" Nicole argued. "That is no type of gift for the woman that gave birth to you."

"The way we get along, sometimes I wonder if she's my birth mom."

"Rashad, I'm standing right next to you so don't think I didn't hear that," Beeva grumbled. "You know damn well I'm your mama. You look just like me."

"No, I don't."

The second the microwave timer sounded, Beeva pushed the button to open the door. She sprinkled a little salt right inside the bag, grabbed a handful, and was about to toss some popcorn in her mouth. She paused.

"Oh, I'm so rude. Want some?"

When no one answered, Beeva shrugged and shuffled across the hardwood floor to the family room; it had a high slanted ceiling and a stone fireplace. Rashad and Nicole followed behind her. There was a large picture window in the rear of the two-story house. The view allowed them to see the huge backyard, which was full of lemon trees.

Rashad noticed two white barking Yorkies playing with each other. Nicole took a seat on a recliner and listened in.

"What's been happening, Beeva?"

"Can't kill nothing and won't nothing die," she declared. She grabbed a few more pieces of popcorn and shook them around in her hand like dice.

"I haven't heard you say that in a long time. Must be them Georgia roots coming out of you."

"Ain't nothing shaking but the beans in the pot, and they wouldn't be shaking if the water wasn't hot."

"I know that's right," Rashad answered with a hearty laugh. There was nobody quite like his mama. It felt good to be home. And family was everything, even if the family wasn't as close as it should have been.

"Anyway, it's sure good to see you, Beeva. This is a real nice place you got," Rashad told her. "You got yourself a nice husband, too. Seems like you hit it big. Again!"

"What he's trying to say is that I've upgraded," Beeva volunteered while nibbling on her snack. "Yes, I'm on my fourth husband. So what? Who's counting? Don't answer that! Anyway, we decided to combine households to save on bills; we living together like sinners, but we'll be married real soon. Did my son tell you, Kiara?"

"How the hell can I tell her what I didn't even know?" Rashad protested, so annoyed with the question that he couldn't think clearly.

Suddenly Beeva squinted and cocked her head. "Wait one minute. This ain't—" She frowned. "This ain't your *wife.*"

"Not yet," Nicole said under her breath.

"No, Beeva, *Nicole* is not my wife. *Kiara* and I are separated. We headed to divorce court."

"What?"

"Yeah, Beeva."

"I know we only see each other about once or twice a year, but that's no excuse not to tell me news like this, son." She turned to Nicole. "I'm sorry for thinking you were the other woman—"

"Beeva!" Rashad said. "Wow, awkward. She's tripping," he said, referring to his mother. "You and I know you look nothing like Kiara," he said to Nicole.

"Mmm mmm, my son." Beeva gave a spirited laugh. "It's been so long I barely remember what Kiara looks like. But what I do remember is that little woman of yours could cook her ass off. Remember that one Christmas a few years ago when y'all had me over? Ooo wee. I ate the shit out of those greens."

Rashad winced. "Glad you enjoyed her cooking."

"So who is this new lady?" Beeva looked Nicole up and down. "Is she any good in the kitchen? Or is she like most twenty-year-old women these days that eat fast food every day and can't fry eggs?"

Nicole, who quietly observed the happenings between Rashad and his mother, stood up.

"Ma'am, my name is Nicole Greene. I'm a southern woman and I can cook pretty well if I say so myself. Your son likes to eat whatever I make for him. And he and I are . . . together."

Beeva finally noticed Nicole's bulge. "I can see that. Shit!" She eyed Rashad. "Is that why Kiara filed on you?"

"Why would you assume she filed on me, Beeva?"

"Excuse me, may I ask you something?" Nicole butted in. "Why do you call your mama by her first name? Why can't you just call her 'mama'?"

"She's sitting right in front of you," Rashad replied. "Why don't you ask her yourself?" Before Nicole could do just that, Rashad kept talking. "You probably can tell that I come from a slightly dysfunctional family."

"Oh, hell, not that shit again," Beeva roared. "Your family was like most other black American families. We niggas through and through. Niggas with money, but still niggas."

"I guess if you gonna be one, at least have some money," Nicole said, amused.

"That 'dysfunctional' shit is a fancy-sounding made-up word that some psychiatrist invented just to take people's money. Everybody and they mama running around thinking something's wrong with themselves, and before they commit suicide, they go and jump on some strange old man's couch. They open up, put their business on the street in an attempt to feel better about themselves, just because of that fucked-up word that is supposed to describe their family. And that doctor gone end up writing a book about all his clients' cases and make even more money off these fools. Ha! Now *that* is dysfunctional."

"Beeva, you may have your little theories about families and what not, but Nicky needs to know that about me. Our family situation wasn't *The Cosby Show*," Rashad said. "Life was kind of rough for me in spite of the money."

It was rare for Rashad to want to admit weakness and vulnerability, but he felt if he was going to be with her, he might as well let her see the good and the bad of his kinfolk. He continued, "She's already finding out shit left and right. And Kiara, man, I think I really turned her into a whole other woman—" He stopped talking.

Nicole came over to him and held his arm. "Go ahead, babe, get out your feelings."

"I'm cool. I'll be all right." He walked over to the refrigerator and opened it. "What y'all got good to drink in here?" He grabbed a tiny bottle of beer. "Is this all? Where's the hard liquor? I know you hiding it somewhere in this house. It's almost New Year, too?"

Beeva released a spirited laugh. "That's my son for sure. I-I have missed you, Rashad. And you know you're free to call me besides on my birthday and Mother's Day. Sometimes I think you hate me or something, the way you avoid me."

"Beeva, I do not hate you. I just . . . I dunno. I-I. Been real busy."

Nicole watched mother and son. His excuse for not seeing his mom sounded so lame. She knew his mother fussed because she needed him.

Rashad awkwardly patted his mother's red hair.

Nicole felt like crying. The man whom she loved and cared about was incredibly human. She was seeing another side of him, a vulnerable side that she didn't know existed.

Nicole puckered her lips and gave Rashad a kiss as he came and sat beside her. "It's gonna be all right, babe. Take your time. You can say whatever you need to say when the time is right."

Beeva burst out laughing. "Oh, shit, y'all enjoying the honeymoon *before* the honeymoon. Let me tell you something, sweetie. You look very young. This your first baby?"

Nicole nodded.

"All that supportive shit only lasts so long—"

"Beeva," Rashad pleaded.

"No, she needs to face reality. Now, my son is a man. A hardworking man but still a man. And although I hate to hear that he and his wife busted up, I ain't surprised. Rashad takes after his daddy. His papa was a rolling stone. Now, to my knowledge he didn't have any stray kids running around, but he sure was acting like he was trying his best to make some, if you know what I mean."

Beeva closely peered at Rashad to see if he was hiding any of his father's secrets. "I wasn't stupid. I knew that he'd step out on me here and there. I didn't like it. I wanted to fuck him up quite a few times while he was in bed next to me in a deep sleep. But I chose to keep my hands to myself. And we stayed married till the bitter end. Marriage is good but it ain't easy. Not assuming that y'all two gonna get hitched. 'Cause babies ain't a good reason to get tied down."

Rashad coughed and stared at Nicole. "We haven't really talked about that yet. I'm not sure what's going to happen. First things first."

"How Kiara feel about you having a second baby on her?"

"What do you think, Beeva?"

"I think you're more like your father than you ever realized. Hell, for all I know, he has a stray running around somewhere."

"He does not, Beeva."

"All right then, but one never knows now, do they?"

Beeva never minced words. It was one of the things that made Rashad nervous around his mother. On one hand, he remembered how much his father's actions had hurt her when he was alive, but once he died, it was as though she transformed into a different woman.

After his daddy died, it seemed his mother started collecting husbands like welfare checks. It made him feel sad and sorry for her. Yet he understood how everyone needed to be loved. He knew he needed to be better at expressing love to her. How could he give affection to another woman if he had trouble loving his own mother?

"Well, Beeva, I need to apologize for taking so long to come see you and I must congratulate you on the new future husband and all that jazz." He hugged his mom. Her skin was soft and warm and she smelled of mint. She scowled like she didn't want to be bothered, but he knew Beeva. She thrived on his attention. She craved his love. Rashad vowed to try to do better. God knows he dreaded having every woman in his life angry at him for not meeting their simple expectations.

The ice had been broken and Rashad felt more at ease.

"This is starting off to be a good holiday. Let's make a toast," Rashad said. He went and found Winston, a quiet, humble man who enjoyed hiding in his room watching television. After Rashad coaxed him to come out, Beeva stood up and started singing a Motown song while she snapped her fingers.

Her smile looked sincere, and Rashad actually felt good that he managed to come and see her instead of changing his mind.

Beeva got some glasses and broke out the champagne that she'd been saving for months.

Rashad took the liberty of pouring everyone's drink and they raised their glasses.

"To my mother, the only mother I know. The one I love and the one who I know loves me, too, even though she may not get a Mother of the Year award."

"That's the worst toast I've ever heard, and I've heard a lot," Beeva said.

"I'm just playing. I know you love me in your own way."

"Who can define love and say how love is supposed to act?" Beeva asked. "If I fed you, kept you clean, bought you what you needed, and taught you right from wrong, I loved you, son. I still do."

"And I love you too, Ma—I love you, too, Beeva."

She clicked glasses with Rashad and took a sip. A warm feeling that she hadn't felt in ages flowed through her. Beeva coughed a few times, pretending like she had a cold. And if there'd been a box of tissues nearby, she would've discreetly wiped her eyes. She thought of Rashad every day and wondered how he was doing. She prayed for him and knew if he needed anything he'd call. But he rarely did. She figured either he was living his life or life was giving him hell. Whatever the case, it hardly mattered. Her prodigal son had found his way home and she couldn't be happier.

The fact that he was an only child made her feel bad. Beeva always wanted to give him a sibling, but it just never happened. She felt guilty that he had no brother or sisters to play with and worried he'd grow up feeling lonely and isolated. Beeva Reese worried about Rashad more than he ever realized.

Rashad Quintell Eason was a part of Generation X. He was born in the late seventies. He was five years old when he first saw the *Thriller* video; he was scared to death of it at first, but he felt better after Beeva tried to teach him the dance moves of Michael Jackson. Ever since he was seven he had a keen interest in both math and mechanics. He liked to tear apart his father's radio. He wanted to know how the voices got in the radio and he wanted to see if little people were inside of it singing and making harmony. He could have become a computer whiz, but his father insisted that he use his hands more than his brain.

"You will always have a job if you know how to use your hands, son," his dad told the little boy. "The computer industry sounds good now, but I don't trust those things. They're probably designed to destroy the world." Little Rashad listened to his father. He played football in middle school and he even wanted to try out for the team when he was a high school freshman. But his father told him they could enjoy the sport by being a spectator, not a participator.

"You need to protect your hands and your body, son. They will make you money if you take care of them. Sports are too risky. The women, the potential injuries, aren't worth it."

So his father told Rashad everything he knew about the construction and renovation business. As he grew older, he became a quick learner, accompanying his dad all around the city to various jobs. They entered musty, smelly houses that looked like they were ready to be demolished and turned them into livable places where families could move in and start new lives.

As the years went on, Rashad knew he would follow in his father's footsteps. By the time he graduated high school, he knew more about his father than he ever wanted to know. He saw the other women, the ladies his daddy flirted with at the job, the woman he often visited during lunch breaks. As a teen, Rashad would sit in the van with the AC running after his father pulled up in the driveway of his "lady friend." Rashad would wait and occupy himself playing with his handheld video game. Thirty minutes later, his dad would return to the van, clothes disheveled, unable to look Rashad in the eye.

By the time his father passed away (his mother claimed that one of his girlfriends poisoned him when he told her he couldn't take her on a day trip for her thirtieth birthday), Rashad was ready to assume the role he'd been prepared for concerning Eason & Son.

He knew he was now "Eason," and that little Myles was "son." He didn't exactly care if Myles became part of the family business, but he still wanted to have a close relationship with the child, just like his father had with him. He yearned for Myles to know he was a good father who wanted to be involved. He wanted Myles to know who he was for himself, instead of the boy learning about his father based upon what his mother said about him.

"Beeva, yes. You are going to have a helluva

year. You're losing a daughter-in-law. But you'll be gaining a new grandchild. Oh, and check this out. Kiara is about to have another baby, too. But that's another damned story. So congrats on all the new life changes. I wish the best for you and Winston."

Beeva stared at her son, quickly drained her drink, refilled her glass, and drained it again.

"You're looking more and more like your dead daddy."

"Damn, Mama."

A hush fell over the room.

"I mean, Beeva."

"My son. Thanks for the well wishes. Thanks for visiting us and telling us what's going on. And I'm glad to meet your new baby mama, but what about that cute little grandson of mine? That's who I really wish I could see."

"Myles is with his mama."

"Oh, so you'll get him tomorrow?"

"No."

"Not even for half a day?"

"No, Beeva."

"No?"

"That's what I keep telling you."

"Let me get this right: You won't see Myles for Christmas? What type of shit is that? She ain't being fair to not let you spend time with him."

"You right about that. And sometimes Kiara plays games with our son."

"I never liked her that much anyway with her bougie ass."

Nicole grinned; she wanted to high-five Beeva, but wasn't sure how the woman would react.

"Ma'am, I could tell you some stuff about Kiara.

She tries to pretend like she's so cultured and reserved, but she can get dirty and ratchet just like the rest of us."

"I know she can," Beeva said and smiled knowingly in Nicole's face.

Later, when Nicole excused herself and went to the powder room, Beeva pulled Rashad to the side. "I haven't known her that long, but watch that one. I can just feel it."

"Beeva, that's where you're wrong. This is my ride or die. She's the realest chick I know."

"If you say so, but don't say I didn't warn you."

Chapter 10

GoFundMe

On the day after Christmas, Nicole was at the mall window shopping. She wanted to buy everything she set her eyes on, but she knew she couldn't, since Rashad told her that his funds were so tight.

She was admiring engagement rings in a jewelry store display when she received a phone call from the 346 area code.

"Hello?"

"Is this Nicole Greene?"

"Yes, who is this?"

"I saw you on television and was inspired by your thoughtfulness regarding those kids that were affected by that fire. I was thinking that you'd know a way to get in touch with them?"

"Yeah, I do." Nicole hesitated. "What do you want with them and why do you want their info?"

"I'm sorry. My name is Geneva Jones. And I just

want to reach out and help the kids. I have started a GoFundMe account; actually two of them. One for the kids so that people can donate money to help with funeral expenses for their mom. I read that they're sending the body to Puerto Rico. I also want to make sure that their future is secure. Hopefully we can raise enough money to help send all four kids to college. Based on the news reports, I understand they didn't have an active father in their lives."

Nicole stopped walking and found a bench to sit on. "Um, yeah, that's true. They have a few family members here but were raised by a single mom. She worked as a manager at a fast food restaurant."

"Yeah, that's so very sad. And, of course, Nicole, I learned from your interviews that you are having a baby next summer, and I just want to do something for you. So many negative things are going on in the world and your compassion for the kids really inspired me. So I set you up an account as well. You should look it up on GoFundMe. Many people have donated. This is for you and that bundle of joy that you're carrying."

"What did you say? Is that a joke?"

"No, no, it isn't. It's very real. So far the kids' account has raised about twenty thousand and I plan to match whatever donations are received. That includes yours, too."

"Twenty thousand?"

"Yes, isn't that great?"

"But I don't understand," Nicole said. She almost hyperventilated. She wasn't used to women being nice to her. She glanced at the number again that was lit up on her phone. She stared at the people near her bench and wondered if her enemies were toying with her.

"What's your name again? Who are you with? And I hope you don't ask me for my Social Security and driver's license number because I'm not with that—"

"Nicole, it's not a scam." She laughed. "It's real. I'm Geneva Gwen Jones. They call me GG Jones. And I'm kind of weird in that I do go around looking for people to help. There are so many needs in the Houston area; so many who are walking around with their heads down and who look like they have no hope. And when I saw you on TV forgetting about yourself and taking time for the kids, well, I just think the world needs more people like you; someone with a good heart who takes time out to care about others."

"I didn't do anything—"

"Oh, but you did. Many that were there stood around looking, then walked away, going on with their lives. But you didn't."

"I know, but you can't say that the people are bad if they walked away—"

"Have you seen the headlines lately? The world is so cruel and people are so angry and ready to hurt one another. We need more real-life examples of positivity. Acts of kindness should be encouraged. Plus, it feels good to be nice," Geneva said.

"I just happened to be there; I didn't do it for money."

"And that's why I want to help: because you did it without expecting anything in return."

Nicole sat in disbelief as the woman talked. By the time she got off the phone, Nicole couldn't believe what had just happened. But after she checked the GoFundMe account online, she wanted to scream when she read the kind notes and viewed the donations that had poured in for her and the children. It didn't really make sense to her, but it had been so long since something so thrilling happened to her, she decided to stay as calm as possible and thank God for her blessings.

She left the mall and drove home as fast as she could.

Once Nicole verified that GG Jones was legit, and the money would be hers, her head felt light and airy.

"Bad things have happened but hopefully better things will start to happen for me." Nicole felt so elated that she began to make plans.

And on New Year's Eve, she decided to announce her news to Rashad.

They got dressed up and went downtown to bring in the New Year. They walked into the joint hand-in-hand around ten o'clock that night. The music was popping and the drinks were flowing.

Nicole knew she couldn't do her usual imbibing, but she was happy that the club offered non-alcoholic drinks. She took a tiny sip on her glass, set it aside, and let Rashad whisk her onto the dance floor as soon as the DJ started spinning a mid-tempo jam.

They began swaying to the music.

"Rashad, babe, sometimes I feel afraid. So happy yet so scared."

"What? Why?"

"I have a feeling this New Year is going to be *my* year. The best I've ever had."

"What makes you think that?"

"They say that what you're doing on the last day of the year is what you'll be doing for the rest of the year."

Rashad grinned and nodded. "And you're with me?"

"I'm dancing, babe. I'm dancing, I'm celebrating and I'm happy."

They moved around the room some more. And when the clock struck twelve, they shared a long, juicy kiss.

Nicole stuffed her tongue so deep in Rashad's mouth he almost stopped breathing. When he came up, he coughed and gasped.

"You trying to kill me, woman?"

"Kill you? With a kiss? That's a new one." She laughed. "I'm so glad we made it to the New Year because I have something to tell you." She proceeded to let him know about the money people around the country had given to her. "It's unbelievable how nice folks can be. I think I need to try that more often." She giggled. "And the first thing I want to do, really two things, is get your mom a gift."

"You don't have to do that. She's okay with those damned fruitcakes."

"No, Rashad. I'm speaking of a wedding gift. When they go to the justice of the peace next month, we'll go, too. And we'll bless her with something amazing."

"Wow! *You* are amazing, Nicky."

"And, Rashad, the second thing I want to do is to buy myself a car soon. I've gone to a couple of dealerships and I'll have more than enough for a down payment."

"What? Why?"

"My Mustang is old and getting run down. The engine has problems. The body has dents in it. Our baby is due this summer and I want to drive around in style."

"I told you no major purchases until after my divorce is final. Can you hold on a little bit longer? Please?"

"But this would be my money, not yours."

"Kiara is already pissed at me for filing. If she sees you driving a new whip, it'll only make things worse for the divorce. So can it wait?"

"Awww, Rashad." Nicole felt heartbroken. It seemed everything she wanted wasn't going to easily be hers.

"Look, Nicky, I know you want nice stuff you've never had before and I get that. But cars and diamonds and designer gear aren't going anywhere. I'm going to get all that for you in time. So hold onto your little money. I will drive you to work if I can. And you don't have to put any unnecessary mileage on your ride. Is that cool?"

"I guess it'll have to be."

Nicole gave in, but deep inside she resented Kiara. She still considered her the woman who got in the way of everything she wanted.

Nicole excused herself to go to the ladies' room. She actually felt sick and ended up kneeling over the toilet and puking. It took her a while to get herself together. When she came back out to the dance floor, she noticed a woman smiling up in Rashad's face. She was a pretty young thing who wore very long burgundy Afrocentric braids. Her lipstick matched her hair color. And she was dressed in a bohemian style that made her stand out.

Nicole walked up to them.

"What's up? What y'all talking about?"

"Happy New fucking Year," the girl said, obviously slightly tipsy. She was a pretty girl who resembled Keyshia Cole. Nicole didn't see any other women hanging with the chick.

"Rashad, what's going on? Who is she?"

"I don't know who she is. She just started chitchatting with me when you walked up."

"Well, that conversation is now over." Nicole grabbed Rashad by the arm far away from the young woman. She told him she wasn't feeling well and convinced him to take her home.

On New Year's Day, Nicole decided to brush up on her mothering skills. She dialed Myles's cell number. To her surprise, he answered.

"Hello?"

"Hi, Myles. How are you? Do you know who this is?"

"Ms. Nicole?"

"Yeah. Wow, you recognize my voice." She laughed. "I don't know if that's good or bad."

"You are in my address book. My mommy put you in there and I see your name."

"Oh, really? What name do you see?"

"N-I-C-K-E-L."

"Oh, okay, I can tell she doesn't know how to spell," she said, sounding agitated. "Anyway, I called you to invite you over to our place. You can stay all night. It'll be fun. Like a sleepover."

"I can't."

"Why not?"

"I'm supposed to go over to Mr. Osborne's house. He has some new railroad cars and tracks and we are going to play with them all day."

His words stung. "I don't think your dad will be happy about that, Myles. Your father really wanted to see you. And I did, too. Are you sure you can't make it? I've made your favorite cake and everything."

"Oh, yeah?"

"Yes. With chocolate icing."

"Wow."

"Plus, we got you a new toy. I'll give you one hint. It flies," Nicole said and crossed her fingers behind her back.

"Okay, I'll come over there."

"You will?"

"Yeah, come get me. Right now."

Nicole told him to get a bag packed. She'd pick him up right away.

On her way over there, she felt so proud of herself. She knew she had the power of persuasion with older men, and now she had skills for young boys, too. First she stopped by the nearest Target and bought the boy an eighty-dollar radio-controlled quad copter.

"He sure better appreciate what I do for him," Nicole said as she stood in the checkout line.

Then, once she was back in her vehicle and driving, she dialed Kiara's number several minutes before she arrived in Fresno.

"Hello?"

"Kiara, hey, um, it's Nicole."

"What do you want?"

"First of all, I want to wish you a happy New Year. And secondly, I again want to apologize for how I behaved that day in the parking lot. I'm pregnant and my emotions are all over the place. I'm sure I said things that were offensive."

"Yes. They were offensive. And your apologies mean nothing to me."

"I didn't think they would and I want to change that. In fact, I'll have to. Because, like it or not, Kiara, we are going to be part of each other's lives forever."

Kiara said nothing.

"Um, which leads me to the main reason that I called," Nicole continued. "I know this is a short notice, but Myles wants to spend time with his daddy tonight if that's okay with you."

"Really?"

"Yes, really. So, be a sweet woman and let him do that. I'm on my way over there now. He's packed his bag and everything. I know that he's looking for me to arrive any minute now."

"Nicole, you've seemed to forget something. You may run things over there, but you aren't in charge of anything in Fresno. There's a proper way to do things and this just isn't happening."

"Kiara, this has nothing to do with being in charge. A man wants to spend time with his kid. This is another major holiday and you didn't make that baby by yourself."

"So are you an expert on baby making these days?"

"Is this your way of saying no? Kiara, how can you be so cruel? So selfish?"

Nicole pulled up in the driveway of the house where Kiara lived. The home was breathtaking just like she'd remembered it. Manicured lawns. Potted plants on the porch. As she got out of the car, she fought the urge to find a brick and smash up all of the windows. Instead, she composed herself and calmly rang the doorbell.

"Kiara, I'm actually outside right now," she told her. "Please let me in so we may talk."

When the door opened, Myles flew through it and ran outside. His mother ambled along right behind him.

"Hi, Ms. Nicole, I'm ready to have fun."

"No, this isn't how we do things." Kiara continued to protest as she scrambled after Myles. He had gotten into the front passenger seat of Nicole's car. She turned to Nicole. "You already know what happens when people show up at other people's houses without an invitation. You'd better be glad I don't have a—"

"Mommy, I'm ready to go."

"Get out of that car right now, Myles. I didn't give you permission to leave."

"I want to see my daddy. I miss my daddy."

Nicole walked up to Kiara, hoping she could convince her to do the right thing. "Do you understand what you're doing? You are traumatizing this child when all he wants to do is be with his dad. You haven't let Myles be with his father for the past three holidays. And this would make the fourth." Nicole was almost shouting. Myles sat in the car with tears streaming from his eyes.

"It seems that you hate the father enough to hurt him, and that's one thing. But do you really want to hurt Myles, too?" Nicole asked. "How can a woman that calls herself a mother do things to hurt a child? He's never going to forget this, Kiara. Never!"

"My God! Okay, you win. I'll let him go. This time." Kiara barely said bye to her son before she returned inside the house.

Kiara rocked back and forth as Eddison held her.

He kissed her every few seconds.

"Go ahead, my love. Get it all out."

She blubbered away in his arms, wetting up his shirt as they sat together that evening on his sofa.

"She plays dirty, Eddy," Kiara sobbed. "She uses people and says crazy things to get what she wants. A master manipulator."

"It'll be all right. In fact, look at it this way. Myles gets to spend time with Rashad and I have you all to myself."

She nodded but felt miserable.

"Wait one second, dear."

Eddison excused himself. When he returned five minutes later he was holding a coffee mug. The sweet aroma of black English tea, lemon, and honey steamed from the cup.

"Give it a few minutes and I want you to sip on this. It'll make you feel better."

She smiled, nodded. "You make me feel better. Every single time."

"Get used to it."

"I want it. I need it, Eddison."

"And you're going to have it."

She was holding a tissue in her hands and dabbed at her eyes.

"I feel so foolish."

"You're not foolish, Kiara. You are human. God gave you tear ducts for a reason."

"Sure, but I doubt he wants me to use them every single damned time."

"You're entitled." Eddison chuckled. "For some strange reason you keep forgetting you're fat. I mean you're pregnant."

She burst out laughing and balled her fist. "Oh, God. What would I do without you?"

He said nothing. When the tea finished steeping, he picked up the cup and pressed it against Kiara's lips. She drank, taking tiny delicious sips. She placed her head against his shoulder and within ten minutes she fell asleep.

Snoring, at peace, and with Eddison protectively by her side.

Even though the New Year started out promising, Rashad's world had gotten so complicated. Three weeks into January, Kiara's attorney filed some motions that required Rashad to have to meet with Lily Tangaro, pay her more money, plus it caused him to be away from his job due to legal battles. To make matters worse, Nicole became grouchier whenever she got sick from her pregnancy. He tried to be supportive but at times he felt the pressure.

By the beginning of February, the only woman he felt he could be around that halfway understood him was Alexis. He hated how things had gone down the last time she popped up at their house; he wanted to make sure that she was all right. He wanted a face-to-face. So he took a chance and drove to her spot.

He got out of the car and went to stand outside Alexis's front door. His underarms were damp. He mopped his forehead with the sleeve of his shirt. He rang the doorbell and knocked. He felt excited to get to see Alexis, his original baby mama.

When the door opened, the smile that was on his face vanished.

"What do you want?"

"Hello, ma'am," he said to Mona Hooker, Alexis's mother. "I'm here to see Skillet."

"Skillet?" Mona Hooker frowned. "Is that what you call my daughter or my granddaughter?"

"Oops, my bad. I'm here to see your daughter so she can let me see my daughter. Are they here?"

"You, young man, will learn how to respect my household or you won't set one foot inside this house. Wait out here."

Mona slammed the door in his face and left him alone. Ten whole minutes passed and he began to pound on the door with his fist.

Seconds later, the door swung open.

Alexis emerged. "Have you lost your mind? Don't make my mama pull out her rifle."

"Oh, it's hunting season for Rashad now. All I want to do is hang out with Hayley and I wanted to talk to you, too. Why is everybody treating me like I'm some damned criminal?"

Alexis's voice softened. She studied him. He looked a hot mess, like he hadn't shaved. "Sorry about that, Rashad. I feel for you and what Kiara is putting you through."

"Does this mean you're on my side now instead of my ex's?"

"Y'all divorced?"

"Not yet."

"But you may as well be, huh?"

"She treats me like I work for ISIS or something. It's starting to piss me off."

Alexis smiled. "I just think your ego is a little bruised. You're used to women throwing themselves at you like you're Michael B. Jordan. But now you're getting treated like you're Columbus Short."

"Wow! That ain't funny. Stop laughing at me."

"Okay, my bad. Um, give me a sec. I'll go get Little Bit, then we can go somewhere."

"I appreciate that."

Alexis smelled good and looked even better. She always knew how to apply just the right amount of makeup. Less was more. Her hair was swept up in a ponytail. She looked five years younger. To him it never seemed like she had any drama in her life, which amazed Rashad. It made him think she had a lot of strength. And that's the type of woman he needed in his life.

Alexis got Hayley quickly dressed in some knit leggings, a cotton-polyester long-sleeved top, and a cute purple hoodie jacket. Rashad insisted that they drive in his vehicle. Instead of arguing, Alexis said okay. While he jabbered away, she discreetly texted Kiara to let her know that Rashad was hanging out with Hayley, and she had agreed to join them. They wouldn't be with each other long.

"Where are we going?" Alexis asked Rashad.

"You got some place to be?"

"I want to be available in case Varnell calls."

"Okay, no problem. We'll just ride around. I just want to be near my daughter."

Rashad drove until they ended up downtown. He turned on Bagby Street. He parked in a big lot.

"What are we doing?" Alexis protested.

"We are here. We are going to have fun. We are going to think about Hayley for a change."

"Rashad! I feel like I've been kidnapped."

He coaxed Alexis out of the car and laughed as he followed behind her. They were at the ticket window for Downtown Aquarium, a six-acre entertainment and dining complex.

"This is nice," Alexis said, "but it's wack at the same time. I'm not prepared."

"I'm disappointed in you. Back in the day, you would've been game to do something spontaneous like this."

"Things have changed."

Rashad allowed Alexis to bitch and moan. He didn't mind. He loved it. He felt happy to spend some time with her and his daughter.

Alexis quieted down once she learned that they'd be seeing some big-ass sharks while they rode a train.

"I've never seen a shark up close," she said. "Except for you."

"Good one, Skillet."

"Why you keep calling me that?"

"You don't want to know why."

Soon they boarded their wooden bench seats. Rashad sat on the left, Alexis on the right, and Hayley squeezed in the middle. A bell began clanging.

"All aboard," said the loud audio recording that described the tour. And they were off.

"Choo choo train," Hayley happily declared.

They passed by tiny ponds and loads of green, exotic looking plants and shrubbery. As soon as they entered the tunnel they were shrouded in darkness. The lit-up two-hundred-thousand-gallon aquarium was filled with all kinds of fish that swam over their heads and in two tanks on either side of the train. Hayley squirmed in her seat and excitedly pointed at the fish.

Alexis shivered in awe. She felt like she was sitting in the middle of the ocean. The light shone on her face. Rashad knew she loved the adventure. While she whispered to their daughter and described the big fish, Rashad discreetly placed his arm around the back of her seat. Then he squeezed Alexis's shoulder.

"What do you think you're doing?"

He smiled innocently, then ignored her.

They watched as Pacific white sharks, swordfish, sand tiger sharks swam through the blue water.

Before she knew it, Rashad grabbed her hand. She let him hold it for a second. Then she snatched it back. "Rashad, what the hell?"

"What?

"You're trying to be slick."

"I thought you were Hayley."

"No, the hell you did not."

"Skillet, c'mon, now cut me some slack."

"You live with a woman. I know she's giving you some night and day. Why you gotta hound me, huh? How would she feel if she knew what you were trying to do behind her back?" Alexis laughed conspiratorially, then covered Hayley's ears. "I do not like her at all and if I was the truly devious type I'd take you up on your offer and fuck the daylights out of you. But I'm not. I got a man. I'm not about to mess it up over some foolishness with you. Now be a good baby daddy, focus on making your child happy, and leave me the hell out of your shenanigans."

* * *

Alexis felt the weight of her reality bear down on her. Some women sought the attention of a man, but the wrong type of attention from the wrong man just felt . . . wrong.

"I wish I were invisible," she said to her friend Regina. They met at a Mexican restaurant where they were enjoying chicken enchiladas and drinks.

"Why would you wish to be invisible?"

"My ex keeps hounding me. Pressuring me."

"Just tell him to fuck off."

"I have. But he's like these big-ass Texas cockroaches. You can spray and watch 'em as they lay on the floor dying. But you know they're going to come back again one day."

"Well, damn. If my man did that, it would make me think that he loves me."

A few months ago, Regina had gotten rid of one married man, just to meet another dude who seemed promising at first, but she was starting to have doubts.

"He hasn't called, has he?" Alexis asked.

"Nah. And it pisses me off," Regina said. "He can call me when he wants to beat up this pussy, but when my car breaks down, or when it's a three-day holiday weekend, I can't get him to pick up his phone. It sounds like he's married, too."

"I wouldn't be surprised."

"Why do I keep putting up with this?"

"You're dumb—"

"I'm dumb?"

"Yes, women who put up with things they don't like, clearly disrespectful things, are super stupid. And they lack self-esteem."

"But I got self-esteem," Regina protested. "I know I look hot!"

"If that were true, you could leave your man behind and concentrate on giving your hot self to someone that really deserves it, am I right?"

"I, um, well."

"Girl, I was proud of you when you eliminated that other man. You had the strength to do what I couldn't even do back then. But I eventually got rid of no-good Rashad. And now?"

Alexis rose to her feet and twirled around in a circle. She stopped and hugged herself.

"I am free. I'm *so* empowered. I got me a real man. And I never would have had him if I had held onto Rashad and continued letting him do me wrong. I only deal with him because of Hayley. But I might have to get Varnell to have a little talk with him. In fact, I think I will."

That night, after Alexis arrived home from the meeting with Regina, she called Varnell. He came right over to her house. They put Hayley in the backseat of his Chevy pickup and drove until they reached Nicole's house. On the way there, Alexis called Rashad and let him know she was stopping by.

"Let that female Shrek know. Tell her right now."

Alexis didn't want any increased bad blood between herself and Nicole.

When they reached the house, Alexis emerged from the car. Varnell followed her with Hayley in tow.

She rang the doorbell and took a deep breath.

Rashad opened the door. He smiled when he saw her. But when she stepped aside and he took one look at Varnell, he came out onto the walkway.

"Why is he holding her?" Rashad demanded.

"Why not? He's with me."

"I don't need another man to hold my daughter."

"Grow up, Rashad. He's not a threat to you. He's my man and he's helping me out because I asked him to."

Rashad clenched his fists.

Varnell didn't flinch.

Rashad jumped at him like he was about to punch Varnell, but the man stood perfectly still. Rashad reached out for Hayley. But she resisted her father and covered her face with her hands as she leaned against Varnell.

"What the fuck? Are you trying to turn my own daughter against me?"

"Rashad, what I'm trying to do is get you to leave me the fuck alone."

Alexis winced. She hated to curse in front of a toddler.

"I'm not too good with these things. Varnell, can you handle this, please?"

"Sure can." Varnell placed Hayley in Rashad's arms. He turned her face into her daddy's shoulder so she couldn't see. And Varnell pointed his finger at Rashad.

"Hey man. Let Alexis go. Do what you gotta do as this child's father but anything outside of that is stepping into my territory. You get what I'm saying?"

Rashad looked like he wanted to explode. But he couldn't. Not then.

He nodded and shot Alexis a hateful, hurt look.

When Alexis felt the message had sunk in, she gently removed Hayley from Rashad's arms.

They quietly got back in the pick-up and went on about their way.

And after Varnell made sure that she and Hayley were safely at her house, he told her he'd call her later. She said okay and gave him a kiss. She stood on the front porch after he left and she placed a call to Regina.

"This love thing is complicated sometimes, but slowly but surely I am finally figuring it out," Alexis told her.

"Tell me, please, because I can use all the help I can get."

"The day you discover your true self-worth is the day you can walk away from anyone who isn't good for you. You can set him free and not give a damn. You won't use the excuse that you 'love' him anymore. When you can walk away, that's when you will realize who you really love."

"Who?"

"Yourself, girlfriend. Love yourself."

A few days later, Alexis was at the home she shared with her mother. The one-and-a-half-story bungalow had always been big enough for two people, but lately the place seemed cramped. Alexis was sick of her mother always getting on her about her life, how to raise the baby, and more.

It was late at night. Alexis quietly gathered some clothing items, Hayley's outfit, and jammed her tote bag with her umbrella, a self-help magazine, a water bottle, and her pouch that was filled with cosmetics.

She strapped her sleepy daughter in the car, buckled her own seat belt, and wildly drove away from her house in her two-seater Benz. Where she was going? She didn't know. But she was desperate to get away.

"I need to sell this shit. Use the money to make a down payment on my own damned house."

She and her mother were butting heads again. And she dreaded the moment she would walk into the house. She knew the fighting would start again. As she blindly drove through the streets of Houston, she couldn't erase the scene that just happened when she tried to get her mom to babysit Hayley:

"Hey, daughter," Mona had told her when she'd snuck and placed her daughter in her mother's bed and told her she'd be back later. "This is the third time this week you had a sudden emergency and dumped your child on me with little warning. I love my little Hayley, but I am not about to raise another kid. I don't have the strength. I feel bad when I'm lying around and she comes in here asking me to play hide and go seek with her."

"I'm sorry, Mama. I really am. But I am not responsible for all the unplanned things that can happen that require me to leave the house for a little while."

"You were already gone for a couple hours last night. I hope you weren't away getting a quickie."

"Mama, don't be ridiculous. I haven't even done anything like that with Varnell. And I told you me and Rashad don't do that anymore, either."

"Well, isn't that breaking news? Heartbroken woman gets a reality check and finally dumps her horny married man. Hell, I lived that life. I know that life." She paused for emphasis. "I must warn you, darling. Rashad will be back in your bed. They always come back. Especially if you got that good-good."

"Ugh, Mama, I refuse to discuss this topic with you. This makes me very uncomfortable."

"Why is that? Isn't this the very thing you talk about with your girlfriends? Oops, sorry. You don't have any friends."

Alexis could only give her mom a horrified stare.

"I'll bet every woman you know has to watch her man around you. You're too damned beautiful. Your body is still in good shape and you were careful not to let yourself go. And anytime a beautiful single woman comes around a couple, that wife will grab her man's hand, pull him closer, not let him out of her sight. Because my beautiful daughter, *you* are temptation. Y'all may not be doing it now. But that married man will be back. Creeping up my stairs, escaping behind your bedroom door, and getting you to undress. I know one thing, you better use a condom. I don't care how much he begs."

"Mama," she finally screamed. "You are not describing me. You don't even know me. I am not that woman anymore. I've never really been that woman."

"What makes you so different now, Alexis?"

"I'm not *you*, that's what."

"Who the hell you think you're talking to, little girl?" Mona screamed at Alexis.

Her mother's voice droned on and on as Alexis quietly made her escape up those eighteen stairs into her second-floor hideaway. That's when she began to pack some things and when she decided to take her daughter with her instead of leaving her with Mona. And Alexis began to realize that yes, even though she felt like a snake for taking Carmen Foster's advice, she was glad that she had finally filed for child support a few days ago. As an administrative assistant, her salary was decent, but she needed more funds if she wanted to adequately take care of herself and Hayley. She'd racked up lots of credit card debt in the past year, plus she had to maintain two vehicles. Things were tight. Perhaps once the child support checks started being deposited into her account she could earn enough money to get her own place.

Because each time Alexis had a showdown with her mother, she felt like she just went through airport security and was forced to comply with a full-body scan by the TSA.

She felt completely naked and brutally judged.

And that's when Alexis McNeil wished she were invisible. She wished that her mother, Rashad, and that no one else could see her, search for her, or bother her about anything. It would feel like she didn't exist anymore. But was it possible to be nonexistent in a bar code, over-tracking world that constantly photographed every freeway, gas station, store, bank, and parking lot? What would a world be like that would give Alexis complete freedom so she could totally breathe?

Alexis continued to drive without a specific destination. It was ridiculously late and Hayley was beginning to fuss. Feeling sheepish, Alexis called Varnell's number. She said hello and explained the situation. She asked if she and Hayley could come over right then and maybe stay over. He said yes. Alexis and Varnell may not have been having sex, but they'd be sleeping under the same roof for the first time—at least for that one night.

Chapter 11

Beautiful Princess

February and March came and went quickly. Eason vs. Eason was in full effect. They'd gone through the discovery process and Rashad knew that Kiara wanted to receive some of his properties, full custody of Myles, a portion of his pension, and spousal support. Kiara's legal representatives informed her that because of the pregnancy, the courts would schedule their divorce hearing after she gave birth.

By April eighth, Kiara was beyond ready for all the monumental changes that would redefine her life. She finally made it to her fortieth week of pregnancy. She'd gained sixty-five pounds and she was very eager for her pregnancy to end.

It was Wednesday at two a.m.; the time of death, for not much moved and stirred at this ungodly hour. But that is precisely when Kiara's eyes popped open as she lay in bed. Contractions had started around midnight. She contacted the hospital, but they told her to go back to bed. And she did. But now her contractions were steady and unrelenting. She could only sleep on her back by then and she began to moan.

"Adina?" Kiara yelled as loud as she could. "It's time."

"Okay, friend."

Adina had been sleeping on Kiara's living room couch for the past few days just in case she went into labor. Adina rose up and took action. The tote bag that she'd packed for the hospital stay was ready and waiting next to the fireplace. Adina fled to Kiara's bathroom and ran some tap water. She quickly splashed her face. She found a clean face-cloth and wet it so she could mop it across Kiara's forehead, which was beaded with sweat.

"Ain't no turning back now," Adina said. "You ready, Mama?"

"Let's do this."

Kiara waddled to Adina's car and soon they were headed to the birthing center.

"I wonder what Myles is doing?"

"As long as he's with his grandma Flora, he'll be just fine. And he'll be so excited to see his new baby brother or sister."

"Yeah. But don't you think he should be used to this by now?"

"You got jokes, huh?"

Kiara may have been trying her hand at comedy, but her stomach was twisted in painful knots. Her face looked puffier than normal and her ankles were swollen. Several thoughts raced across her mind as they arrived at the Sweetwater Pavilion entrance of Houston Methodist.

Kiara and Adina rode the elevator to the third floor and she was immediately admitted, since she'd pre-registered months ago.

"Are you ready for Rashad to see you?"

"Adina." Kiara squeezed her hand so tight she flinched. "I-I'm scared. I don't want to go under anesthesia. What if God decides to punish me for my sins? Or, if I live, what if the baby isn't perfectly formed?"

"First of all, I can't answer that question. Do I look like I'm best friends with the Lord? And secondly, you think the most morbid thoughts of anyone I know. Damn. Be positive, will you?"

"Okay, all right. Pray for me, Adina. Oops! Never mind."

"Girl, as usual you're tripping. I will do my best to pray and we'll see what happens. Meanwhile, stay strong. You must face whatever happens like the resilient woman I know that you are." Adina felt Kiara's pain and she wanted her to know that she wasn't alone.

"You need anything?"

"Just promise not to leave my side."

"I got you."

Kiara got prepared in the birthing room. Soon her doctor, Jimmy Wong, greeted her with a bright, encouraging smile.

"Hello, Kiara. You are one rare woman. These days, many mothers want to know the gender of their child in advance. But I see that you want to be surprised."

"Humph. She'll be surprised, all right," muttered Adina.

"If it's a boy," Dr. Wong asked, "what will you name him?"

"If it's a boy, he'll be called Dietrich, which means leader of the people."

The doctor nodded.

"And if I have a girl she will be named Jahzara, which is Ethiopian for 'princess who is blessed.' Her middle name is Alaine, which is Irish for 'beautiful.'

"Beautiful princess," said Dr. Wong.

"Exactly. We'd call her Jazz for short."

"Got it. See you soon, Kiara."

Right before she was ushered to the delivery room, Kiara grabbed Adina's hand.

"Pray."

Adina immediately bowed her head.

"Are you there, Jesus? Meet Kiara. Ahh, bring her baby to her. And let her see, and um, raise this baby. I guess that's all. Amen."

Kiara couldn't believe it. "That sucked, Adina, but amen."

Just as she feared, Kiara's blood pressure was on the high side. She ended up having an emergency C-section. She was under anesthesia when the baby was taken from her body. While knocked out, she heard the surgeons talking about all kinds of things, but she wasn't able to answer them. She was in a deep state of consciousness that made her feel like she was in orbit and soaring above the earth. But hours later, she finally came to.

Kiara's eyes fluttered until she noticed Dr. Wong standing at her bedside.

"Good afternoon. Here's your beautiful princess." He handed her the newborn.

"Oh, my God, a precious little girl. Hey, Jazz."

Kiara felt groggy and disoriented. But she visually checked the girl's nose and ears, cheeks and fingers. She already knew it was Rashad's child through pre-DNA testing, but she didn't share the info with anyone.

Adina winked. "My prayer may have sucked but it still worked. Congrats, Mommy."

Kiara struggled to smile. "Thank you. Everything is great. And I'm so happy this precious baby is mine. I always wanted a little girl."

"And now you have one. I can't wait to go shopping," Adina said. "I'm going to buy her bows and ribbons and cute little shoes and dresses and—"

"Adina, I must tell you that this is Rashad's child."

She scowled but quickly recovered. "Doesn't matter. I will still spoil my goddaughter."

"What would I do without you? Thank you for being here for me in my most trying moments."

"That's what's sisters do."

"Yes, we are. We're truly a family."

Adina's cell phone rang. "Oh, my goodness, look who's calling me." She held up her phone. The caller ID said, "Remy." Adina answered and put the call on speaker.

"Hi there, daughter."

"Whassup, Mama? Where are you?"

"I'm at the hospital. Kiara just had a little girl."

"Cool. Tell her I said hey."

"What are you doing, Remy?"

"Trying to do what folks do. Getting my little

bit of education. I'm at school now in between classes."

Adina felt so good. Remy had been staying with Marlon these days. The arrangement seemed to be working. All she wanted was for her daughter to live life the right way and for her to be safe and stay out of trouble.

"Well, I just want you to know that I've been helping out Kiara at her house. So if you need me, that's where I'll be. Maybe you can come over sometime."

"I don't remember where she lives."

"I can text you the address."

"All right. I don't know if I'm coming by or not, but I will let you know. I gotta go. My world history class is about to start."

"Okay, Remy. Bye, baby."

"I ain't no baby."

"All right, bye, grown-up woman."

Mother and daughter laughed, said their goodbyes and hung up.

The attending nurse interrupted them to monitor Kiara's blood pressure.

Kiara felt happy and thankful for herself as a mom. But she was also glad for her friend. "Adina, if you could see the look on your face," Kiara told her. "You're glowing."

"I think Remy is finally listening to someone. You know I think it has to do with Marlon having a serious talk with the girl, because Lord knows I wasn't able to get through to her. But we'll see. I'm just happy that she's back in school."

Right then Rashad strolled into the room. "Am I too late?"

"Oh, great," Adina said as she protectively stepped closer to Kiara.

"Hello to you, too," Rashad told Adina. "I'm both surprised and disappointed to see you here."

"Shhh, a baby was recently born. No negative energy in this room, Rashad. My goddaughter is going to live a blessed, happy, prosperous and positive life."

"Thanks, Adina," Kiara whispered.

"*You're* going to be the godmother? Says who?"

"Rashad, we can discuss this later," Kiara told him.

"I'll shut up about that for right now. Anyway, you look very pretty, Kiara. As hot as on the day you had Myles."

"Oh, hush with all that." Kiara blushed. "I'm sure I look a hot mess."

"You look a beautiful mess. Well, enough of all that. Let me see her," Rashad said. "And can you give us some privacy?" he asked Adina. "Every time I see Kiara for some reason you're always in the area."

"Get used to it. Anyway, you may see the baby. You've got fifteen minutes and not a second too long," Adina said before she left the room.

Rashad silently stared at the bundle that was quietly lying on Kiara's chest.

"She smells so good, just like her mama. May I please hold her?"

"Meet Jahzara Alaine,"—she paused—"Eason."

"She's mine?"

"Yes, Rashad." Kiara handed the infant over to him. "Look at her, for God's sake. Can't you tell she's yours by her features?" Kiara was tickled pink as she lay there and watched Rashad carefully examine the child. He inspected her fingers, her toes, the shape of her head, her ears, her feet, everything.

"She has a head full of hair, and look at those cute little lips and her hands. I think she has little fingernails already. She's perfect," Kiara gushed.

Rashad started rocking the baby in his arms. He stared at her with an emotionless look on his face.

"You're sure that this baby is mine?"

"I'm positive. I-I had a pre-DNA test done weeks ago. And it was confirmed. No one knew the results except me."

"You've been known she was mine? I don't get it. Why didn't you tell me?"

"Oh, once you see the hospital bill, you'll know exactly why."

"I don't give a damn about how much it costs. One more bill won't make that much difference. Do you know how stressed I've been? Wondering if I am going to completely lose my family and everything I've worked hard for? Stressing if I was going to lose my wife to another man and worrying if she was having his baby?"

Kiara couldn't respond. She knew Rashad. On rare occasions he grew emotional and reflective. She figured he was having a moment. She just hoped it would be a quick moment and he'd recover and behave rationally.

"Sorry about that Rashad. You don't have to stress anymore."

"Even so, I may get a second opinion. It's important that I be sure."

"Rashad, I'm telling you, she is yours!"

"All right, okay, she is gorgeous so she must be my baby daughter. Mine." He stood and rocked

Jazz for a while. The longer he held her, the better she felt in his arms.

He paused. "What does this mean?"

"It means you've added a new member to your growing roster."

"Kiara—"

"Okay, maybe I shouldn't have said that. And I'm so sorry that I went there because I love this little baby in spite of everything. But really, Rashad, I'm kind of physically and mentally wore out right now. And this isn't the time or place for this conversation. I just had her, for God's sake. I'm trying to make sure she's healthy and breathing. And I want to get my rest and get some morphine or something because these incisions hurt like hell. Then I want to try and breastfeed Jazz if they let me."

"I understand all that, but"—there was hope in Rashad's voice—"I was talking about what happens after you leave this hospital?"

In Kiara's foggy mind, she was screaming, *Do you realize I just had an emergency caesarean*? But she answered her own question. *Nope, he doesn't. He has no idea.*

"Don't even go there. The divorce is still on because you filed on me, remember? And I had to file a counterclaim because I don't want you to try and change your mind. And even though we have a daughter now, I can't forget that our union has been irretrievably broken in so many ways. Don't you understand that? So as far as I am concerned at this very second, I'm thinking we can be co-parents and nothing more. Besides, Rashad, you've obviously moved on with that woman you chose to be with."

"I didn't choose to be with her. You made me leave our house."

Kiara may have done wrong herself but she still hated that Rashad couldn't admit his share of the blame. She felt he was right where he wanted to be and she was sick of his excuses.

"Rashad, I could no longer live with you with all the stuff you were putting me through. What did you expect?"

"But, Kiara, I never really wanted to go. I was all right with staying away for a few days or so until we both figured out what we really wanted to do. Personally, I wanted to try and work things out. But you never gave me the chance. You wouldn't listen to me no matter what I tried to tell you. But now that I know that this is our baby, maybe that means we can have one last stab to do the right thing and make our relationship work." He laughed to himself. "Myles is gonna be so hyped. He loves playing the big brother role. Teaching her how to fly his copters. Bossing her around but still protecting her like the little princess she is." He stroked Jahzara's cheek and thanked God for the little girl. "I'm grateful for all my children. No matter how they got here, they are mine and I love them."

"Please be quiet."

Kiara didn't speak about it much, but it still tore her up that he already had another daughter with Alexis. She respected the little girl because she was a life that didn't ask to be here, so Kiara wouldn't fault her for that. She gradually learned not to blame Alexis for what happened. When she first met Rashad, Alexis may not have known he wasn't single, but a married man always knows that he has a wife.

"If this is my last and final chance to tell you I'm sorry about the past and how much I wish I could have a future with my real family, then there it is. That's where my head is right now."

Kiara yearned for pain-relieving drugs and wished she had a pill that could make Rashad shut his trap. He just couldn't seem to see the big picture. She felt painfully sore and desperately wanted to close her eyes and forget everything that was going on.

Right then Eddison popped his head inside the doorway. A bouquet of flowers was in one hand, and several inflated balloons were in the other. He stood there and evaluated the scene.

Kiara gasped at his appearing there without warning. She never informed him that she was on the way to the birthing center. She realized Adina must have given him a heads-up. Kiara's original plan was to call him as soon as she came out from under the anesthesia, but then Rashad showed up.

Rashad glanced at Eddison, then at Kiara.

"Is this the guy?"

Eddison walked over to Kiara and leaned over to lightly kiss her on the lips. He mouthed the words "I love you." He placed her flowers on the bedside table. He looked Rashad in the eye and extended his hand.

"Hi. I'm Eddison Osborne."

"I don't give a—"

"I heard you just ask if I was the guy. But I'm not the guy. I'm the man."

"If you don't get out my face with that bullshit."

"Hey, man, show some respect to the woman and to the child."

"Cornball here got the nerve to be on a righteous trip—"

"Oh, my God, please, Rashad," Kiara said as she struggled to sit up. "Don't do this!" Eddison rushed to her side. "Babe, don't overextend yourself," he told her. "You need your rest."

Kiara noticed how keenly Eddison stared at her. He glanced at the baby then back at her. She saw desire mixed with hope flicker in his eyes. It floored her that two men in one day looked to her as their savior. She felt regretful that she hadn't informed him about Jazz the second she found out. When she first got the DNA results, she wanted to tell Eddison but found it was difficult to form the words that could potentially break his heart.

"I'm sorry, Eddison, but—"

"Are you sure? Are you positive?" he whispered.

"Eddison, if I could change things . . ."

"Yo, did you not hear her? This baby is mine," Rashad said.

"All right. But may I hold her?"

"Sorry for the letdown, but your services are no longer required, man. No surrogate fathers on standby anymore." Rashad held the newborn in one arm and pointed to the door with his free hand. "Go," he told him.

"I'm not trying to start any trouble."

"Too late for that. You need to bounce up outta here, my man."

Instead of leaving, Eddison took a step closer. He wanted another look at Jazz. "I promise you, I only want to see the baby. Would it be all right if I held her, Kiara?"

"Of course it's fine if he wants to hold her."

"Nope, it's not happening," Rashad argued. "This baby is mine; that means I will get to decide what she does. As her father, I have a say-so and I want to start exercising my rights, right now." Rashad stood his ground and protectively held Jazz closer to his chest.

For Kiara, her daughter's first day on the earth seemed like it had gotten off to an interesting start. And she felt completely embarrassed, since the attending nurse had stood nearby trying to mind her business. She was busy reading charts, but the woman stopped what she was doing when she heard them bickering.

The nurse came over to Kiara. She gently smiled.

"Do you want to hold your daughter again, Mom?"

"Yes, I do."

"No, she doesn't," Rashad said, rocking Jazz in his arms.

"Rashad," Kiara said, "why are you acting so possessive?"

"You know exactly why. Don't you remember the way you've played me with Myles the past few months? You've dictated when I can see him. The exact hours I can see him. By law, you did not have the right to do that. And I don't like how you put me in that position by using our son as a pawn. That will not be happening with our daughter."

The nurse stepped in between them. "Shhh." She hissed. "Whatever issues you have, this is not the time or the place. You all are going to have to lower your voices. Don't think I won't call security."

"But I'm the father. If anything, call security on that guy. He has no good reason to be here."

Kiara's tiredness didn't stop her from chiming in. Eddison joined her. Then Rashad had a few words to say. The nurse clapped her hands.

"Everyone! Calm down and watch your tone. Jazz doesn't deserve this. Kiara is in recovery and this room must be cleared. Come on, give the baby to me right now," the nurse pleaded with Rashad. "It's time to take little Jazz."

"Take her where?" he asked.

"I still haven't held her," said Eddison.

"Give her to me now," the nurse demanded.

But Rashad refused to let go. He asked, "Is this a conspiracy?"

"What?" Kiara said, completely horrified.

"How do I know who this woman is?" Rashad said. "She could have went to a uniform store and walked in this place wearing that outfit and flashing a fake badge. It's not like it's never happened before."

"Rashad, you're crazy."

"This so-called nurse could be one of this dude's relatives plotting to steal my daughter from me."

"You sound like such a fool," Adina snapped as she stepped back into the room. "You have no idea what you're talking about. I've stood outside that door listening. And I've had enough of your buffoonery. This baby is your daughter, all right? And if you keep it up, today will be the last time you ever see her again."

"How dare you threaten me, Adina, over my own child? See, this is why I wish my wife had kicked you to the curb permanently. You're sticking your nose where it doesn't belong."

"I knew her first, Rashad. Who do you think she called when you were treating her like crap, huh?

Unlike you, Kiara can't divorce me. I will always be there."

"Bull, pure BS," Rashad told her.

Kiara sat up in bed. "Leave my dear friend out of this, Rashad. Plus you should be more worried about the next baby of yours that's about to pop out of that awful woman you're living with. Now hand over Jazz to me. I'm demanding that you leave my room right now. Security is on its way."

Rashad was tempted to run out of the door holding his daughter in his arms. She was fifty percent his. And he was sick of Kiara's imperious behavior. He held onto the child for a brief moment longer. The only reason he decided to smile at the baby, tell her he loved her and hand her over to the nurse was because he didn't want to hurt anymore. He didn't want to hurt Kiara anymore. For in some strange way, he still loved her.

Several days later, after Kiara got released, Adina came to pick her up from the hospital. Jazz Eason was in great health and Kiara's spirits were soaring.

"I feel like I'm in a dream," she gushed on their way to her house.

"I'm sure you do. I'm glad for you, girl. A lot of women wish they could have one child, let alone two."

"Well, these tubes will be tied soon." Kiara laughed.

"Oh, does this mean that you and Eddison are done for good? Because I was really hoping that even though Jazz's daddy is you-know-who, I still wanted that good man to stay in your life."

"What man in his right mind would want to be a part of my complicated world, Adina?"

"A man who loves you for you. And if you decide to get your tubes tied, you would completely and totally kill the dream that he might have of being with you and having a child of your own together."

"I haven't made a final decision about getting my tubes tied yet. And Eddison has his choice of eligible women who don't have my issues. I'm sure he'll find someone else in time."

"Kiara, it sounds like you're giving up."

"I am facing reality. I can't bear the thought of hurting him any longer. He's been too good to me."

"Why not let him continue being good to you? Think about it, all right, sweetie?"

"I'll think about it later. Leave me alone," she pouted.

"I will back off. Your life is yours to live."

Thirty minutes later, they arrived at Kiara's house. Instead of going through the garage, Adina insisted they enter through the front entrance. Adina led the way and quietly rang the doorbell.

"You're so silly. Just use my key. It's in my purse."

"No, thank you."

The door swung open. Mama Flora, the woman who raised Kiara, was there to greet them. And John, her grand pop, was standing there, too. Married over forty years, at one time the couple had inspired her with their long union. And although Grand Pop at one time threatened to leave his wife, there he was, still in the picture.

"There's my Sugah and my new great-grandbaby," he said. "And my beautiful granddaughter."

"Hello, you guys. I'm so surprised. And here I

am looking like who did it and why." Kiara grinned at her grandparents.

"You look like a new mom. Now hand her over." Mama Flora took Jazz from her hands and resisted the urge to kiss the baby.

Myles dashed out from hiding behind Grand Pop.

"Mommy, did you miss me?" he asked. "I missed you. Where's my baby sister? I made her a present." She had wanted Myles to visit her while she was in the hospital but due to the emergency surgery, she decided to wait to see her son until she got home.

"Ohhh, my precious Myles, God, I missed you sooo much. I hope you were a good boy while I was in the hospital."

Kiara bit her bottom lip. Seeing her family surround her with their love and support made her so incredibly thankful. And in that moment, she felt hopeful that she'd have the strength she'd need to get through this season of her life. Kiara had always been incredibly independent. Maybe it was time she learned to let those who loved her give her a helping hand.

"You all are a lifesaver," she hollered to Flora and John.

"That's why we are here," said Grand Pop.

Kiara ventured farther inside the house and ran into Tony Fu, her favorite employee among those that worked for her at TSWU. He was in the kitchen, wearing his headphones and putting the finishing touches on some cupcakes that he baked with the help of Myles. When he spotted Kiara, he broke out in a shuffle and made Kiara laugh. "What the hell? Tony, hello, my friend." She couldn't stop giggling. "I never expected all these people to be up in my house. Y'all some sneaky-ass devious people."

Adina had hauled in her travel bag from the car. "Tony, please be a sweetie and go get some more of Kiara's things. They're in the trunk."

Kiara walked into the media room, which was decorated from floor to ceiling with dozens of balloons and streamers.

A huge banner with the words "Welcome Home, Jazz and Kiara" was strung across one wall.

"You all outdid yourselves. And I love you for it."

"Kiara, we'll take care of the baby and settle her in the nursery. You go to your room and maybe get into a nice change of clothes. We've cooked and we're sure you're starving by now." That was Grandma Flora.

"Yes, ma'am. And thank you." She stared at Mama Flora and noticed her maternal ways; Mama Flora loved to dote on Kiara. If she noted a hair out of place, she was standing at her granddaughter's side, putting each strand of hair into place. She was always offering her something to eat, offering her spending money, or just being there when she needed her.

Flora's nurturing presence instantly made Kiara think about her biological mother. Even though she never really knew what it was like to have a mother, Kiara wished so badly that her mom was around to share in this moment.

Pamela Banks had been dead thirty-five years. Kiara had no true memories of her, yet each time a special occasion happened in her life, Kiara yearned for Pamela. She imagined that her mom would be so happy that their family now consisted of three generations.

Kiara took that moment to go and find her daughter. She wished she could tell her everything Flora had told her about the woman. Her daughter was awake. When Kiara looked into Jazz's eyes, she knew it was a reflection of her mother Pamela staring back at her. It was her mom's way of letting her know that, although she was gone, she still knew what was happening in her daughter's life.

"You're a special little girl and I love you very much."

Kiara softly said good-bye to Jazz and handed her over to Mama Flora. As she walked down the hall and into her bedroom, she wiped away a stray tear. Mourning for something you lost was a lifelong process.

Kiara quietly shut her bedroom door and placed her purse on top of her bed. She heard noise in her bathroom.

"What the hell?"

When she opened the door to her bathroom, she saw petals floating on top of some bathwater. Smooth jazz music played in the background.

"You finally decided to come back where you belong," he said, "with me."

Eddison grabbed Kiara in his arms and lovingly kissed her forehead.

"Oh my God. I-I didn't know if I'd ever see you again."

"You know me better than that," he told her.

Kiara threw her arms tightly around Eddison's neck. "I swear you must be the best man, or the craziest man, in the entire world."

"I love you, man," he said teasingly.

Kiara lost it. She slumped to the floor and had a

good cry. Her world felt so unreal and it finally hit her. "I think I've wanted this type of love for so long, that when I finally got it, I could not recognize it. But I get it now, I get it!"

"Babe, everything is going to be all right," Eddison told her in a soothing tone. "Okay, the kid is not my child. We are going to figure out a way to get through this. But the first order of business is for you to take off those clothes. Wait. You don't even have to do that. I'll take them off for you."

And he did. Eddison helped Kiara to her feet. He unbuttoned her loose-fitting blouse and placed it on the bed. He pulled the skirt she wore over her legs. He unhooked her bra and kissed her shoulders. "I feel too dirty," she complained. He hugged her anyway.

Eddison stood in front of her and without his eyes ever leaving hers, he slid her big maternity underwear down her thighs, over her knees, and down to her ankles. He took in her nakedness. The fullness of her breasts, the broadness of her shoulders. Her delicate arms, shapely legs and hips, and even the scar left from her being stitched up after surgery. Eddison's facial expression said he appreciated everything he saw. When Kiara tried to cover her incision, he playfully slapped at her hands.

"You are beautiful."

She willingly fell in his arms. "I don't know why you're feeling me the way you do, but I'm so happy that I have you." She felt grateful that she had a good man whose love was real, genuine, and unconditional.

"I love you, Kiara."

She nodded, kissed his lips. They were hungry for each other, and it felt good to open up her heart and let love in.

They bathed together and she enjoyed every second. Kiara carefully washed Eddison's body just like he washed hers. She noticed some freckles that she'd never seen before. She saw some scrapes and blemishes on his legs. She recognized her man wasn't perfect; he had minor flaws, but the love he had for her seemed to erase his imperfections. His love made Kiara want to try to love again and give it her all.

She felt she deserved that and knew that Eddison deserved it, too.

Chapter 12

Eminence Forever

Five weeks after Kiara gave birth to Jahzara, everyone in the Communications Department received pink, green, and white card stock invitations in their office mailboxes. Even Alexis got one. She stood with her mouth wide open as she read the wording:

You Are Cordially Invited to the Baby Shower
Honoring Nicole Kelly Greene
To Welcome
Her Baby Girl
Eminence Forever

Hosted by Shyla Perry-Fallender
On

Saturday, May 23 at 2 p.m.
at 8423 Dashwood Lane, Houston, TX

Nicole is registered at
Eddie Bauer, Babies "R" Us, and Target

Later that day after work, Alexis decided to pay Kiara a visit. She wanted to see Jazzy and check on how the new mom was doing. After they gossiped a bit and retreated to the large family room, Alexis made sure that the baby was asleep and that Kiara was sitting down before she handed her the envelope.

"What's this?" Kiara asked.

"You'll see."

Kiara read the invite. She stood up. She sat back down.

"What?"

"Yes. Yes."

"She's naming her baby Eminence?"

"Can you believe that?"

"And they are having the shower at her place? Where Rashad stays?"

"I was afraid to tell you, but I thought you should know—"

"How utterly disrespectful. The judge is scheduled to grant the divorce in a few weeks, but for right now we're still legally attached. What would it look like if people come to her baby shower and see that Eason and Son van up in her driveway? Why can't she have her shower somewhere else? That burns me up. I don't know where my phone is. Can you please get Rashad on your cell phone for me?"

Alexis paused and chose her words carefully.

"Kiara, I know you're freaking out about Nicole's insensitivity and you're right to feel that way, but isn't it time that you truly let him go?"

"What are you talking about? I'm not thinking about that man."

"Then why are some of his things still in this house? Little things I've noticed; but with all due respect, stuff that should not be here."

Kiara was tongue-tied as she examined her surroundings. Her eyes rested on the pine bookcase with six wide shelves. It held at least fifteen dusty construction industry reference books. Funny! She hadn't noticed them until now. Upon further scrutiny, she even detected a few mementos that prominently displayed the Eason & Son logo. When she thought about it, she actually still had some of Rashad's personal effects in the closet of her bedroom: Valentine's Day celebration photos, touching little notes and greeting cards, and a couple of giant teddy bears that meant everything to her years ago but disgusted her now. Making a mental note, she realized it was way past time to completely be free of anything that reminded her of Rashad's time as her spouse.

"Alexis, thanks for opening up my blinded eyes. I've been so busy and probably never would have noticed," Kiara said in all sincerity. "All of his shit has got to go. Now I need you to get him on the phone, because I still won't have Nicole Greene continue to act slick and do this highly inappropriate baby shower."

"Yes, ma'am."

Alexis was more than willing to do whatever

Kiara asked. Ever since little Jazz was born, she and Kiara had made a truce.

It happened unexpectedly.

Kiara's body was healing and she was still on maternity leave, but she had cabin fever. When her daughter was four weeks old, she bundled up the baby. They went for a long ride. She ended up outside the building where she worked on the college campus. Shyla Perry-Fallender happened to be walking past just as Kiara arrived and parked. Shyla texted Nicole that the baby just arrived and she should come see. It wasn't long before a tiny crowd of Kiara's staff had gathered next to her vehicle, smiling and waving at Jazz.

When Nicole blurted, "I'm not sure who this baby looks like," Alexis jumped in.

"Little Jazz is legitimate. She's born inside of a marriage. That's the only thing that sensible people need to know."

Nicole shut her mouth. And Kiara knew Alexis had her back from then on. And she promised to do the same for Alexis, no hard feelings.

So after Alexis spoke with Rashad on the phone, the two women chatted and took care of Jazz. Less than twenty minutes later, Rashad pulled up in the driveway of the Fresno house. He got out of the car and felt a jolt of nostalgia. There were the potted plants that he'd bought for Kiara a couple years ago. And he recognized the wooden bench that a carpenter friend had made especially for him.

"Pieces of me are still here," he said with pride as he traveled up the walkway and rang the doorbell.

Alexis let him in.

"Well, damn, it's like that?"

"It's like that," she said.

"And knowing Kiara, she's probably the one that gave you the bright idea to file for child support. I was already taking care of Hayley. So did Kiara put you up to getting the courts involved?"

"You're so off base, Rashad, it's laughable."

"Why'd you have to go and do something like that when we had our own financial arrangement?"

"Because of that insane chick that you live with . . . I had to protect my daughter. Couldn't take any chances. Plus the extra hundreds of dollars a month truly helps out."

"I love my daughter and will do whatever to help her, but don't remind me."

"Bye, Rashad."

At that, Alexis made herself disappear so he and Kiara could have some privacy.

Rashad looked around the house, scoping out anything that seemed foreign and different.

Kiara was waiting on him. He said hello to her before he started rambling. "Man, I miss this house. I can remember the day we closed on this place and moved in. All those damned boxes scattered everywhere. Remember that, Ki?"

"Ki? You haven't called me that in I don't know when."

"Tell me about it."

Kiara discreetly looked at his left hand. He wasn't wearing his wedding band. Good!

"Anyway, it feels weird to be back in this house. It kind of smells the same . . . except more like a baby . . ."

He kept babbling on and on until Kiara said, "Please be quiet, Rashad."

She invited him to go sit in the dining room.

"Have a seat."

He sat.

"There'd be very few reasons that I'd want to see you back on these premises, Rashad, but something has happened that I think you need to handle."

"What? What happened? Are the kids all right?"

"Here, look at this."

She handed him the shower invitation.

"This," she said, "is an insult."

"What? Oh. Yeah."

"What's up with that name?"

Rashad's face contorted with anger as he realized what was bothering Kiara.

"Hold on, don't tell me you're trying to tell us . . . I mean *her* what she can name her baby. That's *her* baby."

"I know, but isn't it shady for Nicole to do something like that? My baby's first name means 'princess who is blessed,' yet she's naming her kid Eminent or some shit like that."

"Eminence. It means 'greatness' or 'prominence.' "

"I see. Prominence Forever. When did she come up with that?"

"It's *Eminence.* And I don't know when she thought of it."

"You know. You know damned well Nicole thought of that name right after I had Jazzy and asked Alexis to send an email to the staff announcing our daughter's birth. I got great feedback from my employees and people texted me excited about Jazzy's name and her baby photos. And I remember back then, someone mentioned that Nicole was supposed to name her child Tristan. To me that sounds much better. So I don't understand how you can let her change her mind and end up printing these invites."

"Kiara, are you blaming me for what Nicole does? Because, guess what? I can't completely control her. And you can't either. You're just going to have to ignore her and stop letting her get under your skin."

"Really, Rashad?"

"Yes, really. Because you can't be calling me in crisis mode every time that woman does something that you aren't feeling."

"You know what. This is rare, but I actually agree with you. She and I are two different women. Why would I expect her to think and behave just like me? I don't know what you ever saw in her."

"Calm down, Kiara, and tell me something. Why can't you simply get Nicole on the phone yourself instead of always putting me in the middle of your beefs?"

"Because it's damn near impossible to hold a rational conversation with her. It's almost like if you're a woman, she wants to fight with you. There's just something off about her. All I know is that she's extremely competitive. And two highly competitive women can rarely see eye to eye." She paused and wished he could understand. "The reason that I get you involved is because you may not control her but you stand a much better chance of reasoning with Nicole. You've got her whipped. And you can try to get through to her for me. Just ask her to reconsider. Make up something. I'll even help suggest alternate names. Just do not let her name that baby Eminence and hold the shower at your house."

"If I do that for you, what are you going to do for me?"

"That sounds like a loaded question. So what exactly are you talking about?"

"Hold on a sec. I gotta use the men's room." Rashad rushed from Kiara's presence and ended up in his former master bedroom. Alexis was perched on a chair toying with her cell phone. She glanced up when he walked in.

"What are you doing in here?" she asked.

"I had to use the men's room."

"Oh."

"May I see the baby? Is she here?"

"I think you'd better clear it first through Kiara."

"Why do I always have to make sure it's okay with Kiara first? Do you know how powerless that makes me feel?"

Alexis said nothing.

"Skillet, you know me. You are probably one of the few reasonable women in my life, even though I hate that you filed on me."

"It had to be done."

He frowned and sighed. "Anyway, why is Kiara acting like this?"

"Are you serious? She's hurt. You hurt her. *I* hurt her. Hurt people do hurt things."

"What can I do to make it better? Make things change so she can stop punishing me?"

"To be honest, Rashad, I have no idea."

"But you were able to get on her good side. I

don't see you two going at it like enemies. Why is that?"

"Maybe it's because I decided I needed to forget about myself and think about Kiara. Putting yourself in someone else's shoes helps you to understand them. Rashad, you can be a selfish asshole and until you change your ways, you'll keep getting the same results. Now I would suggest that you don't bother her about anything. She is still trying to heal from everything that happened, and whether you like it or not, she deserves to be happy."

Rashad studied the ceiling for a moment. It would probably be the last time he ever set foot in the bedroom again and maybe even the house. He remembered how Myles would come and jump in the bed and settle in between him and Kiara so he could go to sleep. Back then he hated the interruption, but now he longed for that experience again. Rashad felt tons of regret, but it seemed too late to change the time. "Thanks, Alexis. I may not agree with you all the time, but you've always kept it real with me."

"Sometimes we need that."

"All right, let me go use the restroom and I'll get outta here real soon. I probably do need to have a conversation with Nicole."

"You do that. And good luck." And she meant it.

He returned to the dining room. "Look, you don't have to do anything for me, Kiara. Forget I ever asked. I will talk to Nicky. The decision, though, will be hers, all right?"

"Thanks for trying."

When Rashad got home and confronted Nicole about the invitations, she feigned innocence.

"Babe, it's all my fault. I tried to change the content on the invites but it was too late. But don't worry. That name isn't written in stone."

"Good," he said, relieved. "Don't decide right now. But once she is born, look at her and the expression on her face will tell you what she wants to be called."

Nicole just stared at Rashad and said, "Will do."

One day before Nicole's due date, she was getting dressed to go to work. She was running late. It was seven a.m. When she was in the laundry room looking for some fresh underwear, her water broke.

"I guess this is it," she said to herself.

Nicole found her cell phone and placed a call to Shyla.

"Hey, girl, what you doing calling me so early?"

"It's time. Can you meet me at the Southwest Memorial?"

"Oh, wow. Do you want me to come get you?"

"No, I think I can drive myself."

"Where is Rashad?"

"Before he left for work he told me he was going to have a very busy day. I tried getting him on the phone, but it went into voice mail. I can't worry about it. This baby is not going to wait on him, and I'm not either. So you gonna have to be my baby daddy for a minute."

"I'm on my way."

It was June fifth.

Nicole felt some kind of way about having to drive to the hospital while she was in labor.

When she tried calling Rashad again, she couldn't get him. She called Shyla once more.

"Where are you?"

"Nicole, I'm on the way. How far along are the contractions?"

"They're not too bad, I guess. Hell, I don't know." She paused. "I need you to call into the job and let the boss lady know I probably won't make it in today. I wish I knew where Rashad was." Nicole hung up and drove to the visitor parking lot. Shyla pulled in a few cars behind her.

They hurried to check in and she was admitted.

"Um, Nicole," Shyla said as she was being wheeled down the hospital corridor.

"Yeah?"

"Our boss is out of the office today. Alexis told me that today is their final court date for the divorce proceedings. They are on the docket for nine-thirty. Actually, I saw this info on the Internet, but I thought you'd have your baby after their case was completed."

Nicole wasn't surprised. In her mind, it seemed that somehow Kiara Eason was always trying to upstage her.

"I'm so sorry. I know you wanted Rashad to be there with you. I know how superstitious you are."

"I hate that this is going on right while I'm in labor, but what else can I do? Ask my doctor to delay my baby's birth another twenty-four hours? It sucks, but even if Rashad can't make it in time, he's going to be an involved father. That much I know."

Hours later, at 1:06 p.m., Eminence Forever came into the world screaming her lungs out. Nicole took one look at her and decided yes, she was royalty, so the name sticks. The bundle of joy had a head full of hair and was a mixture of pink and brown. Nicole was instantly in love and was very happy and grateful for her child, even though Rashad wasn't there to witness his daughter's birth. It didn't matter to her because Nicole was thinking that by the time she returned home from the hospital, her married boyfriend would finally be divorced and completely hers.

The first thing Nicole did after her daughter was born was set up her Instagram account. She posted photo after photo whenever Eminence had any new developments. Her constant hashtag was #EminenceForever or #NicolesFinest.

When her daughter was two weeks old, Nicole wanted to go to the mall. She asked Rashad to go with her. She wanted to be sensitive to him since he had just survived the divorce and she wanted to again clarify the settlement terms.

"So are you sure we are going to be financially all right, babe?"

"What? Oh, yeah. We kept our respective vehicles and will pay off our own credit card bills. We got joint custody, which is what I really wanted to have. And the best thing about it, Eason and Son Contractors was considered separate property since my daddy founded that company. So that's all mine. Our bank accounts were split, even the secret account she tried to hide. But our profit sharing and my retirement were divided. And, of course, they got me good on child support."

"Ouch, that sounds like a whole lot."

"If it weren't for my business, I'd be screwed. I took a little bit of a hit, but it just means I have to work harder, accept bigger projects, and keep grinding."

"Whatever you need to do, I'm here for you, babe."

"Thank you, my ride or die."

When they arrived at the shopping center, she asked Rashad if it would be all right to purchase a few items for Emmy—her baby's nickname. He said absolutely. Excited and grateful, Nicole bought Disney rompers, a dozen onesies, Mickey Mouse bath robes, and a nanny cam.

"Why'd you get this nanny cam?"

"When I go back to work, there's no way in hell I'm going to place my child in a daycare center. So many questionable things go on in those places. I won't take any chances. So I've already started interviewing nannies, Rashad."

"Nannies? Are you kidding me?"

"I'm very serious. Emmy is going to get the best care by a highly recommended nanny. I'll make sure that she really loves children and I will contact as many references as I can. I will hire her a week before I return to work. And you best believe my eyes will be monitoring her whenever she's in our house."

"I don't think we need a hidden camera. That's like an invasion of privacy. We will just have to trust her." Rashad argued with Nicole about the pros and cons of paying for peace of mind. And they both decided to get a nanny but scratched the idea of a nanny cam. Nicole promised to return the camera and get a refund.

The first time Kiara saw Emmy was a day she'd never forget. Five weeks and three days after the start of Nicole's maternity leave, Nicole made a comeback appearance at work.

Kiara had actually just returned from lunch. Alexis went with her that day. They ate at a Louisiana grub hole-in-the-wall near downtown. So when Kiara pulled up to her parking space in the employee parking lot next to their building, she was more than curious when she noticed an unusual scene.

"What the hell is going on?" she asked Alexis.

"Maybe that's the president's car?"

The president of Texas South West University usually was chauffeured around the campus either in his deluxe golf cart or a state-issued luxury vehicle.

"This is not President Hoffman's Escalade."

A sleek black late-model town car was parked at an angle in the lot right in front of Kiara's reserved parking space. A uniformed chauffeur leaned against the passenger side of the car.

"You'd think Beyoncé had just popped by the campus for a visit."

Alexis said, "I think she has. And she must be carrying Blue Ivy." She pointed at Nicole, who was dressed like she was going to the club. She had on six-inch heels and a short black dress that exposed her thighs. She wore dark sunglasses and was pushing a baby carriage that had all the works. Bottle holders on each side. A stroller base and a rocker base. It had a sunshade to protect the child from the sun.

"Is that one of those thousand-dollar strollers that famous people buy? The Orbit Baby travel system. They call them the Lamborghinis of strollers. Look, it even has a paparazzi shade. If I didn't see this sick shit,"—Alexis laughed—"I sure wouldn't believe it."

"This is just ridiculous. She's not rich. She ain't famous. Who does she think she is? Ciara?"

"Ciara has an adorable baby boy, so no—"

"Nicole is such a show-off. Where'd she get the money to afford that type of carriage?"

Then it clicked. Ever since Nicole became known for helping out the children during that tragic fire, the public went out of its way to help her. They deposited over twenty thousand dollars in a GoFundMe account that a total stranger started up for her.

That, combined with the fact that Nicole had hooked up with Rashad's cash, made Kiara feel the entire scenario was so unfair; that this woman had financially benefitted from other people's pain.

"You know what, she can do whatever she wants as long as she doesn't touch me and mine," Kiara decided. "I'm leaving her fate up to God. That's what Mama Flora told me and that's what I plan to do."

"You're so right, because as soon as you start plotting and scheming on Nicole's level, you may find yourself backed into a corner so tight that you won't be able to get out of it."

"One day she'll get what's coming to her," Kiara said. "Like she says, she's going to do her and I think we should let her."

"Agreed."

And the two women walked away together and quickly changed the subject.

Chapter 13

Thinkin' 'bout My Ex

Ajalon Cantu walked down the steps of the Greyhound bus. He'd just been let off on the southern edge of downtown Houston. It was 5:35 p.m. on a Tuesday in early August. He traveled through the busy terminal and out the front door onto Main Street. This was his first time in Texas. He silently beheld his surroundings. Several men who wore tattered clothes sat on the hard concrete. Their backs leaned against the exterior wall of the bus station. One elderly man's bony hand was stretched in front of him.

"Got any spare change?"

Ajalon flipped a fifty-cent piece and watched it drop onto the man's filthy palm. He shook his head in sorrow. The face of Houston's urban plight looked just like his native New York.

Ajalon dodged oncoming traffic as he headed across the street to the McDonald's located at Main and West Gray. He ordered two double cheeseburgers, large fries, and a cup of coffee. He took his time eating his meal. Then he opened his leather wallet. Only thirty-five dollars remained. He also had a prepaid debit card with a hundred-dollar balance.

Ajalon killed some time inside the restaurant by toying with his cell phone and looking up info. He plugged in his wall charger and took advantage of some free electricity. When he finally returned to the streets, the sun was slowly lowering itself. A vibrant streak of orange indicated that the day was over, and night was about to begin.

Ajalon boarded the number 41 city bus; soon he was on his way. An hour later, when he reached the neighborhood he wanted, his shoulders were taut with nervousness. Would she be shocked to see him? His pride told him that she'd be happy and it gave him the strength to continue his journey.

The streetlights were shining down upon the house that Ajalon was looking for. The one-story dwelling appeared quiet and peaceful. He wanted to ring the doorbell, but the van in the driveway made him reconsider.

He glanced at the house once more, then proceeded down the street. He observed his surroundings and noticed several cars that looked like they were at least twelve years old. Luck was on his side when he grabbed the heavy door of a Pontiac sedan and it sprung open. He quietly slipped in the backseat. It smelled of musty laundry and motor oil. Ajalon grabbed a wrinkled beach towel and balled it up. He rested his head on the towel and crouched in the darkness. Tired and anxious, he drifted into sleep.

When morning light woke him, Ajalon's legs were cramped. Yet he was glad to realize that he still had a neck; he was still breathing. His stomach growled and he felt the pang of hunger. For a minute he missed being in the joint. At least he knew they'd feed him while he was there.

When Ajalon grew tired of being crouched in the backseat, he quietly exited the Pontiac. With his light skin and straight dark brown hair, he foolishly wondered if he'd stand out. Ajalon was a handsome man who wasn't aware of his looks. When women passed by him and smiled, he barely noticed them.

He had a lot on his mind and ended up walking all through the neighborhood from morning until afternoon. But when he returned to the little house and noticed a man emerge, get in the van, and drive off, Ajalon felt ready.

He went up the door and pressed the doorbell.

It was the morning of Wednesday, August fourth. The streets were quiet and peaceful.

He heard the padding of house shoes sliding across the floor.

From the other side of the door, a voice rang out, "What the hell?"

The door swung open. There she stood, the woman he hadn't seen in ages.

When he grinned, his dimples sunk in.

"Hi, lady. I just got into town from Seattle. And I wanted to know if I could borrow a quarter . . . till I get my check."

At first she stood with her mouth wide open.

"That's not funny. You ain't been to no damned Seattle."

"Nicole, baby. It's me."

"I know who you are."

"I thought you'd laugh. Why aren't you laughing?" His eyes sparkled with delight.

"'Cause it's not funny."

"Okay, sweetness. I'm no Kevin Hart. But aren't you still glad to see me? Aren't you going to say *ciao*?"

"How about *arrivederci*?" she said sarcastically.

Nicole's remembrance of the Italian word made him chuckle. His heart warmed at the sight of her; the Nicole he knew could usually act sassy and hard. "You're still the same little firecracker."

"Ajalon! What are you doing here? And how the hell did you find me?"

He glanced out at the street. "I will tell you all about it. But can't you invite a bruh in?"

"What? No. I-I can't."

"Why not? I'm here for you! I remembered your birthday is August second."

Nicole's eyes lit up. He was lucky that he caught her at home, which was only because she decided to take off a couple of days from work due to her birthday.

"I wanted to celebrate with you. And I came all the way here because of you. I'm so, so glad to see you."

"Oh, Ajalon."

"I've missed you. *Ti ho mancato.* Did you miss me, Nicole?" He reached out and grabbed both her hands and brought them to his lips.

Speechless, Nicole could only shake her head.

She shivered as he brushed his lips across her knuckles. At that moment, she knew without a doubt that Ajalon had missed her. He was rarely shy about expressing his feelings for her. It was one thing that she loved about him. Still in disbelief, she snatched back her hands and took a good hard look at her ex-boyfriend.

Ajalon was tall and lean, yet his chest was broad and his shoulder muscles looked toned and tight. His body seemed to be in perfect shape. He had nice even teeth and a chipped tooth that gave him character. But it was his eyes that got to Nicole. His eyes conveyed a lot. If he didn't like someone, his facial expression could be brutal and vicious. Yet they also held a kindness she found irresistible.

The sound of a police siren screamed in the distance. Ajalon begged her. "Nicole. Please let me come in. It's hot as hell out here."

She finally smiled. "You're loco. You're from Brooklyn and you should be used to the heat." She glanced out the door and told him, "Hurry up. But you can't stay long."

He smiled back at her and quickly stepped inside the foyer.

"This is nice, Nicole." He walked through the living room and scoped his surroundings. He noticed lots of photos of Nicole and her baby.

"Eh?"

"No, Ajalon. That isn't your daughter."

"Just checking. Next time?"

"Please."

He looked as if he wanted to grab her in his arms. The thought of that frightened Nicole. It all felt like a weird dream and she didn't know how to act. "W-why are you here? How did you find me?"

He pointed at the HD television that covered nearly an entire wall of the living room.

"You're famous, Nicole. I saw you on the news a while ago. On this channel, and that channel. Internet."

"Oh. That. Damn."

"So I knew you were in Houston. And when I got back in the outside world, I went to the place where we used to stay. I saw some old mail that was supposed to be delivered to you. It had a forwarding address label. And—"

"And you decided to head out west unannounced."

"Why do I sense that you don't want to see me? Didn't you care if I was dead or alive? Why did you stop coming to see me? You stopped taking my calls. You never sent me a letter."

"Ajalon. It got too hard for me to deal with. I couldn't take your being locked up anymore. Too much was going on. Things started feeling sad. I wanted to feel happy again."

Nicole's face reddened with shame. She was sure he felt like she abandoned him; that her one hundred pledges of loyalty turned into one hundred disappointments. The man who stood before her used to almost be like her son, except he'd been her lover. She took Ajalon in when he had nowhere else to go; when his family told him point-blank that he had to make something of his life and then treated him like a stranger. Nicole was three years older than he was. Now he was twenty-three. Still young; still virile. Yet he had a hardened edge to him courtesy of the streets and to that two-year bid he served courtesy of the State of Alabama.

"Ajalon, I need you to understand that I had to get away because I decided I needed to start over again. I wanted a new beginning."

"And you need to understand that you hurt me when you left me without even letting me know that you left me. I kept looking for you to visit. Day after day visiting hours came and went. I eventually figured out you weren't coming to see me again. And I felt more alone than I ever felt in my life. I-I sat up in that jail and pictured myself ending it all."

"No more. Stop. Please." His words made her feel like trash. "I-I'm truly sorry, Ajalon. I wanted to tell you my plans but I couldn't. I didn't want to go back to what we used to have. I hated when you'd go on those road trips delivering that dope. I was always scared that one day you wouldn't come home. And I decided I wanted more."

"That's cool. You wanted what I want. I want more, too. With you."

"Oh, Jesus Christ," she said. Confusion pounded at her brain. She could not believe he was in her house. They had been together as a couple for several years. He got arrested and she stuck by him for almost a year. Then she left. When she relocated to Texas last summer, she never thought she'd see this man again.

"When'd you get out, Ajalon?"

He turned away from Nicole and began sniffing.

"Um, ahh, yeah. That's it. That smell brings back memories."

"What brings back memories?" she asked as she stared at him and became mesmerized by his appearance.

Ajalon was a man of mixed heritage whose features made him resemble the rapper Drake or even Vin Diesel. His mother, Callista, was from a wealthy family and was born in Calabria. His dad, Lorenzo, was African-American mixed with Italian. Lorenzo was raised near Birmingham but his family relocated to Brooklyn when he was a kid.

Ajalon was a lighter version of his dad: his wide almond-shaped eyes, unusually thick eyebrows, and ethnic features caused him to get noticed in her home town. Most of the men in her hood didn't look like him and they gave Ajalon a hard time until they got to know him. Even though dating the New York transplant brought negative scrutiny, Nicole had always been proud of the fact that her boyfriend was incredibly handsome, young, and exciting to be around. Even though he foolishly got caught up in the drug game, he had a good heart.

"I can smell your collard greens and sour cream cornbread. I haven't tasted food like that in a minute. And I am hungry, Nicole. I need my strength. Can you feed me?"

"Ajalon!"

"What?"

"My cooking will make you fat." She laughed in spite of herself.

He couldn't stand it any longer. Ajalon placed his arms around Nicole. He allowed his embrace to enjoy her body. Her breasts felt fuller, hips even wider. Motherhood had served her well. And he felt very jealous that the baby wasn't his, and that another man had been with his girl.

"You look better than ever, Mami." He let her go and suddenly pretended like he was running. Lifting his legs high up, he asked, "Remember how we used to go jogging in the park? How we had goals and we would motivate each other to be our best?"

His energy was magnetic. Nicole couldn't forget how much Ajalon inspired her; he made her feel sexy and aware of her body when they'd work out together. But after prison became his home, she had no one else to motivate her. And because he wasn't around anymore, back then she started to let herself go. She didn't care about how she looked when her man was locked up. Being pretty didn't matter anymore.

But now, when she looked at her ex, her memory was awakened.

"We ran. We walked," Ajalon said. "We talked. We held hands. We got fit together. We did everything together! You remember that?"

She grew sober as he excitedly rehashed his memories. He was great at recalling the good. But she wanted him to remember the bad times that made her flee.

"I remember you getting arrested," Nicole told him. "And I remember a lot of us running from the police and nearly getting caught."

"But you got to stay in the free world, didn't you? I set you up with a nice little fence parole. Johnny Law never saw you. And now you are free."

"Am I?"

"But it's all good," he told her. "I got to do my cat nap instead of the nickel term that they gave me. So all is forgotten. Except the good times we shared. They won't ever be forgotten," he said and winked at her.

Nicole's eyes glazed over. The time they spent together in Birmingham seemed a million years ago. It was such an odd yet exciting time. The two of them met through a mutual friend. They hit it off immediately. Ajalon liked Nicole the moment he saw her. He hung around her the way a toddler clings to its mother. He never wanted to let her out of his sight. She was annoyed at first, but because of his persistence, charm, and willingness to prove himself, she gave in. She wanted him in her life. She taught him everything she knew, like how to be responsible, how to deal with his problems, and what it takes to be a good man. And he taught her how to relax, have fun, and take risks.

"I know you want a new beginning. But I want old mixed with new," he said, interrupting her thoughts. "Me. You. We're good together."

"Hmm, Ajalon. According to your family, we're not good for each other."

"Ouch. Tsk tsk tsk. Do not remind me." Then he said, "You're my family. You!"

"Ajalon, that was then. I have a whole new life now."

As if on cue, Eminence began to cry. Her little whimpers tugged at Nicole's heart.

Was she wet, hungry, or hurting?

Nicole ordered her ex, "Wait right here."

She quickly disappeared down the hall. She walked over to Emmy's crib and peered lovingly down at her. Her baby girl's mouth was wide open as she fussed and twisted in her bed.

"You sure are loud. I wonder where you get that from?"

Nicole reached down and lifted up the big girl into her arms. Emmy was now almost nine weeks old.

"She gets her mouth from her pretty mother."

Ajalon was standing and looking over Nicole's shoulder. She could feel the heat of his body as it pressed against her.

"Oh, you scared me," she said and moved away. "Please don't do that. I told you to wait for me."

"I have been waiting too long. I can't wait anymore, Nicole. I am serious. I came here to apologize and tell you to your face that I messed up. I was young. I was dumb. But now I'm a man. I know what I want."

"Ajalon, please."

Emmy squealed even louder.

"I gotta take care of my daughter."

"I'll help you."

"What are you talking about?" She felt annoyed. He always was skilled at getting his own way with her.

"Nicole, you don't seem to understand. I wanted to show you, not tell you. But . . . *ti amo.*"

"Ohh. Hmmm." Her knees felt weak at his confession. In all the years she knew him he'd never told her specifically that he loved her. But he was excellent at showing her and she admired that. While they were together, she would tell Ajalon that she loved him; he'd play it off like it was cool and then change the subject.

And right then Nicole didn't know how she felt about him expressing his love. She thought about her life. Thought of Rashad. And their child who needed them.

"Did you hear me?" he asked. "Do you understand? Let me say it in English. I love you, Nicole Kelly Greene." She adored the way he pronounced her name.

Ajalon stared into Nicole's eyes; she felt herself

getting drunkenly lost, like her blood alcohol level was dangerously high. She wanted to collapse. "I feel like I could use some water."

"I'll get it for you."

Ajalon went straight into the kitchen, opened the refrigerator, and twisted off the cap of an ice cold bottle. He brought it to her and lifted the container to her lips.

"Drink."

She did.

"More."

She drank more.

"Better?" he asked.

"Yes. Thanks."

He drank the rest of the water and wiped his mouth with his hand.

"I can't believe this," she said when he was done.

"Why can't you? Did you not believe you would see me again?"

Emmy let out a piercing wail. Nicole immediately went to grab her daughter.

"Follow me," she told Ajalon.

They returned to the living room and she sat down in a comfortable chair. Feeling shy, she placed Emmy face-down on her chest. She hesitated then she pulled out her breast. Emmy hungrily sucked on her mom's nipple. Nicole thought about how much love she had for her baby. The baby was a great distraction because it felt too bizarre to have her former lover sitting in the room staring at her while her breast was partially exposed. She found a towel and covered as much of herself as possible and continued.

"Look, Ajalon, when I decided to leave Birmingham, I honestly didn't know if I would ever see you again. And pretty much a year ago, I really didn't care—"

"Don't say that. Please—"

"I'm just telling you how I felt . . . back then. I wanted out of that place. I felt like life had stopped for me. You were locked up. My family kept coming down on me and pressuring me about my decisions. Everything was making me crazy. I didn't want to keep going through that. And even though it was very hard, I could no longer picture us with a future together. I wasn't willing to stick around to see what happened. So I-I ended up applying for a lot of jobs out of state. Georgia, Florida, and Arizona. But I got a gig in Houston. That's why I'm here."

"Okay. You didn't want to wait on me. That's a man's greatest fear when he's locked up."

"Oh, I thought his fear was turning into a batty boy."

"It's called making tortillas in prison. I never made a single tortilla. You feel me?"

Ajalon stared straight into Nicole's eyes. She knew he meant that.

The first time they had sex was a little clumsy yet amazing. Ajalon had a tinier frame back then. And she was big boned. So she had to ride him. It was his first time allowing a woman to take over in bed. By the time Nicole was done with him, she had Ajalon screaming for his mama. She aroused sensations that they both had never felt before. They were sweaty, exhausted, and sore. And after they took a break, they did it again. Nicole and Ajalon used to go at it three times a day all over their apartment. These days she and Rashad got it in about once every two to three days.

Nicole continued to breastfeed Emmy and was lost in thought. She never noticed Ajalon lean over. He licked his moist lips and tried to press them against hers. As soon as he made contact, she jerked back. His lips felt dangerously hot and smooth. His breath smelled like mint. A shiver ran through her.

"No," she said and wiped her mouth. "You can't do that. Not anymore."

"You got a Sancho while I was gone?" She knew "Sancho" meant a man.

"How you think I got this baby?"

"So you're serious? This is not my baby?" He pulled back the blanket that partially covered the little child's face.

"Stop it. You know she's not yours. You know what happened to our child." She shot him a daggered look. The pain of the memories weighed on her.

When Ajalon went into prison, she came to see him every day. And when she found out she was pregnant, she arrived at the prison as soon as visitors were allowed. She wanted to spend every available moment with her man so she could break the news that she was having his baby. At first Nicole felt elated. But as the long days stretched into endless weeks, the more despondent she became. Her future looked bleak. She had to make a decision. And when she finally came to see her man after terminating the pregnancy, it was the first time Nicole saw him enraged. He shouted Italian profanities. The guard had to come out to see what was wrong with him. She walked out while he was talking. And that's when she decided she'd had enough. Her love for her man just wasn't enough.

"I'm sorry, Bella," Ajalon said referring to the pet name he called her at times. "If I hadn't been so stupid, I could have stepped up to the plate and been there for you and our child. Put it all on me." Water filled his eyes. She knew prison hadn't made him as hard as he liked to pretend it did. Her Ajalon still had a heart that could feel and mourn and react.

Nicole covered her mouth with her hands and tried to control the achy lump that expanded in her throat. She didn't want to disturb Emmy, who had, magically and mercifully, fallen asleep.

"I'm sorry," she apologized. "I'm having a moment."

"You don't have to apologize to me. I know you. We were almost like a married couple. But I was too young to handle you. I'm older now."

"Ajalon, everyone is older now."

He laughed. She wanted to laugh, too. To Nicole he still sounded young. He was nothing like Rashad, a man that didn't mind going out and working hard every day. In fact, she felt he worked too much. She felt concerned that Rashad's job took him away from her as if his work meant more to him than she did. But he assured her that he was working hard for her and his seed. She felt Rashad didn't need to put in all those hours now that she had thousands of dollars remaining in her GoFundMe account. Something did not feel right, but when she first got with him she ignored her gut and reasoned that Rashad was a businessman and a workaholic.

"Okay, Ajalon. You saw me on TV, you said you're sorry. I accept your apology. But now you need to go back from where you came."

"What?"

"I said you can't be here."

"It's a free country," he sputtered, sounding frustrated. "I can relocate to Texas just like you."

"You're right. It is a free country. But you might lose more than your freedom if you stay here. Texas is nothing like Alabama. These law men will shoot you down in the streets like a dog if you get out of line. If you resist arrest, you're giving the state an excuse to fire at you. All they gotta do is say that they feared for their life and another black man gets a new sign made with his name emblazoned, his own crowd of protestors, and another mother grieving for her son. The cop will get off. And they'll put it behind them and get ready for their next shootout."

"Nicole, thank you for my 'Don't Mess With Texas' speech, but I paid my debt. I was a model prisoner. I hated that place. And I don't plan to go back."

"It doesn't matter. That part of you that got you there in the first place is still inside of you, Ajalon."

She hoped her words weren't hurting him but she knew they could be.

"Are you trying to say once a criminal always a criminal? Are you saying you stopped believing in me because of one careless mistake? Ha! Drugs should be legalized anyway."

"I am saying—"

"You're saying that *you've* changed, Nicole. That you've forgotten where you came from. Or that you were a liar all along and I just didn't know it."

He jumped to his feet and angrily paced the floor, his voice loud with passion.

"You were the one who made me believe in myself at one time. You told me that I had it in me to be a great man, and that I could do good things with my life. And when I come to tell you that in spite of what I just went through, that I believe in myself for the first time in my life, you don't welcome it but you coldly turn me down? You tell me that I am nothing but a criminal who doesn't deserve a second chance at life. Even though you got a second chance you're saying that I cannot have one? Is that what you're trying to tell me, Nicole?"

"I-I don't know—"

"It sounds like that's what you're doing. You forgot about me and moved on with your life. You had a dream like Martin Luther King and you are living it now and you don't want me to mess it up." He paused. "Why do you deny me the right to dream when it's probably because of me that you can even live your dream?"

She had no words. This grown-up Ajalon wasn't going to back down. She stared at him as he pointedly stared at her.

"Bella, what type of job do you have? Where do you work?"

"Ajalon—"

"Where?"

"I-I work at a college. I do a lot of PR activities for our unit and handle a lot of journalism type duties. It's cool because I'm working in my field."

His eyes lit up. "That sounds very professional and much better than that job at Taco Bell."

She laughed and nodded. Taco Bell was where they first laid eyes on each other. Nicole was a spirited UAB student carrying twelve hours a semester and working part-time. And one evening Ajalon Cantu bounced into the restaurant with a friend of hers. Ajalon joked with Nicole, took up a lot of time in her line asking for ridiculous things that weren't even on the menu, and made a nuisance of himself. She couldn't resist his youthful charm and after a lot of relentless persuasion, she gave him her phone number. She was curious. Ajalon seemed different. He called her the very night that they met. They chatted on the phone for three hours, and he had spent his time chasing Nicole ever since.

"I like my job a lot. It's given me everything I need at this point in my life."

"Everything?"

"Just about," she replied, thinking of Rashad and her plans of being his wife.

"And this is where you met the . . . the mysterious Jody and father of your child?"

Nicole lowered her eyes. When Ajalon first got locked up and she went to visit him, he warned her not to let a "Jody" into her life. So she knew he was referring to a man who steals the ladies of inmates. And she resented his implication. "You have no right to ask me that."

"Why not?"

"I just don't want to discuss that with you."

"You don't? Are you ashamed of your Jody?"

"His name ain't no Jody!"

"Then what is it?"

"I ain't telling you."

"Don't matter. I can still find out. I picked up a lot of new skills while I did my bid. Remember, I'm just a criminal."

"Why would you say some young-sounding shit like that? You're crazy."

Ajalon felt he needed to scale back. He didn't want to anger Nicole. So he calmed down.

"If I am crazy, I'm crazy for you. You make me crazy. So tell me about him. What does he do for a living? Riding around in that white van? What is Eason and Son? He's a junk dealer?"

"That's ridiculous. You have no idea what you're talking about," she said, feeling nervous that he had noticed all those details about Rashad. "And I-I just don't think it's right for you to be questioning me, okay?"

Her eyes clouded with anger. His being in her presence was unexpected. Why did he come by bus and why now? She was afraid the happy police had come to snatch away her joy. She'd been through hell and deserved better. Her mother always warned Nicole about karma, but Nicole refused to listen.

Ajalon studied the woman who had turned him into a man. She was deliciously hot to him. She was so unlike the type of women his family pushed him to date. Nice Catholic girls who were seemingly perfect on the outside but crazy as fuck on the inside.

The woman he chose to love was rough around the edges, but he knew Nicole's sweet side. He knew it before, when life with her went from carefree to careless. He was handcuffed and escorted to jail for selling drugs. Nicole tried to hold onto her sweetness until she grew afraid, then tired. Even so, Ajalon realized Nicole still possessed her warm, nurturing quality. He recognized it on the TV screen when he saw a news reporter interview her. She had a quality that allowed her to care about people who had nothing to give her in return. And he remembered how Nicole cared about him when he was an uncontrollable bum running the streets.

"You still love me."

Ajalon stated this like it was a fact. He noticed that Nicole let him in the house where she probably made love with her man. She could have rejected him, but she let him in.

Ajalon lifted her chin with his fingers. "Do you love me?"

"Don't ask me that."

"If we tried again, we could make it work this time."

"I-I don't think so," she said softly.

He snatched her left hand. "You are still single."

She snatched her hand back. "I won't be single forever."

"You say you've been here over a year, and now you have a baby. Why didn't you get married?"

"It's complicated," was all she could say.

"Does your Jody already have a lady?"

"I can't answer that."

"He does, doesn't he?"

"Not answering that, Ajalon."

"Answer this. Does he love you the way I love you?"

That was a good question. Nicole wasn't really sure. She knew how she felt about Rashad, but she wasn't positive of how he felt about her. Sometimes she felt like he was going through the motions, other times she felt like he was captivated by her, and that he appreciated her loyalty. But love? It was still up in the air.

Although the divorce was complete, Rashad never discussed getting engaged to her. With each passing day Nicole got nervous, but still held onto her hope.

"I know he cares about me. He loves our daughter."

"All I can see is that you are single. That means you can be mine. If you marry me, Nicole, you would never be single again. We'd be together till death do us part. Just like all good Catholics."

"Oh, Ajalon, here we go again. You know I'm not Catholic."

"But you could be . . . we could do this, Bella. We could get a place together just like we did in Birmingham. I would apply to study at the university. You could get me in. I'd go to class while you worked. Remember how you encouraged me to give up the drug trade and do that? I could work part-time and help out around the house. And once I earned my degree, I could get a better job and take care of you, the child . . . and we could have our own child again. A handsome son that takes after his father. We could show both our families that they were wrong about us. How does that sound, Nicole? Would you like that?"

"Oh, Ajalon, why do you do this to me?"

Just then Nicole's cell phone rang.

The ring tone was the new song by J. Cole.

Ajalon stood back and watched Nicole as she motioned at him.

She answered, "Hey, babe." She put Rashad on speaker.

"What you doing?" he asked. "Man, I am working so hard I can't see straight."

"He's old," Ajalon said in a loud whisper. "And he sounds like his breath stinks."

"Um, I'm here doing nothing," she said, trying not to laugh. "Feeding the baby."

"I'm the baby," Ajalon said. He pretended to pick up a fork. He pointed it straight at Nicole's breast and acted like he was eating off of it. "Yum. Tastes delicious and juicy."

Rashad didn't hear Ajalon. The sound of a drill operating roared in the background at the same time he'd been talking.

"What you say? I can hardly hear you."

"Never mind, Rashad. Um, anyway, what time will you be back here?"

"I should be home at the usual. You miss me?"

She put him off speaker. "I um, I can't wait to see you. Talk to you later."

Nicole hung up on him mid-sentence. She felt so bad. Rashad asking her if she missed him was extremely rare.

Ajalon's eyes twinkled. "The gods have revealed Jody's real name. Rashad, eh?"

"Oh, my God. I didn't mean for you to know that."

"I've got what I needed." Ajalon rose to his feet. "And I will go now. But I will be back," he told her, "I want to see you again real soon."

All she could say was, "We'll see about that."

Chapter 14

Crazy for You

A few days later, a mere fifteen minutes after Rashad drove off to one of his weekend gigs, Nicole heard the doorbell ring.

She opened the door and placed her hand on her hip.

"Don't think you 'bout to make this a habit." She peeked both ways and then let Ajalon in the house.

She swung around to face him after securing the door. "What do you want?"

He just stared at her with his chipped tooth exposed and grinned.

"I swear to God," she said and left him alone. He followed Nicole, this time to the kitchen.

"Aren't you going to give me a tour?" he asked.

"What? It ain't like this is a mansion. It's just a nice little house. It's home."

"You're just the happy little family now?"

"Please, Ajalon."

"Why do I make you so nervous? You never used to be this uptight. I know what it means when a woman is uptight." He made pumping motions with his hips.

"Ugh," she remarked in disgust. She scuttled around the kitchen preparing Emmy's bottles.

Soon Nicole felt the heat of Ajalon's body against her backside. He pressed his warmth against her flesh.

"Move, Ajalon."

He began to grind against her butt.

It actually felt good to Nicole. She waited a few seconds and managed to squeeze herself past him.

"What the fuck you doing?" she asked.

"I'm doing what you told me to do. I'm moving, baby."

She moaned and sighed. He grabbed Nicole around her waist and started grinding against her. A sexual dance where he took the lead. Soon she was swaying with him. She closed her eyes and rocked back and forth, like she didn't have a care in the world.

He turned her around so he could press his hard-on against her butt. He wrapped his arms around Nicole even tighter. He sniffed her neck and enjoyed the fragrance of her perfume. His lips grazed her neck as he gave her several kisses.

Nicole shuddered and continued to rock with him. She wanted to completely melt at Ajalon's touch. It had been so long since she felt his hands on her body. They used to make love until she was exhausted. She would scream her head off with

Ajalon. Not so much with Rashad, but it was still good.

Just then Rashad's face popped into her head. She stopped moving and broke Ajalon's embrace.

"Look, it's been nice hanging out with an old friend. But I-I can't be doing this. It's crazy. It's too dangerous. I mean, you weren't in my plans. Not at all. I-I'm sorry, but you need to leave. Like right now."

"I can't believe you're acting brand new."

His voice filled with hurt he grabbed his head in his hands in dramatic fashion. "I've listened to you, Bella, and now I need you to listen to me. Do you know how many hours I had to sit my ass on that miserable bus? Gotta sleep with my eyes open in case someone tries to jack me? That's what I went through for you, my love. Traveling on a crowded bus across the entire South just to get back with you, to surprise you for your birthday, to let you know how much I miss you and want you. I plan to remain here in Texas. And this isn't the welcome I wanted to get from you."

"We can't always get what we want."

"And what do you want?"

Instead of replying, Nicole busied herself with the bottles that were almost ready. "Look, I don't want to hurt you. I don't. So, before anything bad happens, I'm saying good-bye. You need to walk out that door . . . and never come back. I'm serious."

"Don't do this."

She pointed to the front door. "*Arrivederci*, Ajalon."

He laughed.

She did, too. But her laugh quickly faded. She heard the sound of Rashad's van pull up into the driveway. It was early on Sunday morning. Rashad liked to play his music loud. He was banging Tupac Shakur's "Shoot 'Em Up."

Nicole began to hyperventilate. "Oh, fuck. My man's home. What am I going to do?"

"I'm glad he is home. You can tell him the news for us."

"What the fuck? There's nothing to tell. You need to get out of here." Nicole raced to the front and placed the double bolt on the door, which was the entrance Rashad usually came through. "You probably will have to leave through the back door. Come on."

"No."

"What?"

"I'm not leaving. He needs to know about me. And if you won't tell him—"

"You're messing with my life now. It's not funny. I don't play when it comes to things like this."

"I'm not playing either. So what are we going to do, Bella?"

Nicole thought quickly. She knew Rashad would try to insert his key in the door any second. She grabbed her ex's hand and dragged him down the hall. She stopped midway then reached toward the ceiling. She pulled down the latch that opened the small door to the attic. The stairs lowered and she pleaded with Ajalon.

"If you love me like you say you do, you won't want to hurt me. I have a child to think about. But he's here now so we gotta talk later. You need to go in the attic and hide out till I see what Rashad wants. Then after he leaves, I'll come get you. We can go out to eat. I may even help you find a place to stay here. But you can't keep coming—"

She heard a loud bang on the front door and her cell phone started ringing.

"It's him. Please, please go upstairs and try not to make a sound."

"Can you give me what I want?"

"I-I'll try."

"Do you love me, Nicole?"

"Oh, Ajalon!"

"Do you?"

"*Ti amo.* Now go."

Smiling, Ajalon sprinted up the stairs and disappeared in the darkness of the attic. Nicole put the latch back. She began praying harder than she had ever prayed in her life.

"Oh, God, please get me out of this. If you do, I swear I will do better. Please don't let anything bad come out of this."

She choked out a quick sob and then recovered.

Nicole got herself composed, ran down the hallway, and undid the double bolt.

Rashad walked in and looked her up and down.

"Why it take you so long to answer the door?"

"I was busy and I didn't hear—"

"Why did you put the bolt on it?"

"Uh, I dunno. I wasn't aware that I did that." She wandered away from his questioning eyes. "You know how some crazy people have found out where I lived since I was interviewed. All kinds of folks been lurking around . . . trying to get me to talk to the media."

"Oh, yeah? Like who?"

"Just people. Nut cases. They pound on the front door and they scare me sometimes."

"Why didn't you tell me?"

"You already have enough to worry about, plus I still have my gun."

"Oh, but you don't want to catch another case. You were lucky enough that the assault case was dropped. But don't get any weird ideas with that gun."

Before Nicole's case went to trial, the prosecutor dropped the charges. Alexis was pissed, Nicole felt fortunate and vowed to never get in trouble again.

"I was very lucky," she replied to Rashad. "I'll do my best to never wave that gun again."

Satisfied with Nicole's answer, Rashad went to the bedroom. He looked around and came back out to Nicole.

"You see my toolbox lately?"

"Um, isn't it in . . . I thought it was in the van?"

"Nah. I got some new tools and I can't remember where I put 'em."

"Do you really need them right now? Like, can't you just go to Harbor Freight and get some more?"

"Not if I've already bought them, Nicole."

"Oh, well." She wrung her hands together and avoided his eyes. All she could think about was the man in the attic. Her clothes clung to her and felt wet and sticky.

Rashad disappeared from the room. Nicole followed right behind him. "Um, I thought today would be a slow day for you. Is this a big job? Are you going to be gone all day? What's your plan?"

"I don't know yet, Nicky. I hadn't thought about it."

She tried to calm down. "I haven't been doing too much. The baby has been fussing a little."

"She has? What's wrong? You need me to stay—"

"Oh, no. No! It's not that serious. I-I will feed her. I've already sang to her—"

"That's what probably made her agitated."

Normally Nicole would tease Rashad back about how he couldn't sing, but she hardly felt like joking.

It grew quiet. A sharp thud could be heard.

"What was that?" Nicole asked, almost in a panic.

"Sounds like it came from above us," Rashad answered. "You want me to go check it out?"

"No."

"You sure?"

"Rashad, don't be silly. I'm tripping. It's probably some type of, um, squirrel on the roof again."

Another thud sounded.

"Can you please go outside? Please, Rashad, go outside right now and look; go see if anything is on the roof. I won't feel safe until you go outside. So go. Now!"

"You sure are acting scared. Afraid of a little harmless squirrel."

"They got sharp teeth, though. And they're just . . . scary."

"If it's on the roof it can't hurt you."

"Go look anyway. Please?"

Her vision was so blurry she nearly bumped into a wall as she followed Rashad and made sure he stepped outside.

She immediately closed and locked the back door behind him.

"I can't take this. This is too much."

A bright light went off in her head. Her mind's eye showed her the last place she saw Rashad's toolbox. She raced to a hall closet and grabbed it before he could get back into the house. She went outside and met him in the backyard.

"Nicky, I don't see anything."

"Don't worry about it, babe. I'm sure it was nothing. Anyway, look what I found. Here you go. See you later. I've already gotten started on brunch and I can finish it and have it nice and ready for you when you get back home."

They walked side by side to the front of the house. Her leg nervously shook as she stood in the driveway and watched Rashad get in his van and put it in reverse. She refused to go back inside until she could no longer see his van.

Nicole went into the house. She locked the door behind her then stood in the foyer and cried for five minutes.

"I dodged a bullet. And I guess this is karma or karma's cousin," she finally said to herself before leaving the foyer and going to get Ajalon and make him leave her home. "But that chick is not welcome in my house."

Chapter 15

Meet Me in the Park

The next time Nicole saw Ajalon was the next Saturday morning in August. She placed Emmy in her fancy stroller and began walking down the street. A neighborhood park was two blocks away. The weather was sunny and beautiful. It was the perfect day to get out of the house.

By the time Nicole reached the park, she felt someone come up behind her. A hand tugged at her elbow. She swung around, her heart beating wildly inside her chest.

A strange man wearing a dark colored hoodie was reaching for her purse and trying to rip it from her shoulders.

"No!" she screamed.

Before she knew it, Ajalon jumped on the man and threw him to the ground. They wrestled for several minutes. Ajalon pulled back his arm and socked the man in his jaw over and over. Blood spurted from the shocked man's mouth and he begged to be let go.

Ajalon stood up, sweating and looking wild with anger.

The attempted robber fled the scene and glanced behind him to make sure he wasn't being pursued.

"He scared me to death and tried this in front of my little baby." Nicole found the nearest wooden bench and sat down. Feeling dazed, she didn't say a word when Ajalon sat next to her. He scooted close beside her. He grabbed her hand, lifted it and kissed it.

She sat next to him and kept wiping her watery eyes.

He let her cry for a couple of minutes then used her phone to call the police. "Don't cry anymore. He can't hurt you now."

"I know. He could have killed me and Emmy. Thank you for saving me."

"That's my job."

"But to be honest, I'm sitting here thinking about what just happened plus everything else that's going on in my life. I thought I would be happy, but I've been stressed as fuck lately."

"Tell me about it."

"Sometimes I wonder if I have post-partum depression."

"Did you act like this before I came into town?"

"Um, no."

He gave her a sad look.

"But I don't think it's all your fault. I think it's just life in general. So much has happened. Some good, some bad. It just gets to me, that's all."

She poured out her heart to her ex and soon calmed down.

"My life is so busy. I rarely have any free time to myself anymore. I love it but I'm still adjusting. And then my man seems to leave me alone to handle things I've never done before. It's a lot to deal with."

Ajalon nodded and firmly held her hand as he listened.

"I guess I just needed to vent. But still, you being out here on the streets next to me feels crazy. What the hell are you doing in Houston? I-I—"

"Shhh, no one can stop fate. It's meant to be."

"But—"

"The day I got discharged from the pen, I went to look for you. But I had to go see my peoples and get the money to do this trip to come see you. It took a whole month. I was sweating like a mass murderer on the run. I didn't want too much time to pass and I end up missing you. So after I got my funds together and closed up some loose ends, I made my way to downtown Birmingham on North Nineteenth street. I bought a bus ticket; but it was storming like hell. Raining like Noah was about to build a brand new ark. But by the time the bus left the Tragic City at two-ten in the morning, the thunder had stopped, the lightning was gone. It was peaceful and calm. And later that morning as we pulled out of Jackson, Mississippi, the sky was blue and crystal clear. The rest of the trip we had lots of sweet sunshine and no road breakdowns. I took it as a sign that it was all right to make this journey. And fifteen and a half hours later, there I was in the same city again as my girl."

"Ajalon, good weather isn't enough for me to sit

up and tell you, yes, we're meant to be together. I need a lot more than that to be convinced."

"I need your help and obviously you need mine, too. How can you be safe when the one who you say loves you is always gone? How can he protect you when he's never around?"

"Rashad went through some financial difficulties and he has to work," she said, agitated.

"No one has to work that much."

"He does. Divorce costs a lot. So does child support. And he has to make back money that he's lost."

"Ah, so he does have another lady."

"Why am I telling you this? Anyway, I think working takes his mind off things. That's why I gotta hold it down for him at the crib."

"Okay. Being with Rashad is wearing you out. I see the tiredness in your eyes. Love shouldn't be so stressful. If you were with me, it wouldn't feel like work."

She listened and said nothing.

"Bella, it's getting hard out here. I have been sleeping in cars—"

"You what?"

"Yes, ever since I got here, my address is an unlocked car on a forgotten part of the street. I've been lucky so far, but what if that luck runs out? I need a place to stay. I want to get back in school. My funds have run out and I need a job. Can you help me out?"

"Wait a minute. Your decision to come here shouldn't involve me. Do I look like a leasing agent, a college counselor, or the unemployment office? When I left you, Ajalon, it was over. Now it seems like you're dragging me back into your life."

"I need you."

She stood up. "This is where all this needing me stuff stops because you're starting to stress me the fuck out."

He stood up, too.

"Are you sure about what you're telling me? That I have no right to need you? Have you forgotten that if it weren't for me, you wouldn't be living such a nice royal life?"

"Ajalon, I don't wanna hear it."

"Because when we were together, you could have had a run-in with the cops just like me. You could be a felon, just like me. Then you'd have no nice house. No pretty baby. No working man. You'd be like me . . . hoping that someone, anybody, would help you."

He told her how he came this close to robbing a Houston homeless woman after he saw her counting the cash she collected that day.

That did it. She couldn't let him return to a criminal life.

Nicole promised that she'd help him and told him she'd call him via cell and that he shouldn't pop up at her house anymore. They departed and she thanked him again for possibly saving her life.

That day Nicole immediately placed some calls. By the end of the week, she had Ajalon set up in some temporary housing. With her assistance, he was able to sign a three-month lease for a reasonable rate. She funded the entire expense and he promised to repay her.

During Nicole's lunch break at work, she submitted online applications for Ajalon and she snuck and created him a professional looking résumé.

On the evening that he moved into his new modestly furnished place, she and Ajalon developed a pattern.

After Nicole laid Emmy down in her crib, if Rashad came straight home, she fussed over him and made sure he had a good meal. Then she told him that she was going to walk on the trails at the park near their house. It was still light outside. She got dressed in her biker shorts and halter top and drove away in her Mustang.

But instead of going to the closest park, she ended up driving a few miles away to Arthur Storey Park, located right off of the Sam Houston Parkway.

Nicole parked her car and began a power walk around the nearly two-mile-long track. A few minutes later, Ajalon, who caught the bus from his apartment, also got on the track and hiked a close distance behind her.

Nicole started out scrutinizing all the bikers, joggers, and children at the park. She hoped no one recognized her, and they didn't. It would take her an hour to complete the walk. That was plenty of time for her to do everything she needed to do.

After a while, she passed by her marker, a retention pond filled with ducks and frogs. She hung around and listened for certain sounds behind her.

"I'm here. It's me," he said loud enough for her to hear.

"Okay," she told him without turning her back.

"What you got for me?"

"I will place it on the next park bench."

"How much?"

"Two hundred."

"Word? Thanks."

Nicole resumed walking. She heard Ajalon behind her. She smiled as she imagined the view her ex was getting of her juicy plump ass. She got wet just thinking about it. But more than anything she wanted to be very conscious of her surroundings. She paced herself and eyeballed any person who caught up with her. After they passed by and when it was clear that only she and Ajalon were again alone on the trail, she spoke up again.

"You still there?"

"You know I am."

"I think I have a gig for you."

"What is it?"

"First of all, none of the leads that I've tried so far have worked out. No openings. They either just hired other people and have no more jobs, or the requirements are out of your league, and so on."

"Okay, so what do you have for me instead?"

"I'm kind of leery because I don't want anything to go wrong, but I've given it some thought and I think you can handle it."

"And?"

"You can work for my guy."

"Your guy? Are you crazy? Why would I do that?"

"It's quick money. And it's tax free."

"Why?"

"From time to time, he pays for manual labor under the table."

"How much? What would I be doing?"

"You'd do whatever he tells you to do. I don't know how much it pays. But I'm sure it's better than zero dollars and no cents."

"You are one crazy lady. I mean that in more ways than one."

"I am crazy," she yelled behind her. "Just like you."

They continued to argue back and forth as they walked.

"I am not feeling this type of setup," Ajalon protested.

"It would only be until something better pops up. You already have bills and you need to make your own cash. And as long as you're very careful, you should be able to handle this. It's just temporary."

Nicole saw an empty bench and sat down. She discreetly placed an envelope with the money on the seat. He sat right next to her. And she hopped right up. He grabbed the envelope and stashed it in his pocket.

And they continued this routine that they kept several times a week through the end of August.

Nicole would work all day and think about Ajalon. She wondered if he was okay. She'd rush home and see the nanny off. She'd cook dinner and wait till Rashad got home. He'd eat and tell her he loved her cooking but he didn't understand why she suddenly starting making more fattening foods. He'd urge her to lose some of her baby weight and said walking would help. He offered to watch Emmy and do the dishes. Nicole would thank Rashad for being so supportive and understanding.

Because of Rashad's helpfulness, Nicole and Ajalon were able to talk and bond and see each other on a regular basis.

A week later, they texted each other and planned to meet again. But instead of arriving at the park and waiting for Nicole to start off first so he could follow her, on this particular night Ajalon walked straight up to her car as she got out.

"Let's go," he said.

"Are you crazy? You can't be seen talking to me. My guy knows a lot of people and they will go back and tell him whatever they notice. Get away from me. I will walk and you follow."

"If they notice everything, they will notice that we are always at this park yelling at each other like two crazy people."

"It's safer for us to yell at each other than it is for me to have long conversations with you on my cell phone. Why leave a paper trail? And right now, I don't want to talk to you. I can't take any chances of being seen with you, Ajalon. Bye."

Nicole broke out into a sprint. Her heart rate increased immediately. Ajalon was so dangerous. She felt like being involved with her ex would bring much trouble to her life. But she also felt responsible for him. It had always been that way.

After a while, Nicole slowed her pace. She walked slowly so she could catch her breath. She listened for the sound of his footsteps.

"Are you there?" she said aloud when she heard the pitter-patter of feet.

"I'm here," said a voice. Within seconds Rashad stepped in place next to her.

"Ahhh," she screamed and grabbed her chest. "You scared the living shit out of me. What are you doing here, Rashad?"

She was tempted to turn around and look for Ajalon, but she was way too frightened.

"I happened to be driving by."

"What do you mean you happened to be driving by? Where's Emmy?"

"The nanny is there with her."

"Oh, Rashad. That's crazy. I-I wish you would have told me about this. We've never had the nanny over at the house in the evening."

"I asked her to come by. Told her it was an emergency. That I'd pay her extra. She said okay."

Nicole froze. "And so how did you find me way over here?"

"Why would you say it like that? I was out and about due to an emergency. I was going down the feeder road after I went to Home Depot. And I saw your car. I'd know it anywhere. I felt so proud of you and your commitment to working out. So I thought I'd surprise my baby."

"You surprised me all right." She paused. "Look at you. You're not even wearing the right clothes or shoes."

"My body doesn't know that, though. I need to exercise just like you do."

Oh, shit, she thought, *he picked a fine time to think about his health.*

"Rashad, that's nice that you want to walk, but I think you should go back right now. I don't want Emmy around the nanny at night."

"What are you talking about? She's with her all day. So why would this time be any different?"

"I don't know. Doesn't she have her own family? I'd think that she'd want a break and time to be with her own kids."

"There you go. Thinking about others before your own needs. But don't worry. Emmy is in good hands. It was a quick emergency, that's all."

"Oh, Jesus."

As Nicole sped up her pace, a wad of cash fell from Nicole's pocket. She was too worried to notice anything except Rashad.

Ajalon had been behind them all that time. He waited until they walked ahead a few paces. He discreetly swept the money into his hand and stuffed it in his pocket.

Ajalon turned around and started jogging in the reverse direction.

"Nicky," Rashad said, "why did you come here instead of the park near the house?"

"I dunno. No special reason."

"Well, you need to let me know which park you're going to in case something ever goes down. I'll be thinking you around the corner and you're not . . . unless you want some privacy . . . ?"

"No, nothing like that. I just enjoy this atmosphere. It's um, very relaxing out here."

Rashad took a look around and saw some sexy looking women running past them. "You're right about that."

Nicole allowed Rashad to walk with her for another two hundred yards. Then she told him she felt sick. She began running in the opposite direction. She felt around in her pocket for the money she was going to give her ex.

"Oh, shit."

When she searched the trail on the way back to her car, she never did see Ajalon. She could only hope that he got the money that she wanted him to have.

Chapter 16

Boss Man

It was almost six-thirty in the morning, a Tuesday morning during the second week of September. The air was unseasonably cool and the sun's brilliant face was hidden by the cloud-filled sky. Rashad had left the house and was driving up to the spot where the day workers gathered outside a Home Depot. It was a sad scene due to all the unemployed men desperate for work. Most of the men struggled to speak English. They were hard workers but Rashad hated the language barrier. He didn't trust anyone that couldn't speak his language.

He got out of his truck, along with Jerry, one of his employees.

"*Hola,*" Rashad said, addressing a small crowd. "*Habla usted inglés?* English speaking only. I need two men."

He was immediately swarmed by ten workers who were jostling each other, ready to jump through the open door of Rashad's van.

"Hold up. Stop! I only need two. What's your name?" Rashad asked the guys. They simply stared at him.

"No. Go! English only. Do you understand the words that are coming out of my mouth?"

Ajalon quietly approached Rashad. He was wearing some steel-toed boots and was dressed like he was ready to work. He forced himself through the circle of men.

"What up, man? I'm Cornell Cantu. I need day work. I can do inside or outside jobs. I'm young and healthy. And I speak perfect English and some Spanish—" He started to say that he was fluent in Italian, too, but he remembered Nicole's warning during one of their walks at the park: *Whatever you do, don't refer to yourself as Ajalon. He knows that name. I don't want any trouble. The second you give me trouble, your ass gots to get the hell out of Texas.*

Cornell was Ajalon's middle name. And luckily for him, he had two driver's licenses, one with his complete legal name, and one which a clerk messed up and thought his middle name was his first name. He never corrected her. Both had addresses in Vestavia Hills, Alabama.

Rashad asked, "Do you know OSHA regulations?"

Ajalon nodded. He made a mental note to ask Nicole about that.

"And what size you wear?" Ajalon gave him his sizes.

"Today's your lucky day, Cornell. Get in," Rashad told him. They shook hands. Then Rashad walked over to the crowd of men. He hammered them with several questions until he found an older gentleman who swore his English was perfect.

"Please hire me, sir. I got a family. They're my motivation. I do a good job for you."

"C'mon, man."

Rashad and the man walked back to the van.

"Cornell, meet Enrique."

"I'm Henry for short," the guy said as he crawled into his seat. He had beady eyes and a big nose the shape of an eagle's beak.

Ajalon was no nonsense. "You may call me Cornell."

Soon they were on their way. During the trip Rashad described the type of work the men would be doing. "We will be tearing down drywall, other basic demos, taking down cabinets, wood paneling and painting."

"Aw that's easy. I can do all that," Henry said as he took a long drag on his cigarette.

"It's hard work. I should have told you this up front, but it pays eleven an hour. And if you do a good job, I'll be back tomorrow, same time, same place. Is that a deal?"

"Sounds good to me," Ajalon told him. "How long does this job last?"

"Two to three weeks."

"When do we get paid?" Henry asked.

"By the day."

"Good. I can handle that. Just as long as you are honest and pay me for the work I do," Henry said.

"If you honestly do the work, I promise that you'll get paid. Just stay out of trouble."

The men were driven to the work spot, a two-story mansion located in the Galleria area. Rashad let them out of the vehicle along with Jerry. "Whatever he tells you to do, do it. He's my eyes and ears. I'll be back to pick you all up later today."

Jerry supplied the guys with uniforms and they were shown all the materials and tools that they'd be using.

The men worked hard and finally took a break for lunch.

Jerry offered to go pick up sandwiches and drinks for them.

"This lunch run will take fifteen minutes," he said. "Your break will last for about twenty minutes after I get back." Jerry had to walk a couple of blocks to a restaurant and he didn't mind. He wanted privacy and he knew they'd probably appreciate the same.

As soon as Jerry left, Ajalon started exploring the house. The home had the tallest cathedral ceilings he'd ever seen.

"I feel like I'm in a damn library or something. Look at all this space."

"Ahh," said Henry. "This is nothing. I've worked in houses much bigger and more expensive than this. It's all right."

Ajalon ignored Henry and continued inspecting every room. He noticed the pricy fixtures in the kitchen and bathrooms. "An athlete must live here. This spot gotta be worth one mil easy."

Henry enviously looked at the top-of-the-line kitchen appliances.

"Cornell, the boss man must really trust us," Henry said with a wry grin.

"He has no reason not to trust us. I'm here to work. I hope you are, too." Ajalon left the man looking stupid as he went to the bathroom. He saw all sorts of raw materials lying around the place. But he didn't care. Being tempted to steal wasn't one of his vices. He had a plan and he was sticking to it.

All that morning, Ajalon wished he could speak to Nicole, but he knew it was too risky. She'd already warned him that Jerry wasn't to be trusted.

"Don't talk to him any more than you have to. He is sneaky as hell. So watch your back."

Ajalon listened and agreed to Nicole's instructions. But now he was starting to miss her. He picked up his cell phone and started to call her. Then he had another idea.

He used the bathroom and went to find Henry, who was puffing on his third cigarette. He flicked the ashes in the sink and didn't bother to rinse them down the drain.

"Hey, you think you should clean up after yourself, dude?"

"This ain't my house. I ain't gotta do shit."

"Whatever," Ajalon said as he gave Henry another steely look.

"Hey, man. I need to make a personal call but I can't get a signal on my phone in this place. You got a cell I can try to use?"

"I don't hand over my phone to strangers."

"What? We're stuck here if you haven't noticed. It's not like I can run outside and jump in my car."

"It's not like you can't run outta here and race away on those young, strong legs you got, either."

Henry was on the older side, so he was probably one of those guys who always felt he was in competition with the younger workers.

"Whatever, man."

"But you can try using the phone they have here. There's one upstairs. The landline is working."

Ajalon swiftly ran up the spiral staircase of the gorgeous mansion. He walked around and recalled that he had seen a phone installed in the wall of the master bathroom. The bathroom had a huge tub, two walk-in showers, a sauna, and double sinks. It was bigger than Nicole's entire house.

Ajalon opened a cabinet door and picked up the phone.

He heard a dial tone.

He glanced at his cell phone and then punched in Nicole's number.

She didn't pick up. He decided not to leave a message.

After a while he heard a commotion downstairs. He went on down and saw Jerry handing Henry a white paper sack.

"Hey man, where were you? What's upstairs that you had to go up there?"

"Nothing." Ajalon shrugged. "I needed to use a working phone. No big deal."

Jerry stared at him, then handed him his sack of fried chicken wings.

"Y'all got ten minutes, then it's back to work."

"But you said we had twenty," Ajalon protested.

"And now I'm saying ten," Jerry snapped.

"Yes, sir," Henry told him. "Ten minutes only."

By the end of the third day at the mansion, Ajalon was used to his routine. At the urging of Nicole, he searched the Internet on his cell and learned quite a bit about OSHA regulations; he was quick and accurate with his work.

After completing their work for the day, they

waited in front of the house for their ride back to Home Depot. But this time, instead of Rashad coming to get them, another dude whom Ajalon didn't know picked them up.

Usually they got paid as soon as they got back in the van after their shift ended. But the guy sitting in the driver's seat said nothing as he drove them back to the parking lot.

"Where's boss man?" Henry finally asked.

"He ain't here."

"I can see that," Henry said as he retrieved a fresh cigarette.

"You want one, Cornell?"

"Nah, I don't smoke."

When they reached the Home Depot parking lot, the driver pulled to the side and popped the locks. The men waited in the van. The motor was still running and the driver said nothing. Henry, who was about five feet three, crawled over Ajalon to sit behind the guy.

"Hey, thanks for the ride, but you got something for us?"

"I ain't got nothing for you. You'll have to see the boss man tomorrow."

"Hey," Jerry said. Although he was a salaried employee, he was always looking out for Rashad's best interests. "What's up with that?"

"You heard me. If they wanna get paid, come back tomorrow. Now get the fuck out."

Henry picked up his cell phone and tried to make a call. The man reached back and slapped the phone out of Henry's hand.

Livid, Henry popped the driver on the back of his head with a closed fist. "We ain't leaving this truck till we get our fucking money."

The man protected his head as Henry slugged him again. When the man still wouldn't pay up, Henry pressed a lit cigarette against the man's neck. Tiny particles of his hair and skin began burning. The smell was unpleasant, like smoked pork. The startled man jerked and screamed, then bolted toward the door, trying to get out of the van. Jerry pressed the button and locked him inside.

"Where's our money?" Henry screamed.

The driver emptied his pockets and threw almost three hundred and fifty dollars in the back seat.

Jerry exploded. "You were going to steal from the boss?"

"Rashad owes me."

"Then you needed to bring that up with him and not take the money from these workers."

"Fuck them and you, Jerry. You owe me five dollars your damned self."

Ajalon picked up the money off the seat, then he and the other men got out of the van. They watched the disgruntled man drive away.

"He's history," Jerry said. "That piece of shit will never work for Rashad again."

Ajalon counted up the cash and gave everyone their pay.

Jerry shook both their hands. "Thanks for handling that. You two are pretty cool. See you in the morning."

The next time Ajalon and Henry saw Rashad, he offered them more work.

"Next job is a big one. And I got you, Cornell. Jerry told me what happened. And don't let that dude scare you. He was on his way out anyway. I caught him stealing from one of the work sites. And I tested him by giving him some cash and seeing if he'd pick y'all up and pay you your money. I wasn't worried about no four hundred dollars. And I don't let people work for me who I don't trust. Don't forget that, you hear?"

"We hear you," Ajalon told him. With that he made plans to keep coming back to work for the man who held the key to giving him everything he planned to have.

Chapter 17

Stormy Weather

Kiara was adjusting to her new life. She finally went through every square inch of her house and unloaded each item that reminded her of the past. Eddison suggested she give Rashad's things to the Salvation Army, but Kiara packed his belongings into some garbage bags and gladly drove away to the nearest dump. Eddison couldn't help but laugh and beam at her with pride. She then recovered all of her ex-husband's books and sold them at Half Price Books. She only made fifty dollars out of the deal, but it was enough to buy tickets to the State Fair of Texas for herself, Myles, Eddison, and the baby. It was held in the Dallas area. They woke up that Saturday morning in late September and drove up I-45 in a rented SUV. The road was clear and the weather felt perfect.

She sat back in her seat and sighed with contentment.

"What are you smiling about?" Eddison asked as he glanced at her profile.

"Happiness, babe. I never dreamt I could be this happy."

"Well, I'm glad to hear that."

"Jazz did well at her recent check-up. I've lost all my baby weight. Got rid of all that trash." She giggled.

"I didn't want to say anything, but now that you've gotten rid of items that you should have dumped a while ago, your mind is going to be a lot clearer. You will be able to see the things that you were blinded to before."

"And how do you know that?"

"Because it took me years to get to that point after Nina passed. So actually you are doing better than me."

"That sounds impossible, too, Eddy."

"But it's not. I am learning you and I can see the pep back in your step. You are becoming a more complete woman."

The sweet words he spoke to her made her desire him in ways that she knew she could do nothing about. They were going to drive up to Dallas and stay at a Marriott one night, then head back home the following afternoon. The kids were in tow so love-making was out of the question.

"Hmm, I have you to thank for the good things that have happened. I mean, look at you. You are stepping up. I thought you would have changed your mind, but you didn't."

"I told you," he said. "You don't listen to me."

"I plan to listen to you from now on."

They arrived in Dallas hours later and were immediately struck by all the sights and sounds. They had fun exploring one pavilion after another. They munched on turkey legs and funnel cakes, played games, showed Jazz things she'd never seen before, and let Myles explain to them all the fascinating details about the animals that were housed at the farmyard exhibit.

Kiara thought it hilarious that he became an expert at a place he'd only just discovered.

"See that baby calf? He's only a few hours old, yet I think he weighs more than me. And that exhibit over there is where the chicks are going to hatch when they peck through the egg. And they are very curious and will wobble around, eat some food, then they'll close their eyes, lean over, and fall asleep with their feet up in the air."

"Sounds like someone I know," Kiara teased Myles.

"Yes, that sounds just like you, Mommy."

They all laughed and continued to let Myles act as their tour guide.

Life certainly was good. Kiara's family felt complete and she no longer cared if anyone gossiped about her or their judgment. It's what her family thought of her that counted.

At the beginning of the next week, Rashad was pleased with his work and decided to promote Cornell by increasing his responsibilities and upping his salary twenty dollars per day. During the last week in September, Rashad explained to his crew that he had to go on a trip that would keep him out of the city for ten hours. By then Ajalon had been in Texas for exactly two months. Life was going good. But he still wasn't where he ultimately wanted to be.

That Tuesday night after his shift ended, Ajalon's adventurous side motivated him. Instead of waiting for Nicole to show up at Arthur Storey Park like he usually did, he decided to catch the bus to her house.

It was twilight by the time he arrived on her doorstep. He rang the bell and was shocked when an attractive woman answered.

"Hello, may I help you?" The woman was holding Emmy in her arms and softly singing to her.

"Aww, Emmy. Such a pretty little girl," he said. "Is the child's mother or father home?"

"Um, who are you?"

"You must be the nanny. I don't remember ever meeting you. I'm a friend of the family."

"Your name?"

"Call me Cornell."

"Like the university?"

"Like the rapper Nelly."

"Oh! Well, neither she nor her husband is here."

His eyes clouded. "Excuse me? Did you say her husband?"

"That's what she calls him. I think. I'm not sure. Just forget it."

"I see. Um excuse me, miss, but is it all right with you if I come in and wait?"

"I am not allowed to let strangers in the house while my employers are gone." She started to close the door in his face, but he reached out and stopped the door from shutting all the way.

"I understand your concern. The parents are

very good to put you in charge of their child while they're not here. What's your name again?"

"Um, I am Miss Nadia."

"Nadia. That's a pretty name for a very pretty lady."

Ajalon hoped that Nadia was a sucker for a compliment. It looked like it as she began to relax and soak up his attention.

The sound of thunder ripped through the air. At sixteen weeks of age, Emmy was able to let out a healthy, piercing scream. Nadia grew worried as she peered up at the darkening sky. "I think it's about to storm."

"Are you all right? You look very afraid, Nadia."

"I hate thunder."

Lightning suddenly brightened up the sky. More thunder boomed. The atmosphere felt very static.

"Oh, my Lord," Nadia said. "The ground is shaking like we're in an earthquake."

"If you want, I will stay with you. There's nothing to be afraid of as long as you close this front door and think happy thoughts." Ajalon slickly slid inside the doorway but wouldn't go any farther.

"I will wait inside until this storm passes over. I'm sure it won't take long. Maybe the man and his wife will be back soon?"

"Oh, no. Mr. Eason is gone for the entire evening. I am waiting on his wife to return from buying groceries. She doesn't like to shop and try to look after her daughter at the same time. Sometimes I go with her, but tonight the baby was fussy. So she said she'd make a quick grocery run and would be back soon."

"You're a very caring woman to help her out like this."

"Why don't you come have a seat in the living room instead of standing there by the doorway? What if the lightning gets inside the house?"

He followed her inside. "I'm not worried about that. You'd have to be the unluckiest person in the world to get struck by lightning, Nadia. Wow, you have such a pretty name. And your eyes are so beautiful."

"Ohhh, thank you." She blushed. She invited him to sit down as she sat near him. The television was playing a music video channel. Nadia resumed singing to Emmy and smoothed her hair. "Are you the godfather?" she asked.

He said nothing.

"Cornell?"

He ignored her.

"Mr. Cornell, are you all right?"

"Oh, sorry. I was so mesmerized by your beauty I could no longer hear or speak. Forgive me."

She giggled and grew more comfortable.

"Are you married or single?" she asked.

Suddenly Ajalon looked up at a display on a table directly across the room. It was filled with a variety of stuffed animals. He stood and calmly approached the table.

"The baby has lots of presents and toys, eh?"

"Yes, she does. She's a little princess and gets whatever her parents want to buy her."

"I see."

Ajalon picked up the largest teddy bear. He began to feel around the stuffed animal, from its head to its paws to its feet.

"Cornell, what are you doing with the baby's toy?"

"Just looking." He located a zipper in the back of the teddy bear. Ajalon unzipped the cloth and continued fiddling around with the animal. Soon he found what he was looking for.

He produced a teddy bear spy cam and held it up. "Do you know what this is?"

She shook her head no in response.

"I'm afraid that your bosses don't trust you. This is a hidden camera. Who knows how long it's been there and what info it's picked up. I hope that it hasn't shown them anything you wouldn't want them to see."

She gasped and stood up. "Oh, my God. Maybe you should leave."

"I'm not trying to scare you, Nadia, but you should just stay aware of everything you do inside this house."

"Are there any more cameras?"

"Let's find out." Ajalon thoroughly investigated the remaining stuffed animals that were displayed on the table. Then he went into Emmy's nursery, where he found another one in her crib.

He returned to the living room holding the device.

"Got it."

"Thank you for what you've done. But won't my employer be upset to find out that you removed the cameras?"

"Would you rather I put them back? You tell me."

"Oh, okay. I'll pretend like I know nothing about it." She paused. "Thank you."

Ajalon thought quickly and ran into the hallway. He pulled the string that opened the door which led to the attic. It was there that he stored the hidden cameras.

As soon as he was done and returned from the attic, a thunderclap boomed so loud the house vibrated.

The baby cried even more. Ajalon gently removed Emmy from her nanny's arms.

"Shhh, it's going to be all right."

The front door opened and Nicole burst through the door. She exchanged an awkward glance with Nadia.

"What's going on?"

"Um, ma'am, Cornell came by and wanted to see you and your husband."

Nicole studied Nadia. "Okay. You shouldn't have let *Cornell* in here while we were gone. But it's okay. He's one of our employees." Nicole removed the baby from Ajalon's arms.

"Nadia, you may go now."

"A-are you sure?"

"Yes. It's fine. Everything is okay."

"Okay, ma'am."

She saw Nadia to the door and closed it firmly behind her.

"What are you doing here?"

"I thought we were going to walk but it is raining hard." He looked calm. "I knew that you probably wouldn't go to the park tonight."

"True. But still. You shouldn't have . . ."

"It's okay. Call your husband."

"Huh?"

"Call him. You're concerned about him. You want to make sure he's okay on the road. That he's reached his destination. You want him to know that you are fine and you're riding out the storm." He sounded authoritative as well as seductive.

Ajalon being there in the house with Nicole made her think of Rashad. Many days he didn't arrive home until his dinner had gotten cold. He wouldn't answer her questions about why he was so late. He'd say, "Business matters." And now he was gone out of town. She fought hard to believe whatever he told her. But occasionally she wondered what he was really doing. Who was he with? It was at those times that she was glad she had Ajalon to talk to. He was familiar. They had each other's backs. And she felt she needed him in more ways than one.

Soon Nicole was on the phone dialing Rashad's number. They spoke briefly. He assured her that he reached his destination, on the outskirts of Louisiana. And he informed her he'd be back tomorrow, but he couldn't tell her exactly what time.

"I just need to wrap up some loose ends here. Kiss the baby for me," he said. He was on speaker phone.

The thunder clapped again.

"Are you sure y'all will be all right?" Rashad asked.

Nicole had put Emmy in her crib. She was nice and snug and had even fallen asleep.

"We'll be perfectly fine," Nicole told Rashad as she stared at Ajalon. "See you sometime tomorrow."

She was trembling as she hung up.

Ajalon was leaning against the wall in between a doorway. She saw his silhouette. He was very quiet. But Nicole knew he was watching her.

She set down her cell phone and decided to go get something cold to drink.

As soon as she stepped into the kitchen, all the lights flashed then went completely out. The noise from the TV went silent. They were in total darkness.

"Are you all right?" she cried out.

"I'm wonderful."

Nicole couldn't see Ajalon anymore. But soon she smelled him. He groped around in the dark and managed to find her inside their house.

He reached out and found her hand and held it.

"Everything's going to be all right, Bella."

She swallowed deeply. Her mouth felt completely dry.

"I, um—"

"Shhh, come with me."

Heart beating wildly, she followed the voice that had given her the command. She walked in the darkness with Ajalon leading. He went through the house until he came to the back door that led to the backyard. They had a covered patio. It had a small slanted roof and an area with some patio furniture, several chairs, and a few potted plants situated around the covered area.

"What are you doing?" she asked.

It was totally dark outside, too.

"There must be a blackout. I hope it won't last long," Nicole said in the shadows of the night.

The sound of rain drizzled in her ears.

"Wait right here," Ajalon told her.

She waited.

Soon he returned. He fumbled around in the dark on her patio.

"What are you doing?"

"Shhh. You're about to have the most unforgettable time of your life."

She squinted and felt him standing in front of her. He pulled her down until she was sitting on the floor. But she knew she was on a thick blanket that he must have found when he went back into the house.

He had his cell phone with him and shone some light on her face.

She looked scared.

He began laughing.

"This isn't funny," she protested.

Soon Ajalon was sitting in front of Nicole. He leaned in and gave her a sweet, hot kiss. She was shocked. But she gave in and kissed him back. She soon closed her eyes. The darkness would hide her sins. She'd wanted to make love to her ex ever since the day he'd come to find her.

With the sound of thunder and rain in the background, Ajalon began to undress his love. His fingers felt cold yet warm as he removed her shirt and pulled it over her head. She kept her eyes closed as she felt his lips kiss her on her neck, her arms, her fingers, and her back.

He cupped her breasts in his hands and licked her skin over and over. It was so sexy. Nicole moaned and tilted her head. She felt like she was in a dream.

"Oh, Ajalon."

He quietly and confidently lowered her panties over her hips. He got undressed too quickly removing his shirt, wifebeater, jeans, and boxers. Together they fell back on the blanket. He started caressing her mound, rubbing it over and over as waves of pleasure made her shudder and groan. She was totally wet, completely his.

They kissed each other, allowing their lust to diminish their logic. Nicole had thought the love she previously had for him had died, but now she knew it was resurrected. She was born again and knew she wanted this deliciously desirable man inside of her. Rashad had been acting distant, but Ajalon was the one who gave her constant attention. His fingers caressed her until waves of pleasure made her tremble. Nicole grew hotter and hotter with want. As she stroked his body and covered it with kisses, she knew she hadn't planned on any of this happening. Not really. But now it was too late. Who knew what their future held? He was doing such a good job proving his love for her, even those things that Rashad couldn't always do.

Using his legs, Ajalon maneuvered her legs with his thighs and got ready to plunge himself inside her. As he pounded into her over and over, Nicole became completely lost in him. He built up a nice steady rhythm that grew more and more violent as he bucked and jerked. She moved with him, their bodies creating a sensual orchestra. Nicole never wanted that good feeling to end. She exploded in one orgasm after another. As the raindrops fell, she muffled her screams by sticking her tongue deeper and deeper in Ajalon's mouth.

He placed his ear against her mouth. "I've been waiting to make love to you for two years."

"Oh, Ajalon, what are you doing to me?" She bit him on his shoulder.

He moaned and said, "I'm loving you like I've always wanted to do."

"Ohhh," she responded.

She caressed his head as he pounded into her. It hurt but it was a good kind of hurt. Nicole came again and again and she finally murmured the words she knew he'd been dying to hear.

"I love you. Yes, I love you so much, Ajalon."

Nicole was enjoying herself to the fullest. Plus, she knew that no one could see them. It would be their secret. She'd do it with him this one time and get it out of her system. She loved him but she hadn't yet figured out if that meant she could try and be with him.

Like a couple on a honeymoon, Ajalon and Nicole fell asleep naked on top of each other on the patio floor. She stirred in her sleep then woke up abruptly.

"Oh, shit," she said. The power had been restored. The floodlights shone upon the backyard. She grabbed the blanket to cover her nudity. To her it felt like the lights had eyes and they were staring at her without blinking.

She woke up Ajalon and they went back into the house. She immediately began turning off all the lights.

"Why are you doing that?"

"It just makes me feel better."

"But we're in the dark again."

"I-I know that."

She deserted him to go check on her daughter. Thankfully, Emmy was blissfully asleep. Nicole quickly thought of something. It was a little after midnight.

She packed a plastic Kroger bag with panties, a bra, a shirt, some jeans, and a toothbrush.

"Um," she said when she returned to the living

room, "I don't think we should stay here. It would feel weird. I can't shit where I eat."

"I see. So what is your plan?"

"We'll go somewhere else."

"What about the baby?"

"Of course she's coming with us."

"I love it when you say things like that."

Nicole ignored his youthful flirty ways. She packed up Emmy and made sure the house was locked. They got in her car in the darkness of the night. She made Ajalon slump down in his seat as they drove out of the garage.

"Shit shit shit," she said to herself after they'd driven a couple of miles away from the house. "You can sit up now."

"This shit is wilder than Birmingham." He laughed.

"This isn't funny, Ajalon. I have no fucking idea what I'm doing and it feels so dangerous, as if I'm playing with gasoline and matches."

"But don't you like it?"

"Somewhat, yes. But I'm a mommy now. I can't be dragging my infant daughter out of the house just to be with my felon ex-boyfriend."

"What? Why did you give me a negative label like that? I am not that man anymore. That was one moment in time. It shouldn't totally define me."

"I know," she said, "I'm sorry. I'm just trying to figure out things. You gotta give me time."

They entered the freeway. Nicole jerked in her seat every time a car sped past them. She felt like a fugitive. Like her name and face was on the walls of every post office in the country. Even though it was night, she wished she'd worn a wig and some dark sunglasses. But it was only her conscience bothering her. She questioned if what she was doing would cause Rashad to be angry, but with his mysterious trips out of state she herself wondered if he was doing things that would make her angry, too.

When they found an out-of-the-way motel, she made Ajalon check in at the front desk while she and Emmy waited. Once he got a key, they drove around the parking lot to their room.

"What's the number?" Nicole asked.

"Room one sixty-six."

"Are you serious? Get another room. I don't like that number. That does not sound like a lucky number."

"You're being paranoid."

"Someone has to be."

To make Nicole feel better, he drove back to the front desk office and asked for a different number. "One on the second floor."

This time they got a room that was more suitable.

"Room two twenty-six," he said when he returned to the car. "Better?" He grinned.

"Perfect. Nice job."

They parked and walked up the concrete stairs with the metal railing to their second-floor room.

Ajalon waved the key and they went in and locked the door behind them.

"Why is it so cold in here," she complained.

"The cold is the last thing you should be worried about."

"Of course, humping is all you care about."

"I've wanted you, and last night was just the beginning, my love."

She smiled in spite of herself. It felt good to be chased instead of being the chaser. They set their things on a table and made sure Emmy was settled in her portable crib.

"Damn." Nicole yawned. "I am so exhausted. I'm going to call in sick in the morning and it seems like you will have to call in as well. There's no way I'll be able to go into work after the night I've had."

He had stripped down to his boxers. His muscles were taut and solid.

"Damn, you look good. I gotta give you that."

"Glad you like it." He came and sat on the bed and pulled the covers back so she could join him. She fell into his arms and enjoyed warming up next to his body.

He kissed her forehead. "Just relax. You aren't married. You aren't even engaged. So technically, you've done nothing wrong."

"But we've lived together for months. In Texas, you're considered common law if you live together for six months."

"But you two don't go around calling each other husband and wife, right?"

"No."

"But your nanny thinks so."

"That was a little glitch. Trust me. Rashad and I are not married."

"What are you waiting on?"

"Who in their right mind wants to get divorced one day and get married a few weeks later?"

"But isn't that what you want to happen?"

She nodded. "All I can tell you is that I prayed to God that if it is meant to be, let us be married. So I'm waiting."

"Until then you can enjoy being with me."

"All right."

He made Nicole sit up. They reminisced and laughed for another half hour. And when Ajalon gave her the look, she nodded. He slid down her body and let his tongue start working on her mound. She loved how he licked her clit over and over until she squirmed and jerked around in bed.

"You taste delicious," he said as he watched her facial expressions.

They made love until the morning.

Ajalon was deliriously happy. The one wish he wanted was granted. In his mind, she belonged to him again. Their destinies were intertwined. Feeling content, he fell asleep in his Bella's arms.

Nicole watched her ex spread out next to her. She couldn't believe that after all the progress she'd made with Rashad, now she felt like she was standing at a fork in the road. She still loved Rashad very much but was it possible to also love her ex, too? Although at first she didn't want to accept it, she realized that she and Ajalon had unfinished business.

She turned over in bed and tried hard to fall asleep. But all she could do was think about the man who was breathing soundly next to her. And she lay stiffly all night long wondering what she was going to do about her and Rashad.

By that Wednesday afternoon the storms had slowly moved out of the Houston area. Eddison was taking an extended lunch break from his job at TSWU. He had just arrived at a local park to get in a workout. He lifted his gym bag from the back seat of his Chrysler 3000. He reached inside and pulled out a tiny box. He carefully slid it into his gym pants and secured the zipper.

A few minutes later he was leaning against his vehicle as Kiara pulled up in her car right next to him.

They greeted each other and minutes later they began to walk on a trail in Memorial Park, which was located near the college campus. The sky was slightly cloudy but Eddison didn't care.

"This is one thing I love about being a manager in my position," Kiara told him. "We can take those much-needed extra-long lunch breaks and get in a nice workout."

"I agree with you on that one. I love getting to see you outside that place."

"Hey, Eddy." Kiara smiled, noticing that he was in a peppy mood. "Why are you grinning like that?"

"I have no reason to frown. I'm right where I want to be . . . almost."

"Almost? Oh, you mean out here getting your jog on?"

"Except we're walking so slow you can't call this jogging, woman."

"Oh, yeah?" She giggled. "I can take a hint." And at that Kiara bolted into a quick run. She zoomed far ahead of Eddison and could imagine him gasping for breath as he tried to catch up with her. She heard him yelling her name. And she finally had mercy on him and came to a stop.

"Damn, you are fast. And thanks for stopping. I wouldn't want to draw attention as a black man running real fast in a city."

"Oh, so sorry." Kiara laughed. "I didn't mean to put you in a position like that."

"I get it," he said. "You enjoy being chased. You know your worth and you feel like you're worth chasing."

"Am I?" she beamed.

"I think so."

"You think so? Humph."

"Tell you what. Let's go have a seat on that bench and discuss this in more detail."

"Okay," she said and casually walked toward the bench, which was a few yards ahead.

"You do the honors first," he commanded.

"Fine, I could use a break. Get some rest. From all this running I've been doing."

He laughed and lowered himself next to her on one knee.

"Why are you kneeling?" she smirked. "Proposing?"

"What? No! I'm actually stretching." Eddison placed one hand on his knee and began to do a vigorous stretch. He thrust his hips forward and moaned as if flexing his muscles felt good.

"Now, see, if you would be doing your job and taking care of me, I wouldn't have to be out in the park stretching in order to moan." Eddison's voice was sexy. He held the stretch and then repeated it with his other leg.

"Okay, you can stop with the lies." She flushed. Indeed, she thought he was going to propose to her. Maybe she was imagining things.

"Eddy, you know I enjoy taking really good care of you in bed and out of bed."

"Do you?"

He got up and sat next to her. It was then that she noticed the bulge in his long pants.

"I'm looking at the effects I have on you right now." She playfully attempted to touch the peculiar shape next to his groin.

"I got you hot and bothered out here in Memorial Park," she said as she fumbled for his slacks. But he stopped her before she could manage to get a solid grip on the box that he had hidden in there.

"I don't want to run anymore, Kiara."

"Okay."

"I'm serious. No more running. No more chasing." He expertly produced the box out of his zippered pocket. When Kiara realized what he was doing, she nearly screamed.

"Is this what I think it is?"

"It's whatever you want it to be, my love." Eddison pulled out a fourteen-carat rose gold ring. It featured two hearts filled with round diamonds. Kiara's name was engraved on the left side and Eddison's was on the right.

"This is so beautiful." She was stunned and happy and completely overwhelmed.

"I love you, Kiara. This is a promise ring. I want you to know for certain that I'm here for you. My heart is yours if you would have me. But I know that you've gone through a lot. And this is why I bought this to signify my commitment at this point in your life."

"My goodness, Eddy, I don't know what to say. Except I love you, too, baby. I'm committed to us being in each other's lives. You've made me very happy today."

She asked him to place the ring on her right hand. It fit perfectly.

"You are so devious." She laughed. "Now I know why you asked me all those questions a while ago. All my sizes, favorite colors, really personal stuff. And you did it just before I went to sleep so that I'd think I dreamt it all."

"You're not dreaming, sweetheart. My love is for real."

They kissed one another in the middle of the jogging path on a cloudy day.

She was so grateful that although her first marriage had ended, she was able to come to terms with it. If Rashad wanted out, and got the joint custody deal that he requested, so be it. As long as Nicole didn't harm her kids, she would be all right.

So that day in the park, she accepted the path where life had brought her. There with Eddison, Kiara's heart was bursting with happiness, and she finally believed her Mama Flora, who told her that God would give her the wings to help her fly and feet to help her safely land.

Chapter 18

Ride or Die

The month of October had arrived. Rashad told Nicole that he must return to Louisiana. It was early Saturday morning and he had a rare morning off. He'd be leaving Houston the next day and said he'd be back on Wednesday. She felt disappointed, but helped him pack his overnight bag.

"I hate leaving you. But I thought I told you that I have a case. Someone is suing me for damages for an injury that happened on a construction site. I was a party named in the suit. Their headquarters are in Louisiana. The suit was filed there. This time I will be gone a few days. This is bullshit, but I will deal with it."

"I guess I'm seeing the other side of business. A side I didn't realize existed."

"Exactly. And lawsuits come with the territory."

"Damn, that's all we need is more legal trouble. I hope you win your case."

"Thanks, Nicky. I'll make it up to you."

Since Rashad had given her a heads-up, Nicole had time to bake him a quick pan of banana bread.

"This smells and tastes good," Rashad told her. "Sometimes I think you're too good to me."

She didn't respond; she turned her back to him as she packed him a cooler filled with water bottles and fresh fruit.

"Just be safe on the road."

"I will," he said. "What do you plan to do these next few days?"

"Oh, same old same ole."

He just stared at her. "Well, be good and don't do anything I wouldn't do."

His words sent a chill down her spine.

Does he know what I've been doing behind his back or is his choice of language a mere coincidence?

Nicole decided not to worry about it. She felt Rashad still cared about her or else he wouldn't be with her. In fact last night was the best time they had together in a while.

He came home early last night.

And he brought in bag after bag of seafood. Shrimp, lobster, snow crab, and loads of stuffed mushrooms.

"What's all this for?" Nicole squealed.

"Just because. Mommy needs a break from cooking and changing diapers and working and trying to make sure I'm okay. Plus, you still find time to try and exercise."

"Oh, wow," she said. "Rashad, you are shocking the hell out of me tonight."

"I forgot to tell you. I specialize in that sometimes," he replied. "It's just that I've been so busy with work and business matters that a brother just plain forgets sometimes. I told myself that I would never do that again. But, dammit, I still do it. Have you noticed?"

"Have I? Never ever," she teased. And right then Nicole felt good and encouraged. She hated herself for sometimes not feeling as ride or die as she should. She felt she should just weather those relationship storms and maybe one day everything would work out between them. But Nicole was impatient and demanding. She needed constant encouragement to feel that her life was in order.

Rashad gave her his undivided attention after dinner. They played with Emmy and both marveled at her personality. Their child had Rashad's determination and Nicole's feistiness.

And with that memory fresh on her mind, Nicole felt it was time that she really showed him that she was down for him.

She had a sudden idea. "Before you head out of town, I want us to do something special today. As a family."

"Oh, yeah," he said. "What's that?"

"I know you mentioned that Myles is about to come over. And I think it's time we went to see the wild animals that he's always talking about."

"The Houston Zoo, right?"

She laughed. "Where else? We don't have time to go to Africa in a few hours."

"Hmm, all right."

"C'mon, it'll be fun. It's a great day to be outdoors. I will get Emmy dressed. Be ready soon."

And right on the dot, Kiara pulled up in front

of Nicole's place. She had a huge smile on her face when she dropped off Myles. Nicole overheard Kiara telling him to be a good boy. When Myles saw Nicole, he waved. "Hey, Ms. Nicole."

She waved back, then walked around to Kiara's driver's side. She peeked in the backseat.

"Hmm, Jazzy sure looks jazzed up today. Is that a corduroy headband? Where'd you find that?"

"I ordered them off the Internet." Kiara hesitated. "Etsy dot com from that Baby Bloomz Boutique."

"That sounds like my type of place. Well, you did a great job; Jazzy looks beautiful."

"I want to believe you, Nicole but—"

"I'm being genuine. Your daughter is my child's sister. Emmy may want to grow up and be like Jazz. I guess I'm trying to say that we all need to do better."

"Well, thank you, Nicole. I appreciate your words. But I need some action too and I am requesting that you watch over my child like he was your own."

"I promise. He's in good hands," Nicole said and waved as Kiara drove off.

After a while, the entire family piled in Rashad's sedan and was soon on its way.

"I'm pumped, Daddy."

"Oh, yeah, son? Why is that?"

"You're finally taking me to the zoo."

"I could have been taking you. But you said you weren't feeling these Houston animals."

"I'll take what I can get." Myles giggled. "Next up? Africa."

"Keep dreaming, son."

"Rashad, you know you ain't right," Nicole

chimed in. "I think it would be great if you took Myles to Africa."

"Oh, yeah? Why is that?"

"Because even you said so. It's his dream. And he deserves to have his dreams come true."

"We'll see," was all Rashad would offer.

The family arrived at the zoo and purchased their tickets. Myles ran through the entrance ahead of everyone, eager to observe the sea lions. His eyes were lit up with excitement as he pointed and jumped up and down.

"He acts like he's never been to the damned zoo before," Rashad said.

"It's not the zoo, babe. It's the fact that you followed up on a promise," Nicole explained. That's why he's so happy, and I can't say that I blame him."

Later they visited the African Forest, the elephants, ostriches, and spent time in the petting zoo.

But Myles was eager to see the bird exhibits, which included flamingos, macaws, and other endangered animals.

"Hey, look, Daddy. There's a cassowary. We learned about them in school."

"That's a big-ass bird," Rashad exclaimed.

"They look like they wear faded haircuts," Myles informed him. "But that's not real hair. It's feathers. And some of them are tall, way taller than me and you, Daddy."

"Okay, son. Calm down. You're starting to make me feel short."

Next Myles asked to see the homing pigeons. "No matter where you take a homing pigeon, no matter where in the world, it will always find its way back home. Daddy, how can it remember where to go when it's let out in a strange place that it's never been before?"

"I guess if it tries hard enough, it eventually finds its way back to where it belongs."

"So when are we going to see them?"

"I hate to tell you this, little man, but I don't think they have those kinds of pigeons."

"Aww, Daddy."

"For some reason," Rashad told Nicole, "he's always been fascinated. At least that's what Kiara tells me."

"Oh, you still talk to her about petty stuff?"

"It's not petty if it has to do with Myles."

"I didn't mean it how it sounded; it's just that I didn't know y'all still talked."

"Nicole, please. You already know we discuss the kids. Nothing slips past you."

"Apparently, it does, because I honestly didn't know. At least not how much you two talk. Remember we were supposed to be open and honest? So if you need to speak with your ex-wife, I don't mind if you do that in front of me, Rashad. I really want you to understand that."

Rashad didn't answer. And Nicole thought she knew exactly why. She was aware whenever Rashad arrived home later than usual. But if it honestly had to do with meeting up with Kiara about their children, she could understand that. She just wished he'd tell her instead of being secretive, assuming that was his reason for being late.

At that very moment, Nicole realized that Rashad shut down. He walked alongside Myles while she was left behind pushing Emmy. She hated feeling neglected.

Nicole couldn't take it anymore. If they were going to make it, she needed Rashad to know that she was down for him in every way. As his woman. As a potential stepmother. As a genuine mother figure to Myles. She spoke up.

"Hey, you all. Let's go visit the cheetah display. We haven't done that yet."

"Yayy. Let's go," Myles said.

Rashad eyed his watch. "I got to be getting on the road soon."

"C'mon," Nicole coaxed him. "It'll only take a few minutes. It's on the way to the exit so it's not an inconvenience. Plus, Myles is turnt up and I love it when he's happy."

Rashad didn't argue. He trailed behind Nicole, who continued pushing Emmy in her stroller. Myles ran ahead squealing. Once he came upon the cheetah exhibit, he maneuvered his way past the other kids who were staring down at the animals. Some cheetahs were partially hidden out of view as they stood at the opening of their cave. Others lazed around a pool of water. Their claws were long and vicious looking. Their spotted coats were beautiful. The cats looked like royalty.

Nicole calmly approached Myles and squeezed past a couple of kids to stand directly next to him. "Wow, those are so cool. Can you see?"

"Not really."

"You're too short to see clearly over this wall."

"But I can see a lot better if you pick me up. I'm not heavy. C'mon, Ms. Nicole."

"No, that's a bad idea. Since I'm taller than you, how about I take a few video clips through my phone and you can see the cheetahs that way?"

Myles pouted. She felt bad that he came all the

way to the zoo and couldn't get to see some of the animals that he really liked.

Nicole tried to ignore Myles's pleading. She examined the pit in which the cheetahs were housed.

"Here kitty, kitty, kitty," she called out. One curiously opened its eyes as it sat on the grass. She had an idea. She reached in a pocket inside Emmy's stroller and grabbed a bag of snacks that she liked to store for herself when she took the baby for walks.

"The sign says don't feed the animals," remarked an elderly man with large black glasses. He carefully watched Nicole.

"Oh, these PETA maniacs won't feed these animals what they want, which is the big piece of chicken. And it's a damned shame," Nicole told Myles.

"They are actually being deprived of food. So I think it would be fun if you just tossed some trail mix in their pit, don't you think? You can go back to school and tell all your friends how brave you are because you helped out an endangered mammal."

Rashad soon approached them. "What's going on?"

"Nothing." Nicole shrugged. "Just talking." She glanced over his shoulder. "Hey, look over there at that concession stand. They have cotton candy and snow cones. Please go get some!"

"That line's too damned long. I don't have time."

"Please, Daddy . . ."

Seconds later Rashad started walking toward the concession stand. Nicole immediately lifted

Myles by his arms until he was slightly hanging over the stone partition that separated the animals from the zoo visitors. "Go ahead. He's hungry. Throw the food at him."

At first Myles was all game. But then he sized up the display and hesitated. "This looks dangerous."

"I thought you loved animals. And let's face it; this is as close as you're ever going to get to a safari camp. Just throw a little bit of food and we'll be done."

He shrugged and said, "Okay." He leaned forward ready to toss some snacks.

Nicole tried to hold Myles securely but he felt heavier than he appeared. In fact, she was sweating so much that beads of water covered her forehead. She looked down into the pit. Two other cheetahs weren't paying attention, but the other one's long legs advanced near the wall right below Myles. The cheetah seemed to lock eyes with Nicole.

"Uh oh, by the look he's giving me, I don't think Mr. Cheetah is into trail mix. We'll just take video like I suggested before."

"Okay, Ms. Nicole."

She tightened her grip on Myles, preparing to pull him back toward her.

Myles's foot slipped. He began to dangle by one arm. His leg hung helplessly. The cheetah stared at the boy as he wildly jerked back and forth.

The cheetah circled beneath Myles's leg. Nicole saw his long teeth.

Myles screamed and yelled, "Mom."

Nicole completely froze. She couldn't believe what he called her. It was music to her ears.

"Mom, help me."

"Okay, son," Nicole said, "hold on." She tugged hard on his arm, and managed to safely pull him up.

Rashad finally returned as he watched Myles being placed firmly on his feet. When he saw what was going on, he dropped the snow cones and popcorn on the ground.

"Daddy," Myles said, choking back tears. "He-he-he almost got me, but I was too fast for him."

Nicole knew Myles was being overly dramatic for the benefit of his father. But as she thought about what could have happened if she hadn't had the strength to pull him up, she wanted to cry herself. She fell against Rashad and hugged him so tight she nearly choked him. Then she pulled Myles in and they all embraced one another.

"What happened back there?"

"I wanted him to feed the animals. So I thought if I picked him up, it would help. But he slipped a little. Nothing bad happened, though."

"You saved Myles's life?"

"Nooo, it wasn't that extreme. That's an exaggeration. I did what I had to do to keep him safe. Thank God he's fine now."

"I'm shocked as hell. By all of this. But thanks, Nicky. Thank you so much for what you've done."

Rashad hugged and kissed her again. He said he wished he didn't have to leave them to go out of town. But she said everything would be all right. She promised to watch Myles the next day and she knew that she would. And right then Nicole knew that being a good mother to all the kids and being true to Rashad were the only things that really mattered. She loved little Myles and she wanted more than anything to be with his dad in the proper way if fate allowed.

When Rashad departed Houston and arrived in New Orleans, he checked into his hotel—alone. He concentrated on his notes regarding the litigation. He met with his attorneys. And he lay in bed at night thinking about Nicole. Wondering if she could be wife number two, or questioning whether she was yet ready to be the woman he felt he needed in his life.

The case went well and he returned to town and got back to work. And as usual, as he'd been doing for several weeks, he agreed to meet with Remy Davis. Marlon Davis had asked Rashad to take her under his wing. The young girl had been doing well getting resituated in high school and she finally thought she'd want to study construction management.

Rashad laughed. "You don't look like the average foreman on a job site, but I guess you will do. In fact, we need more minority females in this industry."

Marlon, who was there when Rashad first met with Remy, laughed, too. "My daughter is going to defy the odds. She's got some ratchet in her but I am hoping she will grow out of it. She needs to hit those books and gain some experience even if she just volunteers. I would appreciate it if you could teach her a few tips about your business, man. Every other day after school for a couple of hours. Or once a week if you can spare the time."

Rashad's schedule was very hectic but he said okay. He and Marlon originally met when Rashad had done a Career Day speech at Remy's high school. Marlon was impressed that Rashad was a successful small business owner and felt Remy, as well as some other classmates, could use the guidance.

The only reason he didn't tell Nicole about what he was doing was that Remy was a pretty young female. And he knew she'd flip. So he avoided the topic and hoped that his woman would grant him the trust he felt he deserved.

Chapter 19

Tricks and Treats

It was all Eddison's idea. He brought it up to Kiara when he came by her house that evening.

"It's a couple of weeks until Halloween," he said. "Can you believe a year has passed already?"

"I know, right."

"So what if you get all the kids together? Take them to a studio and sit for a holiday photo?"

"All the kids?"

"Myles, Hayley, Jazzy, and Eminence."

"Hmm, interesting. They sound like a hip-hop group."

"Kiara, I'm being serious. Don't you agree with me that it's about time?"

She folded her arms across her chest. "I'm trying to work with Nicole on these things but I still feel skeptical. I'm cool with Hayley. But I'm not one hundred percent sold on Emmy."

"With all due respect, Kiara, everything simply can't always be how you and only you wants things to be. These kids are siblings and they need to know one another. Because, like it or not, their parents won't live forever."

"Eddison," she shrieked. She didn't like how that sounded. She never wanted to think about bad stuff like death and not being on earth anymore with her children. It was too much to handle. "I thought you were on Team Kiara. I thought you'd want to do anything to make me happy."

"I am on your team and you know that. You're wearing my ring and we are committed to each other. But I am simply suggesting that we start doing little things that encourage all of them to be around one another. Because how would you feel if you knew you had siblings out there, but someone was preventing you from getting to know your sister or your brother?"

Kiara had never thought about his question. For all she knew, she wasn't an only child. But she'd never been told otherwise. It would have been great to have a piece of her mother, Pamela, somewhere in the world. Maybe bonding with a sibling would make her feel more complete. And if that's what she would have wanted as a grown-up, how much more did the kids deserve such a chance?

"Hmm, so you think that I should coordinate a photo shoot with the children?"

"I feel it's the right thing to do."

"I know Myles would be game. He even talks about Hayley all the time. And he loves Jazz to death. But it's Emmy that I'm worried about."

"How can a four-month-old worry you?"

She laughed out loud. It did sound ridiculous.

"Use your power. You can group these baby moms together and make some moves. Score major points. And be the happy mediator. Everyone will love you for it."

"Even Nicole, who's added me to her To Do list?"

"Even Nicole."

Kiara thought about it and texted Kiara and Nicole. "Bring the kids," Kiara said. "Come on over to my place."

"What's this about?" Nicole texted back.

"You'll see."

Nicole showed up first. Eddison opened the door. Feelings of envy burned at her soul when he warmly invited her into that big beautiful house.

Some people are born to have everything they want, she thought as she walked past Eddison into Kiara's home. It was lavishly decorated with fresh flowers arranged all around the dining room. The family room was filled with gift-wrapped presents. And there was a table filled with catered refreshments.

"I'm shocked," Nicole said. "And I'm really curious now. What is this about?" She noticed a new pretty ring on Kiara's hand and thought it was just a nice piece of jewelry.

Kiara laughed. "Eddison has an idea and I wanted to run it by you. I'll let you know what it is as soon as Alexis arrives, okay?"

Nicole shrugged. "Fine by me."

"May I see the baby?" Kiara asked.

Nicole handed over Emmy to Kiara. A beautiful purple bow was wrapped around Emmy's hair. She wore a cute little sweater and onesie.

"She is so freaking adorable," Kiara admitted in a small voice. At first, holding the nineteen-week-old girl felt strange. But as the seconds went by, and the more the baby stared into her eyes, the more Kiara knew she had the strength to be good to this innocent soul. When Emmy smiled, Kiara grinned back at her.

Suddenly Myles entered the room.

"Hi, Mom," he said.

Both Kiara and Nicole said hello to Myles and they all burst out laughing.

Rashad had told Kiara what happened at the zoo. She was shocked and thankful but still a little skeptical about Nicole's motives. This is why she made sure to get hidden cameras installed in Nicole's home. And it all had to do with Jazzy, not Rashad. Since he was going to be with the woman, she wanted to make sure that her child was safe in Nicole's presence. She had honestly forgotten about the cameras, but made a mental note to check any footage.

Myles proceeded to pour Nicole a glass of punch. A little later, Alexis arrived with Hayley. Everyone settled on couches and chairs in the living room.

As Kiara gazed around the room, it was almost surreal: all her husband's babies in her house. Eddison noticed the dazed look on her face. He spoke up.

"What Kiara wants to say is, first of all, thanks for coming by. She wants you to feel at home. And she has an idea for all the kids to get dressed up for a photo shoot. It would be next weekend and they'd have to wear some type of Halloween outfit."

"That's a cool idea," Alexis said. "Count me in."

"Ladies," Kiara began. "Now I'll admit I haven't been the best woman in handling certain situations in the past. But I'm at the point where I want all that to change. These kids are adorable. I mean, look at them. Myles, so smart and helpful. Hayley, so innocent and comical. Little Jazzy, the best little baby in the world." She stopped talking.

"What about Emmy?" Nicole demanded.

"And Emmy, the little princess herself." Kiara laughed. "We couldn't leave her out. So with that being said, I think it would be a wonderful idea for the kids to get together and take the photo and then have a little party afterwards. How's that sound?"

"Since Alexis already gave you her approval, I guess that leaves me." Nicole stood up and walked around the room looking at Kiara's lovely furnishings. She thought about her own house, which was cool but nothing on this scale. She knew that Kiara got a nice settlement including a couple of vacant lots that were worth at least seventy thousand dollars.

"Why do you get everything you want?" Nicole asked. She knew it was an odd question. But she couldn't help herself. Everyone just stared at her. "You had the man. I somewhat have him."

"Nicole, that has nothing to do with saying yes to a photo," Alexis said. "Stop making everything about you and cooperate so these kids can have fun. Can you do that?"

"No, I can't. I'm struggling, okay?"

"What do you mean you're struggling?" Kiara asked.

"He doesn't just give me loads of cash. If it has to do with the baby we're all good. If it has to do with buying things for the house like food and paying a bill, he's all for it. But I can't remember the last time he's bought anything nice just for me. And I got student loans to pay. I still drive around in that raggedy Mustang that's on its last legs."

Nicole wanted to say how she'd been dipping into her GoFundMe money since Ajalon came into town. She still had a good eight thousand left, but she wasn't foolish enough to give her ex every dime she had. So she lied to him and told him that she was almost broke. And she was running out of options.

"Tell me something," Nicole said to Kiara. "Are y'all really hooking back up or not?"

"Girl, you sound like a fool," Alexis said. "Don't you see that ring on her finger? It isn't from Rashad."

"Oh, no. I'm sorry. I had no idea what it was or who bought it. I mean no harm, y'all. I just want to know if I'm wasting my time with him."

"Oh, my goodness, we came here to talk about Halloween," Alexis said. "Make a decision so you can get out of here and we can have some fun and not have to listen to your side mama setbacks."

"Hold up," Kiara said. "Clear the room. Me and Nicole only."

The room cleared out and Kiara asked Nicole to have a seat. "Look, Nicole. I don't know what type of woman you think I am, but I am too old to be playing relationship games. Rashad and I are done. I'm sure you've already searched online records to see the final decree. So my guess is that if he isn't giving you a lot of money or even proposing to you right now, don't worry about it. Maybe the way you get him is the way you gotta keep him. As a woman it hurts me to see other chicks thinking that latching onto a certain man is the only key to her happiness. It doesn't work like that." Kiara pointed to herself. "Once I got that man out of my system, I began to learn what it's like to live. I focused on motherhood. I did all I could to make sure the kids were happy and safe and secure. I thought less about having a relationship. And when I stopped stressing is when I received total fulfillment. Eddison is just a bonus and trust me, I am not rushing to marry him. He gave me a promise ring and yes, we are committed. All I know is that you seem very focused on the wrong things. That type of mentality can drive a good man away. And I'm at the point where I couldn't care less about you and your drama over your man. Now for the last time, I don't want him. Can you get that through your head?"

Nicole looked distraught. "Then what's up with him? Why doesn't he come straight home to me like he used to? Is it because I had a baby?"

"Anytime a side chick becomes the main chick, her position is up for grabs again. But that's just my assumption."

"I-I don't know what to say."

"Whatever you're going through with Rashad, I'm sorry. I really am. But think about your child, please. Don't punish the kid because you don't understand the man."

"All right," Nicole said in a humbled voice. "Emmy can participate in the photo."

Rashad hung up from Kiara. And Nicole was there to listen to their entire conversation.

"Well?" he asked.

She giggled. "Thank you for including me in the conversation."

"Nicole, I swear I'm not intentionally trying to leave you out of anything that has to do with Kiara and my kids. I just forget. You gotta believe me."

He got on one knee and placed his arms around her waist.

"You believe me?"

"Oh, Rashad. You're acting silly."

"Not as silly as you've been acting. You're the type of woman that overanalyzes shit to death. It ain't even about that half the time."

She patted him on the head. "Now I really feel silly."

"And you should. Stop worrying."

"My mother would say the same thing. She said that when I was eleven years old I asked her to give me some antidepressant pills."

"You lying."

"I swear to God. Funny thing is I don't even remember anything like that."

"Good. That would be a terrible memory for a kid." He paused. "Damn, I should have really asked you about your family's mental history before I even allowed you to give me head."

"Arg," she screamed. "That is so unfair. But I love your silly butt anyway."

They made love that night for the first time in a week. She had to get used to his hands on her body again. And once he explored every sensitive crevice, it was on and popping. Things felt good and right. And that's all she wanted. For things to get back to good and grow even better.

* * *

One week later, Myles led his sisters into the photography studio. He was wearing a gold Iron Man costume with an arc reactor that lit up.

"Good job, Myles." Alexis clapped when she saw him emerge from Nicole's beat-up Mustang. It was Rashad's time to keep Myles and Nicole agreed to oversee his costume and bring him to the studio. She struggled to get out of the car and was trying to unbuckle her daughter from her car seat.

Alexis went over to the car.

"Need some help?"

"No. I got this."

"You need help, girl, and you know it." Alexis assisted Nicole in unstrapping Emmy. She held the baby while Nicole grabbed her day bag.

"Once you get real, you'll let all that foolishness go," Alexis continued. "It's okay to ask for help."

The women had been getting along fairly well, but Alexis noticed that whenever Nicole displayed insecurity the daggers came out. Alexis paid the woman no mind but she wasn't about to let her run over her.

"Nicole, please stop. You bleed just like any other person out here. Oh, forget it. It's going to take you going to hell and back before you understand what life is really about."

"I hope you're wrong about that."

They went and quietly waited in the lobby until they saw Kiara arrive.

"Sorry I'm late. Thanks, Nicole, for picking up Myles for me."

The ladies met their photographer, Robbie, and he instructed them on what he wanted to do.

"We'll get several shots. First I want the two youngest to sit in this pumpkin patch."

Both Nicole and Kiara agreed to arrange the girls so that they were huddled together. Even Nicole had to admit that the shot would be something special.

"I wish my mom was here to see this," Kiara said.

"Where is she?" Nicole snapped. "She abandoned you when you were born?"

Alexis was at Nicole's side in an instant. She shoved her hands against Nicole's chest and pushed her until she hit a wall.

"You have gone too far. And I'm sick of it."

"It's all right, Alexis," said Kiara. "The children. Think about the children."

Alexis calmed down and let up off Nicole. She immediately felt regretful. "Look. I shouldn't have done that. I apologize. But I don't think you understand. Kiara's mother is dead."

"Oops. I didn't know. I messed up. I'm sorry."

Kiara couldn't think of what to say.

She finally regrouped. "Let's just continue with this photo shoot. Stay focused."

The rest of the shoot went well. The children seemed to have a good time. Myles enjoyed being in the center of all of his female siblings.

"This was a really good idea," Alexis said. "And as much as you irk me, Nicole, I want to thank you for allowing Eminence to be a part of this. She really is a little baby doll. Look at her fat little thighs."

Nicole hesitated. She didn't know if Alexis was sincere or trying to throw shade. "Thanks. I think."

When the photo shoot was over, and Alexis and Kiara stood on the curb holding a conversation about the kids, Nicole felt bad that they didn't invite her to join them.

But a few minutes later, when Kiara waved her over, Nicole swallowed her pride and joined them.

"We were just saying how much Jazz and Emmy favor. They have the same cheeks, even the same teeth. Have you ever noticed that?" Kiara asked.

Nicole smiled. "I didn't before, but I see it now. I see a lot of things now that I never saw before." The three women chitchatted about the kids and Nicole felt better than she had in a long time.

Kiara was excited. Jazzy had just turned twenty-seven weeks old. It was the third Sunday in October. And Kiara had given Jazzy her morning bath and dressed her. She was now sitting on the couch staring at her daughter, who was sitting on her backside talking to herself.

"What you talking about, Jazzy?"

Suddenly, the baby spotted a colorful big ball that was located a yard away from her next to a case of books. Jazzy got on her knees and started scooting toward the ball.

"Oh, my goodness, go Jazzy," Kiara said in delight. She felt embarrassed to learn that she was alone in the house, a rarity. Myles was with Grandma Flora. And Eddison had some maintenance work to take care of regarding his house.

Kiara felt that odd pain that struck her once in a while.

"I wish Rashad was here to witness this."

But he wasn't.

She tried to FaceTime him, but he didn't answer.

"This sucks."

Soon she was on the phone with Adina. "Girl, I

know this sounds crazy, but if I had to do it all over again, I think I would have fought for my marriage." She explained how she just witnessed her daughter's latest achievement. "I mean, no marriage is perfect. And I think if we would have worked on our relationship at the first sign of trouble, my ex would be with me right now. Both of us would be enjoying our daughter's developments together. Instead of . . . it's so sad . . . I don't want my children to suffer . . . not Jazzy or Myles . . . we need each other, Adina. We really do. And it's sad that the man that used to be there, just near enough to talk to, is someone I can barely get in touch with anymore."

Adina couldn't listen any longer. "Stop it, Kiara. Because what you're failing to do is appreciate the blessings you have right now, as in right this very second. Yesterday is gone. It'll never repeat itself again. All you have is the present. And the perfect present is that good man, Eddison Osborne. He is always right there with you whenever he has time, watching everything that Jazzy does. So before you mourn for the past, value what is in your face on a daily basis."

Adina's words had to sink in. "What on God's earth would I do without you, Adina?"

"You'd make a whole lotta stupid mistakes. You'd repeat the same damn mistakes I've made and regretted. I won't let it happen to you, girlfriend."

Kiara smiled, agreed with Adina, and it helped her to realize that hanging onto the past wasn't beneficial unless it helped her value the present. She decided to make peace with one more person in her life. A person whom she loved even though she didn't really have the person in her life the way she wished she did.

Cemetery. It had been years since Kiara thought of this place.

Eddison remained behind in the car. Kiara walked the grounds searching for the tombstone that said:

Pamela Arlene Banks
Born June 10, 1957
Died August 25, 1980

When Kiara came across the weathered and chipped stone that bore her mother's name, a chill surged through her. She'd never been to the graveyard before. For anyone. Ever.

She felt like she was on holy ground. So she got on both knees and faced the tombstone. She placed her hands on its cold hard surface and choked back a hundred tears.

"Mommy, it's me. It's Kiara. I hope it's okay if I call you that. Even though I barely remember you, it hasn't stopped me from loving you. To this day, I wonder what you'd be like if you were still alive. Would you be proud of me? Would I look like you? Would you be there for me to help me and listen to me when I had problems?"

A weird gasp escaped from Kiara's mouth. It felt like the entire world was staring at her as she talked to a piece of stone. But she didn't care.

"Oh, Mommy, life hurts so bad. Sometimes I feel like I know what to do. But sometimes, I just don't know. Please, Mommy, please help me to deal with everything, especially Myles. You'd love Myles if you knew him. I think he takes after you in some ways. I heard that you were stubborn and strong. Hey, I am, too. I can't help it. I have so much I want to tell you. And I pray to God that you can hear me, Mommy. Hear me. Love me. And help me somehow. Send me a sign. Let me know that you're still with me even though I can't see you. Oh, how I wish you were here. If you were here I know I could make it. I-I . . ."

Kiara frowned, not sure of what else she could say to the spirit of Pamela Banks. She sniffed and wiped her tears.

"I better go now. I just wanted to say hello. I'm sorry I didn't make time to come visit you before now. But it was just too hard." She shivered and looked around at all the symbols of death all across the grounds. The vast land filled with dreams that were now buried underneath the earth.

"I feel a little better. And before I leave you, I have one last thing to say. Why didn't you ever tell me who my father is? I really want to know that. If there's one last thing I want in my life, it would be to know who he was. But even if that never happens, I've got to let you know that I have a new man. A great man like no other. His name is Eddison. I think he is the one. He's loyal. He loves your grandson and your granddaughter, Jahzara Alaine. He's amazing, Mommy. And I think you sent him to me. I really do. So thank you for watching over me. All right. Gotta go."

She rose to her feet and noticed that her knees hurt from being on them for so long. She felt that the pain was worth it.

"Good-bye. Love you," she whispered.

Kiara began to back away and grew startled when she bumped into someone. Eddison was there behind her. He stretched his hand toward her. She grabbed it. They started walking.

"Um, how long were you standing there?"

"Long enough."

"How much did you hear?"

"I heard everything you said about me."

"Oh, shit."

"And I loved everything that you said about me."

She giggled and smiled. And Eddison did, too.

Chapter 20

Let's Get Married

Rashad had been thinking about it ever since Nicole proved her love for Myles. She seemed to be taking her role as a stepmother more serious. And although she had a long way to go, Rashad knew that she'd been through a lot with him. The divorce. His long hours. Him having to wait to give her anything of great monetary value. But he had won his recent case and was awarded damages. And he felt now was the time to do something nice for her.

So the following Wednesday, when Nicole was on a three-day vacation from work, Rashad surprised her by driving them to a Jeep dealership.

"What's this?"

"Go in the showroom and take a look at that Jeep you've been talking about."

"Are you serious?"

"I wouldn't be here if I wasn't."

As Nicole walked around the showroom, she was overwhelmed. She recalled a conversation they had one night a few months ago when they were watching cable and saw a Jeep commercial. She admired the car and mentioned it without really thinking about it.

"So I can get a new Jeep? Are you playing with me?"

"No!"

She jumped up and down and laughed. "But are we trading in my Mustang?"

"For what? We'd barely get five hundred for it. We may as well keep it and sell it ourselves."

"Sounds good to me, Rashad."

Hours later Rashad and Nicole signed the contract to purchase the new car. He put the deposit on the vehicle and she agreed that she could make the monthly payments. The vehicle would be in her name. It was big, bulky, black, and beautiful. She could picture herself riding through the streets of Houston with everyone staring at her. As Nicole and Rashad rose up from the seats in front of the salesman's desk, she shook his hand and beamed from ear to ear. The salesman looked with a big smile while she waited in the lobby for a serviceman to prepare her vehicle before she could drive away in it.

"This is totally unexpected," she said excitedly to Rashad.

"That's just the beginning."

"What are you talking about?"

Suddenly all the salesmen and women gathered together in front of them. Rashad slowly lowered himself on one knee right in front of a model

Jeep. He reached in his pocket and produced a black velvet ring box.

"Nicole, will you accept the honor of marrying me?"

"What?" she screamed. She covered her mouth with her shaking hands. "Are we on *Punk'd*?" Everyone laughed. When Rashad convinced her he was serious, she nodded.

"Yes. Absolutely. I accept. I want to be your wife."

After he slipped the engagement ring on her finger, Nicole slumped in her seat and stared into space. It seemed like she just crossed the finish line of a marathon. A marathon in which she experienced falls, bad weather, bomb threats, you name it.

But finally, Nicole Greene felt like she was getting everything she ever desired.

The next evening, Nicole called Nadia and asked her to come over and watch Emmy right away.

Nadia said she'd be right there.

Nicole put on her running shoes and biker shorts with a matching Nike shirt. She placed a fanny pack on her waist. She stood outside the house waiting for Nadia to drive up.

It took her no time to get Nadia situated with Emmy.

She then hopped in her Jeep. It still smelled brand new and she was so grateful to have reliable transportation. "I'm going to need you more than I've ever needed a car," she said to the Jeep. She grabbed her smartphone and clicked the Internet icon. She hadn't heard from Rashad since early that morning. When she tried to call him, he did not answer or call back. Not knowing where he was made her feel nervous even though she did have his ring.

Nicole knew Rashad's log-in info for his phone. And she retrieved the GPS info. It showed her exactly where Rashad was. Feeling nervous, she started the engine and was on her way.

She drove until the GPS directed her exactly to Rashad's car.

He was driving his sedan. He rarely drove that car so she figured he must've had meetings. The car was parked at a gas station. It appeared as if he was there and had gone inside the station to pay the cash to fill up his tank.

Oh, that's cool, she thought. *He ain't up to nothing.*

Satisfied, she decided to leave the station before he could notice her and think she was following him. But as she started to drive past the car, something caught her eye. She noticed movement in his car. She circled around the other pumps and pulled up right behind Rashad's sedan. She got out of her Jeep and began walking toward the car.

Nicole peeped inside the driver's side window. It was empty. But when she got closer and scoped out the backseat, she saw a tiny figure lying on the floor.

"What the fuck?"

She grabbed the door handle of the car. It was locked.

"That asshole never locks his car door," she said, almost shouting. She pressed her hands against the glass to get a closer look, but the figure stayed facedown so Nicole couldn't tell who it was. All she saw was some long braids.

Nicole went into the store. She saw the back of Rashad as he stood in a very long line of customers. She walked up to him and tapped him hard on his shoulder. He turned around looking annoyed. When he saw her, he looked as if he was expecting her.

"Hey, babe. I was going to call you."

"Don't say shit to me."

He shrugged like he wished she'd believe him.

"Can you step out of the line, please, Rashad? We need to talk."

"All right," he said in a calm voice. "What's happening?"

"I want to know what the hell is going on."

"You want to know what the hell is going on?"

Rashad was facing the outside of the gas station. He had a clear view of the gas pumps. He tried to pay attention to Nicole.

"Yes, it seems like you are carrying something in your ride that shouldn't be there."

"What? Oh, yeah, right." He nodded. "I forgot. I bought some beer and I guess it shouldn't be visible right next to me on the front seat. Is that what you're talking about?"

"No, you bastard. I'm about to show your lying ass what I'm talking about." She grabbed Rashad's hand and marched him to his sedan. She watched his face as she pointed to the backseat of his ride.

"What the hell is that chick doing there? Who is she?"

He looked in the backseat. "I don't see anybody. So what are you talking about?"

"She was just there. Open the car door."

Rashad popped the locks. Nicole stuck her head in the door. "Where'd she go? I know I'm not going crazy." She looked around the big lot and saw no one with long braids.

"Pop open the trunk."

"No, I ain't doing that."

"Why not, Rashad? Is that where that hoe is hiding?"

"What hoe? What you talking about?"

"You scumbag. Don't think I don't know the game. I invented the game and sold the t-shirt and taught the class." She laughed in pure amazement. "Who was I fooling? My mother always told me you can't turn a hoe into a housewife."

"Nicole, you're tripping."

Nicole grabbed him by the arm. "Look at me, Rashad. Why did you propose to me?"

"Because it's what you wanted."

Her heart sank. "So, you didn't ask me to marry you because you love me?"

"That has a lot to do with it, too. I wanted to be with you like you want to be with me."

"The way you said that sounds so insincere."

He stared in her eyes. "Okay, tell you what. I know what this is all about. And you're right. So here goes: I asked you to marry me because like I've always said, you are my ride and die, Nicole. You've proven your loyalty time and time again. I never have to wonder where you are. You work, you cook, you clean, you make love to me when I need it. You listen to me, you gave birth to my youngest child. And you have a decent heart. Wounded but decent."

She calmed down and allowed his nice words to soothe her hurt feelings.

Maybe her scandalous ways were making her imagine that he was cheating on her. But she knew that she saw what she saw. But now she could not prove it.

"All that sounds nice, Rashad," she told him. "But you still haven't told me the most important reason for anybody wanting to marry someone else."

"Okay, I'm telling you now." He waited, paused then said, "I asked you to marry me because in my own way, yes. I do love you. I care about you. I think about the woman I met last summer and how you cooked for me. You listened to me. You made me feel important. But at times I feel like you aren't that woman anymore. Maybe it's because a lot of your time is dedicated to Emmy. And that's cool. But don't forget about your man and your man won't forget about you."

"So, you do love me, Rashad?"

"That's what I've been trying to tell you."

She thought about love and what it's supposed to mean and how it's supposed to make you feel. She knew that someone could tell another person that they loved them in one breath, and in the next moment, that person could point a gun at the one they "love," pull a trigger, see their blood and guts spill out of their body, and watch them take their last breath. What type of love was that?

What type of love did Nicole want and need?

She looked at Rashad, the man for whom she sacrificed so much, and told him. "Thank you for telling me that you love me. But love spelled backwards is pronounced evil."

"Huh? What are you saying?"

"I'm saying that for some people, they are going to feel the true feeling of love, but for others it is going to mean something entirely different."

She started walking away from him toward her Jeep.

"I just want to make sure I know which definition of love you're talking about." And she got in her car and drove away.

The next time Nicole was able to return to work was the following Monday. She drove up to the employee parking at five minutes to eight. That was when most of the department arrived at work. She wanted everyone to see her. She sat in her brand new thirty-six-thousand-dollar Wrangler Unlimited Rubicon Jeep, black trimmed in green, with seventeen-inch rims. She relished in the fact that every jealous eye was on her in her new ride.

Shyla, who got a text that Nicole was on her way in with instructions to meet her in the staff parking lot, practically ran when she saw Nicole in the Jeep. She parked in a spot, but the motor was still running. "Well, look a here."

"I've been dying to tell you all these unbelievable things that have happened. But I wanted to show you and not just tell you over the phone."

"C'mon, girl, sit next to me and check out this interior." Shyla hopped in and allowed Nicole to show her all the features. She used exaggerated movement with her left hand as she pointed at the CD/radio system.

"What the fuck?" Shyla grabbed her left hand. "Is that a diamond engagement ring?"

"I know it's kind of small, but yep, it's real, girl. I accepted his proposal . . . of marriage."

Shyla screamed and they hopped up and down in their seats.

"You are one lucky woman. What's your secret?" Shyla asked. "I can't believe you kept this to yourself all weekend."

"It was tough but I did it. I'll tell you all about it at lunch. My treat."

True to her word, at the noon hour, Nicole and Shyla walked out to her Jeep and hopped in. Nicole chauffeured her friend to a little Italian restaurant, one that they'd never patronized before.

They both ordered pasta dishes and salads and dug in.

"Your life has truly turned around. You even seem like a different woman," Shyla announced. "I'm glad for you, but I've got to know how you did it. The ring is kind of tiny, but that's beside the point."

"It's not the size that matters. It's the thought."

"That's my point. Did he really think about it? I would hate to believe that he just got anything just to appease you."

Nicole wanted to hide her hand. When she compared her jewelry to Shyla's it was like pitting the queen of England against some ghetto fabulous crack hoe living on the street. The more she thought about it, the madder she became.

"Shyla, you of all people should be happy for me. You know all of what I've been through and how hard it's been for me. So can you please stop throwing shade at the size of my ring?"

"All right, okay. I'm just trying to look out for your best interests."

"I know, but the way you're doing it is truly getting on my damned nerves."

The lunch suddenly tasted like it had no seasoning. Nicole felt the tension between herself and her friend. And it was in that moment that she wondered if karma would ever leave her alone. She felt that each time she took one step forward, she had to take another step backward. Could she ever get ahead in life? Would everything she desired come with a struggle?

Nicole completely lost her appetite. She didn't even want to engage in conversation with Shyla any longer. So she left three twenties on the table and told her friend she wasn't feeling well. She advised her to call a taxi. Then she picked up her purse and hurried out of the restaurant.

Blinded by tears, she ran to the vehicle that she was so happy to get not too long ago. She jumped in and started the engine. Nicole drove and drove, not really knowing where she was going. The thrill of riding in a Jeep felt empty and pointless.

Shyla kept dialing her number, but Nicole wasn't in the mood to talk and ignored the calls.

Feeling fraught with worry, she drove around without paying strict attention to where she was headed.

She ended up getting on a major street and driving wildly. She ran a couple red lights and switched lanes without signaling. It was like a cry for attention. Nicole wanted to get caught. She felt she needed to be punished for her sins. For getting involved again with Ajalon. For not being very respectful to

Kiara and Alexis. And for not consistently being the best woman that she could have been to Rashad. She wanted to get pulled over. But no cop car was around.

"Just like the fucking HPD. They are never around when you need them."

Nicole impulsively decided to turn into the parking lot of a Home Depot. She felt she could find a vacant parking space and just think.

She was zipping through the spacious lot on an afternoon in which a lot of people were shopping at the store. Her music was banging and she was distracted as she fiddled around with the controls to try to lower the volume. For a split second, Nicole took her eyes off the road. When she looked up, her eyes enlarged in horror.

A young woman was directly in the path of Nicole's Jeep.

The girl stopped, looked at the oncoming car, and froze.

Nicole screamed, pumped her brakes, and the car's tires began to screech as she grabbed the steering wheel and tried to maneuver past the woman without hitting her.

The Jeep came within a half an inch of the chick without hitting her.

But she stood there trembling like she was freezing to death and kept staring at the driver that almost hit her. Unable to imagine what just could have happened, Nicole flew out of the car and went to see if she was all right.

"I'm so sorry. I got a little distracted. Thank God I didn't hit you."

The girl stared at her, nodded, then opened up her mouth. "You stupid old-ass bitch. You need to watch where you going and keep your fucking eyes on the road. I'm sick of you non-driving bitches always texting, or stuffing your mouth with a hamburger, or applying mascara when you supposed to be concentrating and looking where you at. I swear to God, bitch, if you would have hit me, my man would have fucked you the hell up. Do you understand what I'm saying? Slow your old ass down, this fucked-up world ain't going nowhere, so ain't no need to rush."

The girl regained her composure and walked into Home Depot. Nicole stared at the woman and noticed a lightweight jacket she wore with the word "REMY" applied on the back in large letters.

As Nicole looked at the young woman, she realized she was the same girl that she swore she saw hiding in Rashad's sedan last night. Nicole felt like she had to look for the girl again and this time she'd find her. She briskly walked through the entrance of the large store. And she kept going until she crossed paths with the chick again. She was in the hardware department looking at mechanical tool sets.

Nicole quietly approached her and tapped her on the shoulder. "Excuse me? Is your name Remy?"

The girl looked at her. "Who wants to know?"

"I'm sorry, but I wanted to say I didn't mean to almost hit you. I'm very sorry about that."

"Apology accepted."

"And I had another question."

"What is it?"

"You look like a girl I saw a while ago. Do you know a man named Rashad Eason?"

Remy's eyes enlarged.

"Oh, you. I thought I recognized you. You his crazy-ass woman that he had me hiding from like I was a bank robber. He saw you somehow and thought you was following his ass, so he asked me to lie down when we pulled up to that gas station."

"But who are you?"

"I sure ain't kicking it with that old-ass man. He's like, what, almost thirty-two or something. I'm still in high school. My boyfriend would kick my ass if he thought I was cheating on him."

Nicole wanted to smile. And then shout.

"So, lady, I don't know what your problem is, but you better trust your man. He's just my mentor. He does things like tutor me and my classmates after school and teaches us stuff about the construction industry. That's it. Now can I please be left alone? Or do you have another question for me?"

"I will leave you alone, Remy. And thanks so much for telling me—"

"Bye, lady. Ugh!"

Nicole humbly walked back to her vehicle. She revved up the engine and returned to the campus of Texas South West University. She took a deep breath, quietly parked her car at the far end of the employee lot, and made her way into the building. Alexis didn't give her any odd stares as she passed by. That meant that Shyla had kept her mouth shut. And when she went into her office, Shyla was sitting in a guest chair right next to her desk. Nicole sighed in relief, closed the office door, and the two women quietly hugged each other. Nicole rocked back and forth and told Shyla, "I had a moment. I'm so, so sorry. Forgive me, please girl."

"You know I do. Don't even sweat it."

And that day, Nicole knew she'd gained much

more than the hope of a wedding, new transportation, and a peace of mind.

She knew she'd regained a true friend.

In the week leading up to Halloween, Rashad and Jerry went to pick up Henry and Cornell to help out with some renovation work. But before dropping them off at the day labor parking lot, Rashad told the men, "Hey, I got to make a quick stop. Something's going on at my crib that I gotta check on."

Ajalon froze up. He knew he shouldn't have agreed to get picked up at the day labor lot. He was on the verge of quitting but wanted to stay on another week or so before joining another company. Things between him and Nicole had cooled down and he wasn't feeling the Eason & Son work any longer.

When Rashad pulled the van up in front of his driveway, he got out of the vehicle and started walking toward the front door. He turned around and said, "Hey, y'all. Come on in. This won't take but a second. If you need to use my bathroom or get a drink from the fridge, make yourself at home."

Ajalon was the last one to exit the van. His legs felt like steel as he walked inside. It had been awhile since he'd been inside this house. He stood off to the side. Jerry, though, walked around and started looking at anything that appeared interesting. He picked up a stuffed animal that was sitting on a table.

"Cute, huh?" he said with a grin. "This reminds me of my grandson's teddy bears."

Ajalon said nothing.

Moments later, Nicole walked out. She stopped when she saw the men. She exchanged a worried glance with Ajalon but he refused to say a word.

"Hey, guys," she said. "How are you doing? What's going on?"

"We wondered the same thing," Jerry said. "Rashad indicated you have a problem going on here?"

"Oh, yeah, the washing machine won't stop leaking. There's water all over the floor. It's dangerous. I thought that it might harm the flooring and wasn't sure how to stop the water from rising. Rashad is handling it, though. He'll be done soon."

She excused herself. Ajalon and Henry went into the kitchen. Ajalon took a chance and opened the refrigerator.

Henry muttered, "You shouldn't get that familiar with the boss's things, man. Be respectful."

"I am respectful."

"You should ask before you go in the man's fridge, Cornell."

"He already said it would be okay."

"Just because he said it don't mean he means it."

"Have you ever been over here before?" Ajalon asked.

"No. Have you?"

"Nah, man. But it's cool. He already gave his okay."

Henry looked pissed that Ajalon was doing something first again. He didn't like that the much younger guy wore confidence on his sleeve. Though Henry talked more shit, he still acted timid.

"Watch what I'm telling you! I've been in this situation before, young man. It's a test. The boss is always testing. The walls have eyes."

"You're paranoid."

"No, I like to know things." He paused. "Have you heard that something may go down with our company? Like, our jobs might be in jeopardy?"

"Yours may be, but mine sure isn't," he replied, just to mess with Henry.

"Oh, that is because you are a brown-noser if I ever saw one. I could never kiss ass. Got too much pride."

"You're one stupid old man. I've been dying to say that." And Ajalon left Henry in the kitchen all by himself.

As Ajalon returned to the living room, he saw Jerry still fiddling with the stuffed animals.

He laughed at him. "You two are some weirdos, man."

Jerry only smiled.

Nicole then returned to the living room. "Hey, sorry, guys, I forgot something in here." She began searching. Suddenly Henry was at her side. "Is that an engagement ring?"

Nicole blushed. She had never told Ajalon what happened between her and Rashad. She wished Henry would keep his mouth shut.

"It's just a ring."

"But it's on the ring finger," Henry argued. "Is the boss getting married again and he didn't tell us?"

"There will be a lot of things that the boss won't tell you," Nicole snapped. Henry grabbed her hand, looked and laughed.

"It must be true what they're saying on the streets."

"What are you talking about, Henry?" Nicole asked.

"They say that Eason and Son is going bankrupt. Soon we'll all be out of a job." He grabbed Nicole's hand again. "Tell us the truth. I have a family to feed and he has been giving me a lot of work."

"I-I don't know what you're talking about. I haven't heard any such thing about the company going bankrupt."

"Someone is lying," Henry said accusingly.

"Man, shut the fuck up," Ajalon told him. "If that rumor was true, our boss would tell us himself. He wouldn't leave us out of something as important as that."

Nicole wanted to pat Ajalon on the back.

But she said, "Ajalon is right."

"What?" Henry demanded.

"I mean, Cornell."

"Why'd you call him that name?" Henry asked.

"Why don't you go and wait in the van for Rashad. All of you. We are having a family emergency right now and it's best that we handle it privately."

They all filed out back to the van.

And Nicole could have kicked herself for calling her lover by his real name.

Nicole decided to go to the park anyway. It had gotten darker by the time she reached it. But there was plenty of lighting on the wide paths. She was stressed out and felt going on a walk would do her some good. She had been walking about ten minutes when she felt a presence join her.

"Hello, Bella."

"Ajalon."

"Don't be mad. It's a free country."

"I thought you were mad at me. It's like you didn't want to talk to me anymore."

"No, that would be you who couldn't talk."

"Hey, I'm sorry that I wasn't able to tell you that Rashad and I are going to be married. But I wanted to tell you now, to your face."

"Congratulations."

"I know it's not what you want to hear, Ajalon. I'm sorry for hurting you."

"I will survive. I have survived much worse things than losing the only woman that I've ever loved."

She touched his shoulder and wasn't worried about anyone seeing them. It was so dark outside she was sure any observers could only see murky shadows. And who could actually say for sure what they'd seen?

"Ajalon, did you have anything you want to say to me before I go?"

"I will be quitting that job you got me. I'm going to strike out on my own."

"Oh, I see. Well, good luck with that."

"One last thing. I still love you, Bella."

She bit her bottom lip. "I still love you, too, Ajalon Cornell Cantu. But in a different type of way."

He looked so sad that she decided to give him one last sensuous kiss on his lips.

It was her last hurrah, and the streets of Houston would never be the same.

Chapter 21

The Last Betrayal

Alexis was poking around on her computer when she decided to review some video footage. It was the day before Halloween, a Friday. She was at her workstation in the open area of the department's main corridor. The day was quiet and she was bored. She selected the icon to start the playback of the film; at first she didn't see anything. Images of the house presented nothing significant. But then she noticed Nicole enter the living room. Alexis saw an unfamiliar man and a pretty woman in the room with them. The three spoke briefly and the woman disappeared. Then Nicole and the man were alone.

Alexis whispered, "What the hell?" as her eyes remained glued to her computer monitor.

She continued to watch Nicole and the man and she wondered who he was and what he was doing in Nicole's house; then the screen went dark. Alexis saw nothing. She knew the camera was still rolling because the device that was recording was battery operated. But it also was motion-activated. So it would make sense that the playback stopped.

"Oh, well. I have no idea what happened, but it doesn't look good." Alexis picked up her office phone and called Kiara.

"Um, if you aren't busy, could you come by my office? Like, right now? I have something interesting to show you."

It took several minutes before Kiara arrived.

Alexis's face was serious. She pointed at a chair near her.

"Pull up a seat and try to remain calm."

"Sure."

As soon as Kiara sat down she knew what she was watching. "You finally found something?" she gasped.

"At first I wasn't sure. But now I got the real spill."

Both women intently watched the screen in front of them. They saw the dark shadows, the man, the woman, their subsequent disrobing, their nakedness, their lying down on the floor, and them having sex outside during the rain.

"I simply do not believe this," Kiara said. She could barely watch.

"Keep looking," Alexis said.

Right then Nicole and Shyla Perry-Fallender walked past them. Alexis and Kiara kept their heads down. Nicole noticed the two women huddled close together but she didn't have time to worry about it. She had a wedding to plan. Nicole waved at the ladies as she passed by. They barely spoke to her.

As soon as Nicole disappeared from sight, Alexis started snickering. "Damn, now I know what that woman looks like with no clothes on. I want to throw up."

"You? I should call CPS on her. I am quite sure that her baby had to be in the house that night. Who else could she call to babysit? She is such a skank."

Kiara stopped the playback. "I've seen enough."

"So what are you going to do?"

"I am not doing anything. He made his decision. He got who he wanted. Let him suffer the consequences."

"Oh, Kiara, that ain't right. He's not such a bad guy."

"How can you defend my ex? Are you still fucking him, too?"

"Now you know good and well that ain't happening. I thought you had more faith in me than that."

"I apologize. You've been better than most women who are in your position."

"I'm no hero, that's for sure. And even if you are upset about Rashad and hate his guts, he's the father of two of your kids. Two beautiful kids. They deserve better than Nicole. I think he seriously trusts her, too, which is a shame."

"I don't hate the man, but men like Rashad get everything they deserve. If a husband wants to leave his wife for the other woman, let him. It may take him getting treated like trash by Nicole to finally learn how to honor a decent woman."

"I guess." Alexis thought it over. "I think we

should meet with him, especially since he's given her a ring. Then we can figure out how to handle this."

"Okay," Kiara said, "but I really don't know what good it'll do."

Kiara invited Rashad over to her house that evening. She told him it was important and it had to do with Jazzy's latest milestone.

But when Rashad came over and saw Alexis sitting next to Kiara, he knew there was more to it than what his ex-wife told him. They had Rashad sit down at the dining room table and Alexis started the playback of the video footage.

"Now do you believe me?" Kiara asked Rashad. "The proof is in your face; now what you gonna do about it?"

Stunned, Rashad wanted to punch a wall. He felt like an idiot.

"So you planted these spy cameras in my house? On my patio?

"Months ago."

"Months?"

"*Yes,* Rashad. I didn't trust Nicole and didn't know what type of shit she'd be doing to Myles behind my back. And I asked Jerry to handle everything for me. He and I remained friendly even after you and I broke up. So remember when she had a baby shower and wanted everyone and their mother to give her stuff for Emmy? I purchased some cameras and asked Jerry to place them in some teddy bears that I bought. And he brought them over to the house and told Nicole that the gift was from his wife. Of course, Nicole fell for it, especially since there were three crisp hundred-dollar bills attached to the bears. That's how I was able to get it done without Nicole suspecting a thing."

"Damn. And what about the footage from the patio?"

"Well, the devious side of me told me I'd better keep an eye on her outside the house, too. So at my urging, Jerry also brought a few plants over to your house and that's how he was able to set up the camera on the patio. He was happy to do it. And I swore Jerry to secrecy because I didn't want you tripping. You know how stupid you get over her. But as you can see now, it had to be done, and for good reason."

"But that means you've been watching me and everything I do, too?"

"Yes, Rashad. That's what we had to do," Kiara explained. "But it's not like you have anything I haven't seen before."

"Don't matter. I still feel violated."

"But everything isn't about you, sweetheart."

At first Rashad was angry. Women were too damned unpredictable, every single one of them.

"Where exactly was this camera on the patio?" he asked.

"You ever notice a little plastic plant? Well, it's fake. And it had a wifi spy cam set it in."

"How much it cost?"

"I paid over one thousand dollars for this shit," Kiara said. "Using your money. Thanks, honey." She couldn't help but laugh.

Kiara may have thought it was funny, but Alexis noticed how hurt Rashad looked. It was something she rarely saw. Feeling a little foolish, she told him, "Sorry we had to act like *Charlie's Angels.* But it was the only way we could get you to open up your eyes."

"Did you say 'we'? You were in on this, too?"

"Hell, yeah. I care about Myles and Jazzy as much as I do Hayley. We're family."

This was almost more than Rashad could bear. But it finally settled in. He felt their love. And it blew his mind.

"Well, damn. Y'all two are golden. And now I really know what I'm working with. Two devious geniuses. How much y'all charge for your services?"

"Don't get any crazy ideas," Kiara teased him. "This ain't about you. It's about all our children."

"Damn, damn, damn," was all Rashad could say. Regret filled his heart, but it was too late for all that. He had to focus on the future.

"Now that you know the truth," Alexis asked, "what are you going to do?"

"Well, I've thought about it."

"And?" Kiara asked.

"Nicole wants to be married to me, right? And I think I'm going to give her exactly what she wants."

"Say what?" Alexis asked. "Aren't you pissed at her?"

"Yeah, you know I am. But I ain't sweating it. If she wants me, she can have me. Every single fucking thing that goes along with having me." Rashad had a steely look in his eyes. And only he knew what he planned to do. Neither Kiara nor Alexis could figure out his motives.

Later that day, Rashad was driving in his van on his way to pick up his work team. He couldn't get the vision of Nicole and Ajalon/Cornell out of his mind. Now he realized who the dude really was. He clearly recalled that the man wanted to go by the name Cornell. And how did he miss the fact that the young man had just arrived from Alabama? He did good work, that's how. And good workers made him look good. And Rashad couldn't believe that his employee made love to his woman right in their own house. "That sounds like some type of shit I'd do," he said to himself. "It would be funny if it weren't so fucking scandalous."

He tried to calm himself down as he figured out how to confront the people that he trusted the most.

Around the same time that Rashad was driving to get his workers, Nicole was in a festive mood. She felt like she'd gotten Ajalon out of her system. When they shared one last juicy kiss, they both agreed it was time to move on. He would never bother her with his dreams and schoolboy wishes again. He was on his own.

"*Ti amo,*" he told her as she drove off. "No, she will never forget me. And I will never forget her."

And on the late afternoon the day before Halloween, Nicole felt freer than she had in a while. She wanted to party. She was engaged. Rashad told her he loved her and life was looking more promising. She vowed to stay out of trouble and she meant it.

Nicole was in the middle of deciding which costume she wanted to wear. She and Rashad were going to a party on Saturday night, and she couldn't wait for it to start. She had two different outfits that she could choose from. It would either be the black witch outfit that was always a big hit at a party, or she'd wear something different yet stylish: her beautiful Egyptian Cleopatra outfit that she adored. Right then she decided to try it on. It was a three-quarter-length black halter dress with sequined armbands and drapes that hung off her biceps. There was also a multicolored collar and a headband. She picked out the perfect pair of skimpy heels and had just practiced applying this new green-and-black eye shadow that would give her the smoky eye look that she wanted to have.

"I look pretty good," she said to herself as she gazed at her reflection in the mirror.

She heard the doorbell ring and went to see who could be ringing it.

Before her stood two strangers: a beautiful, elegant looking white woman and a darker-skinned man.

"May I help you?" she asked.

"We are looking for our son. Are you Nicole Greene?"

"Yes, I am, but who is your son?" Then she looked in the woman's eyes and she immediately saw Ajalon inside of them.

"Oh, my God. What are you doing here? How did you find me? Oh," she said. "Never mind."

"May we come in?"

"Now is not a good time." She laughed nervously. "Um, I am about to go to a costume party," she lied.

"I see," Ajalon's mother, Callista, told her.

"We don't mean to intrude. We will only stay a second," said his father, Lorenzo.

"Well, what can I do for you?"

"Take us to our son," Callista said. "We are just checking on him and want to make sure he is okay."

"All right. I need to get my baby, and then I'll show you where your son is."

Nicole may have looked like a queen but she hardly felt like one as she drove to the Home Depot day worker location. She knew Ajalon's schedule. And she knew that he'd get dropped off soon. She just wanted his parents to follow her Jeep, point to the drop-off spot, and go on about her way. Whatever they wanted with him had nothing to do with her. She just wanted to show some Texas hospitality, but she couldn't forget the stories her ex told her about how his family disapproved of her. They made her feel like she wasn't good enough, yet he was the one with the criminal activities and subsequent record.

She pulled over to the spot and parked her Jeep. With the motor still running, she walked over to their rental car. It was a Chevy Suburban. Big, expensive, and classy.

Lorenzo rolled down his window. "He works with, um, with someone I know," Nicole explained. "And this is where he will get dropped off. It should happen in ten or fifteen minutes. So just wait. You'll see the van. Eason and Son. You can't miss it. Bye."

"Thank you for your time."

By the time Nicole spotted Rashad's van, it was too late. She wanted to run as fast as she could to her Jeep, jump in it, and speed off. But with her wearing the stupid high heels, she got slowed down. She decided to play things off so as not to bring attention to herself. She started walking slowly toward her vehicle.

She was almost about to reach her door handle. But she saw a strange man race to her Jeep. He beat her to the door and jumped in.

"No," she screamed. "My car."

Within seconds Rashad's van pulled up. The guy put the Jeep in reverse and attempted to back out. But Rashad blocked him in. Then his side door opened. And Ajalon jumped out. He ran to the door of the Jeep and yanked it wide open. He grabbed the strange man by the collar and pulled him out. The next thing you know, both Rashad and Jerry came over. Jerry held him down and let Rashad punch him over and over in his face and kick his legs. They took turns thrashing the man so badly he limped away after they got done whipping his ass.

Nicole couldn't believe it. She felt so ashamed yet so grateful. When the melee was over and Ajalon looked up, he yelled in exhilaration when he saw his beloved mother.

"*Madre,*" he said and smiled at Nicole. "*Mia madre.*"

She could only smile back at him.

"Thank you," she whispered.

Rashad watched them all along. He said goodbye to Jerry and shook Ajalon's hand.

He looked him in the eye. "Thanks, Ajalon."

Nicole froze. She quietly boarded her Jeep. She waited. And she wasn't surprised when Rashad opened her passenger door and hopped inside.

"You want to explain to me what the fuck is going on with you? You were supposed to be my ride or die."

"What are you talking about? I can't help it if those people came to the house looking for your employee—"

"I'm not talking about that and you know it. You know good and well what I'm talking about. Cornell Cantu? That's your boy from Birmingham. Your little Afro-Italian lover."

He shook his head. "I've been the biggest fool. I thought I was the shady one, but you got me beat by a long shot."

Nicole's eyes were dry. She had no words to argue with him. She heavily sighed. "Sometimes we don't know why we do what we do. We only know what we regret."

"That's the truth if I've ever heard the fucking truth."

"So? What now?" she asked, trembling. She was petrified. More afraid than she'd ever been in her life. She still wanted Rashad but she wasn't certain that he could ever muster up enough strength, heart, and willingness to love her in the way she needed to be loved.

And if Rashad couldn't love her, then who could?

"We'll talk about it," he finally told her. "Meet you back at the house."

As she pulled out of the parking lot, she watched the continued celebration of a son being joyfully reunited with his parents. She could only hope Rashad gave her the same chance.

* * *

Before she went home, Nicole had the mind to call up Shyla. In all the excitement, she nearly forgot she had Emmy in the backseat of the Jeep. She knew how foolish she'd been to keep her daughter in the car with her keys still in the ignition and the engine running.

Shyla heard the latest drama and agreed to keep Emmy the entire night. "Go home and fix things with your husband."

Nicole said, "You are a true friend."

"And don't you ever forget it."

Hours later, after Rashad and Nicole talked, really ironed things out and gave each other their thoughts, fears, and expectations, Nicole knew she'd nearly dodged a fatal bullet. Any other man would have tried to kill her.

She gratefully held Rashad's hand.

"I know I don't deserve you, babe. I'll admit it. I don't always do the right thing. But I do want to try and learn from my mistakes. I want another chance. And I promise to be the best wife you've ever had. You have my word."

"Everyone makes mistakes," he calmly told her.

"So does that mean you honestly forgive me? Because, Rashad, and I swear I don't say this too often, but I am so fucking sorry that I wish I could start the entire year all over again."

"You do. That's different! How would you change things, Nicole?"

"I think that it's possible you and Kiara might have broken up anyway. Because maybe somehow she would have found out about Alexis and Hayley. She may have decided no, she didn't want her marriage anymore. And she may have decided to leave you and start over with someone else. And if that happened, I would have been able to meet you the honest, organic, and systematic way. It sounds old-fashioned, but I think I would have waited until you were completely unattached. And then we'd be just cool at first. No sex."

"Are you saying that you are sorry for relentlessly pursuing me?"

"I beg your pardon. I'd hardly call it that. It's just that when I noticed you were spending more time with me, and less with her, the handwriting was on the wall," she scoffed. "I didn't invent hooking up with a married man. Your precious Alexis is proof of that."

"You're right in that assessment, Nicole. To understand people and why they are how they are, you'd have to go way back in history. Biblical times, even. Because I'm not a religious man, but even I remember the story about Samson and Delilah. She saw the man that she wanted and she made sure to do what it takes to get him."

"I hope you aren't comparing me to Delilah. Because I believe that our modern-day situation is very much different than that story."

He silently studied her. Then he said, "Yeah, right."

She allowed herself a cautious laugh. "Because in the Rashad Eason and Nicole Greene story, you were a carpenter, so to speak, that originally wanted to help me to fix some things. And those things required you to come over to my house. But you could have sent one of your other men. But you, Rashad, chose to come and help me. And you came and got my problems fixed up real nice and pretty. And you talked to me and made sure that we became friends. And you took me out for my birthday last summer, to a beach, for God's sake, and you brought me back home and you made love to me. And so that ruined any chance for our own relationship to grow organically just like in a storybook. And I think you have to realize that in spite of its dirty background and origin, you must admit you played a role and now, in spite of everything, you do love me. And if things had been different, I believe you'd have gotten me a two-carat diamond ring instead of this plastic thing you found in a Cracker Jack box."

He heartily laughed. "Ahh. About the ring . . . I was only testing you to see if you still loved me no matter what the size of the diamond. Some men do that just to see if the chick's heart is right. Some women pass the test." He shrugged and gazed at her. "Other women miss out."

"Oh, okay." She felt foolish and immature. "I feel dumb. Again. And it's the one thing I'm committed to changing." She let go of his hand and starting toying with her fingers.

"Rashad, I know for a fact you could have walked away from me and never talked to me again. I can't say that I'd blame you. I'd be hurt. But I'd understand. But the fact is that you are kind enough to forgive me. Why, it's an honor that you're giving me another chance. I feel like I've died on the operating table and was suddenly brought back to life."

"That's a nice way to put it." He pondered his words. "Well, Nicole. You haven't died. You're very much still alive. And yes, I'm giving you one more chance to prove yourself. Just once more. Don't blow it."

She sighed in disbelief. "You are an *amazing* man. And I mean that."

"I think I'm amazing, too. I really do." He knew in his mind Nicole Greene really didn't have one more chance like he told her.

And Rashad thought about all the treacherous things he could line up in his mind to make this woman regret ever messing with him, his family, and his business.

Amazing indeed.